# City Essentials

## An Introduction to
## Financial Mathematics

Published September 2009

ISBN 9780 7517 5393 6

British Library Cataloguing-in-Publication Data
A catalogue record for this book
is available from the British Library

Published by

BPP Learning Media Ltd
BPP House, Aldine Place
London W12 8AA

www.bpp.com/learningmedia

Cover photo by Terence O'Loughlin

Printed in Great Britain

Your learning materials, published by BPP Learning Media, are
printed on paper sourced from sustainable, managed forests.

£40.00

# Contents

# INTRODUCTION

The purpose of this book is to introduce the mathematical issues underlying investment and finance. It is assumed that the reader already possesses a basic understanding of mathematics, though it is appreciated that this may be a little rusty. As a result we begin with a reminder of the important basic mathematical issues that we will be relying on when we develop the investment and finance ideas that form the core of this book.

Although all the techniques in this book are illustrated and can be performed manually, it is recognised that modern calculators and spreadsheet programmes can undertake many of the mechanical processes far more efficiently. Blindly punching numbers into a calculator or spreadsheet without understanding the ideas is, however, a recipe for misinterpretation, misunderstanding and mistakes. In order to minimise this possibility, the objective within each section is to explain the ideas being introduced and used in order to maximise effectiveness for the reader. This book has, therefore, been written as generally as possible and is independent of whatever support (calculator or spreadsheet) that the reader may be using.

Finally, we introduce and apply many mathematical expressions throughout this book, some of which are quite complex. Many readers will be happy to accept the formulae provided, preferring to concentrate on being able to apply them correctly – the main aim of this book. Others, however, will prefer to understand where these formulae have come from. Within each section we try to provide an explanation or justification for any formulae introduced, though for the more complex formulae where the derivation may obscure its understanding and use, this derivation is consigned to a chapter appendix that the reader is free to study or ignore as they wish.

BPP LEARNING MEDIA

# 1 Mathematical relationships

## Contents

## Introduction

As noted in the introduction to this book, it is assumed that you already possesses a basic understanding of mathematics, though it is appreciated that this may be a little rusty. The purpose of this section is to remind you of some of these basics.

# 1 MATHEMATICAL RELATIONSHIPS

## 1.1 Mathematical operations

### 1.1.1 Mathematical notation

There are some standard mathematical notations that we assume the reader is familiar with but that we lay down here for completeness.

| | |
|---|---|
| + | plus or add |
| − | minus or subtract |
| × | times or multiply |
| ÷ | divide |
| / | divide (an alternative to ÷) |
| ( ) | brackets used for grouping parts of a calculation |
| ± | plus or minus − used in an equation with two alternative solutions, one where something is added, one where that same something is subtracted |
| = | is equal to |
| ≠ | is not equal to |
| ≈ | is almost equal to |
| ≡ | is equivalent to/may be restated as |
| > | is greater than |
| ≥ | is greater than or equal to |
| < | is less than |
| ≤ | is less than or equal to |
| ∞ | is infinitely large |

Remember that multiplication is often abbreviated in formulae through the omission of the multiplication symbol, especially in the case where brackets or variables are being used. For example, where a, x and y are three values or variables.

$$3(6 + 5) \equiv 3 \times (6 + 5)$$

$$a(x + y) \equiv a \times (x + y)$$

$$ax \equiv a \times x$$

# 1.2 Mathematical precedence

One of the key fundamentals within any mathematical relationship is the order in which the calculations should be undertaken, the order of *mathematical precedence*.

## Example

For example, how should the following equation be evaluated?

$$x = 5 \times 8 \div 2^2 - (7 - 3) - 4 \times 6 + (2^3 - (2 + 3))^3$$

## Solution

You cannot simply work from left to right, there is a strict mathematical order that must be followed which is sometimes referred to using the mnemonic **BIDMAS**, which means

1.      **Brackets** – Evaluate the contents of any brackets before moving on to any other part of the equation. Where brackets are nested (brackets inside brackets) we must start from the innermost bracket and work outwards. At each stage we must apply the order of mathematical precedence within the brackets being evaluated.

2.      **Indices** – Evaluate any indices (powers or roots).

3.      **Division** and **multiplication** – Next, undertake any multiplication and/or division. Note that the order of execution here does not matter, i.e. whether we multiply first then divide, or divide then multiply is irrelevant.

4.      **Addition** and **subtraction** – The final two functions to undertake are addition and subtraction though, once again, the order between these two does not matter.

**Brackets**

Applying this order we would start with the two bracketed elements. The first of these is easy to evaluate

$$(7 - 3) = 4$$

The second, $(2^3 - (2 + 3))$, is a little more complex since it contains a nested bracket which we must evaluate first as follows

$$(2 + 3) = 5$$

which reduces this second bracket to

$$(2^3 - 5)$$

To evaluate this correctly we must apply the BIDMAS order and evaluate the index element (the power) before undertaking the subtraction. The index element is

$$2^3 = 8$$

reducing this second bracket to

$$(8 - 5) = 3$$

If we now substitute in these values in place of the bracketed items, the original formula

$$x = 5 \times 8 \div 2^2 - (7 - 3) - 4 \times 6 + (2^3 - (2 + 3))^3$$

is reduced to

$$x = 5 \times 8 \div 2^2 - 4 - 4 \times 6 + 3^3$$

## Indices

The next step is to evaluate any indices (powers and roots), and again there are two, the third term and the last term. Looking at each in turn.

$$2^2 = 4$$

$$3^3 = 27$$

reducing the equation to

$$x = 5 \times 8 \div 4 - 4 - 4 \times 6 + 27$$

## Division and multiplication

The next stage is to undertake any multiplication and division which involves the first three terms and the fifth and sixth term. Looking firstly at the fifth and sixth terms, we have

$$4 \times 6 = 24$$

reducing the equation to

$$x = 5 \times 8 \div 4 - 4 - 24 + 27$$

Considering now the first three terms, we have

$$5 \times 8 \div 4$$

and, as noted above, it does not matter whether we undertake the division first or the multiplication first.

If we undertake the division component of this first

$$8 \div 4 = 2$$

this reduces these first three terms to

$$5 \times 2 = 10$$

If, however, we undertake the multiplication component of this first

$$5 \times 8 - 40$$

this reduces these first three terms to

$$40 \div 4 = 10$$

As we can see, we get the value of 10 either way – the order between division and multiplication is irrelevant.

Having evaluated these first three terms, our equation is now reduced to

$$x = 10 - 4 - 24 + 27$$

Before moving on to complete this evaluation there is one more issue to raise, specifically when multiplying numbers together their order does not matter. For example

$$5 \times 2 = 10$$

and

$$2 \times 5 = 10$$

Whether the 2 or the 5 comes first is irrelevant, when two numbers are multiplied, the result is the same irrespective of their order – the order doesn't matter.

### Addition and subtraction

The equation has now been reduced to simple addition and subtraction which can just be followed left to right (since there is no priority order between the two), giving

$$x = 10 - 4 - 24 + 27 = 9$$

### Conclusion

We have managed to reduce the equation to

$$x = 9$$

but only by correctly applying the strict order of mathematical precedence. We shall continue to apply this strict BIDMAS order throughout this book.

## Exercise 1

Work out all the answers to four decimal places, using a calculator.

(a)  $(43 + 26.705) \times 9.3$

(b)  $(844.2 \div 26) - 2.45$

(c)  $(43.756 + 26.321) \div 171.036$

(d)  $(43.756 + 26.321) \times 171.036$

(e)  $171.45 + (-221.36)\ 143.22$

(f)  $66 - (-43.57) + (-212.36)$

## 1.3 Expanding brackets

### 1.3.1 Introduction

Following on from our order of mathematical precedence is the idea of expanding brackets. For example, how would we evaluate

$$x = 3(4 + 5)$$

Remember that what we have here is standard (albeit abbreviated) mathematical notation for

$$x = 3 \times (4 + 5)$$

As we noted earlier, whenever we see a value or variable placed immediately in front of a bracket then the bracket is being multiplied by that value or variable.

Given this interpretation, and following the BIDMAS rules above, we can now evaluate the expression. Firstly we would evaluate the contents of the brackets, i.e.

$$(4 + 5) = 9$$

and then we would undertake the multiplication, giving

$$x = 3 \times (4 + 5) = 3 \times 9 = 27$$

An alternative approach that proves to be very useful in certain circumstances is to expand the bracket.

What we are doing in this example is multiplying the value of the contents of the brackets by three. As an alternative, we could have multiplied the value of each and every element inside the brackets by three before evaluating the bracket, i.e.

$$x = 3 \times (4 + 5) = (3 \times 4 + 3 \times 5)$$

Now applying BIDMAS to this right-hand version gives

$$x = 3 \times (4 + 5) = (3 \times 4 + 3 \times 5) = (12 + 15) = 27$$

So in conclusion

$$x = 3(4 + 5) = 3 \times (4 + 5) = (3 \times 4 + 3 \times 5) = (12 + 15) = 27$$

Generalising this idea, if a, x and y are three numbers, then

$$a(x + y) = (a \times x + a \times y) = (ax + ay)$$

This last term being where we apply the abbreviations $ax = a \times x$ and $ay = a \times y$

## Conclusion

For any three numbers or variables a, x and y

$$a(x + y) \equiv (ax + ay)$$

That is, $a(x + y)$ is equivalent to or can be restated as $(ax + ay)$ for all values of a, x and y.

# 1.4 Negative numbers

The next mathematical issue for us to consider is that of negative numbers, particularly the addition, subtraction, multiplication and division of negative numbers.

## 1.4.1 Addition and subtraction

### Addition

When we add a positive number to another positive number, the positive value increases, e.g.

$$12 + 9 = 21$$

It logically follows that when we add a negative number to another negative number the negative value increases, i.e. it must be that

$$-12 + -9 = -21$$

Note, some people prefer to bracket the second number, (−9), for clarity, i.e.

$$-12 + (-9) = -21$$

Though this is not strictly necessary in this example, it is advisable in general as it is helpful when applying the BIDMAS priority order in more complex problems.

Whether we use the brackets or not, however, for the logic to follow the evaluation must be

$$-12 + (-9) = -12 - 9 = -21$$

and so we can see that **when we add a negative, we subtract the value.**

## Subtraction

Subtraction is simply the opposite of addition and so the same logic applies. When we subtract a positive number from another higher value positive number, the positive value decreases, e.g.

$$12 - 9 = 3$$

It logically follows that when we subtract a negative number to another higher value negative number, the negative value decreases, i.e. it must be that

$$-12 - (-9) = -3$$

For the logic to apply, what we must have here is

$$-12 - (-9) = -12 + 9 = -3$$

and so it must be that **when we subtract a negative, we add the value.**

## Conclusion

When we add a negative, we subtract.

When we subtract a negative, we add.

## 1.4.2 Multiplication and division

## Multiplication

Multiplication can be viewed as repeated addition, for example

$$4 \times 3 = 4 + 4 + 4 = 12$$

And we can state that **when we multiply a positive number by a positive number, the result is positive.**

It follows from the above that the rules we established for addition apply equally to multiplication, and so

$$(-4) \times 3 = (-4) + (-4) + (-4) = -4 - 4 - 4 = -12$$

The conclusion we can draw here is that **when we multiply a negative number by a positive number, the result is negative.**

We noted above, however, that when we multiply numbers together the result is the same irrelevant of their order. It therefore follows that

$$3 \times (-4) = -12$$

From which we can conclude that **when we multiply a positive number by a negative number, the result is negative**.

What if we multiply two negatives together, what if the problem is

$$(-4) \times (-3)$$

Going back to the bracket point mentioned earlier, this could validly be written as

$$-4 \times (-3)$$

Now, applying strict BIDMAS to this, we should do the multiplication before the subtraction, which we could illustrate by bracketing as follows

$$-(4 \times (-3))$$

Now based on the above, the inside of this bracket reduces to

$$4 \times (-3) = -12$$

and so

$$(-4) \times (-3) = -4 \times (-3) = -(4 \times (-3)) = -(-12) = +12$$

Note, we have included the '+' sign here purely for emphasis. The conclusion we can draw, however, is that **when we multiply a negative number by a negative number, the result is positive**.

## Division

As we are all aware, division is simply the opposite of multiplication. Therefore since

$$4 \times 3 = 12$$

then

$$12 \div 3 = 4$$

and

$$12 \div 4 = 3$$

That is, **when we divide a positive number by a positive number, the result is positive**.

Using our multiplication example above as a basis, we had

$$(-4) \times 3 = -12$$

It therefore follows that

$$-12 \div 3 = (-4) \text{ or } -4$$

and

$$-12 \div (-4) = 3$$

The first of these examples illustrates that **when we divide a negative number by a positive number, the result is negative**.

The second illustrates that **when we divide a negative number by a negative number, the result is positive**.

Also, since

$$(-4) \times (-3) = 12$$

It follows that

$$12 \div (-3) = (-4) \text{ or } -4$$

and what we see here is that **when we divide a positive number by a negative number, the result is negative**.

## Conclusion

You will probably have noticed that the conclusions for both multiplication and division are identical. Summarising what we have seen, we have

| Multiplication | Division |
|---|---|
| Positive × Positive = Positive | Positive ÷ Positive = Positive |
| Positive × Negative = Negative | Positive ÷ Negative = Negative |
| Negative × Positive = Negative | Negative ÷ Positive = Negative |
| Negative × Negative = Positive | Negative ÷ Negative = Positive |

Which could be summarised further as follows: when either multiplying or dividing

**Same signs give a Positive,**

**Opposite signs give a Negative**

All of the illustrations so far have, for simplicity, used integers, i.e. whole numbers that may be either positive or negative. The rules we have established, however, apply equally to all real numbers, that is any value (including but not limited to integers) that may be either positive or negative.

## Exercise 2

Work out the following.

(a)     $(72 - 8) - (-2 + 1)$

(b)     $8(2 - 5) - (4 - (-8))$

# 2 FRACTIONS DECIMALS AND PERCENTAGES

## 2.1 Introduction

Though in some instances we may wish to refer to whole number (integer) values, much of the time we may wish to refer to only a part of something, which we can describe by using fractions, decimals or percentages.

Fractions, decimals and percentages represent three alternative way of dealing with real number values, and should be viewed as completely interchangeable.

Note that whenever we refer to a number in this book we are referring to real numbers, if we wish to limit ourselves to whole numbers we will use the expression integer.

## 2.2 Fractions

### 2.2.1 Definition

A fraction represents an alternative notation for division and, in the BIDMAS context, should be viewed as a division component within any formula or equation. For example, the mathematical expression

$$2 \div 3$$

may alternatively be represented as the fraction

$$\frac{2}{3}$$

A fraction, then, has two components – the top line (the numerator) that is being divided by the bottom line (the denominator). That is

$$\text{Fraction} = \frac{\text{Numerator}}{\text{Denominator}}$$

Where the numerator is less than the denominator we may describe the fraction as a proper fraction. Where the numerator is greater than or equal to the denominator we may describe it as an improper fraction.

## 2.3 Special case

We will all be aware that any number divided by one is simply itself, e.g.

$$5 \div 1 = 5$$

However, applying the definition of a fraction above

$$5 \div 1 = \frac{5}{1}$$

an improper fraction. Hence it follows that

$$5 = \frac{5}{1}$$

or more generally, any number, x, may be expressed where necessary as

$$x = \frac{x}{1}$$

## 2.4 Reciprocal

The reciprocal of a number, x, is 1 divided by that number, i.e. $\dfrac{1}{x}$

Reciprocals are very important in the context of dividing fractions as we will see shortly. An important attribute of a reciprocal that should be noted is that the product of any number and its reciprocal is 1. For example, for any number, x

$$x \times \dfrac{1}{x} = x \times (1 \div x)$$

Now, since when we are multiplying and dividing the order doesn't matter, then

$$x \times \dfrac{1}{x} = x \times (1 \div x) = x \times 1 \div x$$

and so

$$x \times \dfrac{1}{x} = x \times (1 \div x) = x \times 1 \div x = x \div x = 1$$

Extending this idea a little further, for any two numbers, x and y, which may be integers or may themselves be fractions

$$x \times \dfrac{1}{y} = x \times (1 \div y) = x \times 1 \div y = x \div y = \dfrac{x}{y}$$

The important conclusion here is that for any two numbers, x and y

$$x \div y = x \times \dfrac{1}{y}$$

That is, dividing one number by another is equivalent to multiplying by the reciprocal of the other, which represents the most convenient way of dividing with fractions.

Before we leave reciprocals there is one final point to consider, specifically the reciprocal of a fraction which we will need to deal with dividing by fractions below. A little earlier we introduced the special case of

$$x = \dfrac{x}{1}$$

and based on our definition, the reciprocal of this is $\dfrac{1}{x}$.

Pulling these two ideas together, for any number, x or $\dfrac{x}{1}$, its reciprocal is $\dfrac{1}{x}$. What this illustrates is that to get the reciprocal of a fraction we simply turn the fraction upside-down, making the numerator/denominator of the original number the denominator/numerator of the reciprocal.

More generally, therefore, for any fraction, $\dfrac{a}{b}$, its reciprocal is $\dfrac{b}{a}$.

For example, the reciprocal of $\dfrac{3}{4}$ is $\dfrac{4}{3}$, and the reciprocal of $\dfrac{5}{12}$ is $\dfrac{12}{5}$.

## 2.5 Multiplication and division

### 2.5.1 Multiplication

To multiply fractions, we multiply the numerators of the fractions to get the new numerator and multiply the denominators of the fractions to get the new denominator. For example

$$\frac{2}{3} \times \frac{4}{7} = \frac{2 \times 4}{3 \times 7} = \frac{8}{21}$$

More generally, for any two fractions, $\frac{a}{b}$ and $\frac{c}{d}$

$$\frac{a}{b} \times \frac{c}{d} = \frac{a \times c}{b \times d} = \frac{ac}{bd}$$

### 2.5.2 Division

To divide one fraction by another we must apply the idea established under reciprocals above, specifically we multiply the first fraction by the reciprocal of the second, i.e.

$$\frac{2}{3} \div \frac{4}{7} = \frac{2}{3} \times \frac{7}{4} = \frac{2 \times 7}{3 \times 4} = \frac{14}{12}$$

More generally, for any two fractions, $\frac{a}{b}$ and $\frac{c}{d}$

$$\frac{a}{b} \div \frac{c}{d} = \frac{a}{b} \times \frac{d}{c} = \frac{a \times d}{b \times c} = \frac{ad}{bc}$$

## 2.6 Addition and subtraction

The addition or subtract of two integers is reasonably straightforward so long as we remember the rules established earlier in relation to negative numbers.

The addition or subtraction of two fractions must also follow these rules but brings with it an additional problem, though it may be considered in quite a simple way. Looking at a very simple example

1 apple + 2 apples = 3 apples

In other words, to add anything the units must firstly be the same (here all apples). It follows from this that

1 fifth + 2 fifths = 3 fifths

when we are adding fifths rather than apples, i.e.

$$\frac{1}{5} + \frac{2}{5} = \frac{3}{5}$$

What we can see from this example is that where the denominator is the same for the fractions being added, the denominator of the sum is this common denominator (5 in this example) and the numerator of the sum is the sum of the numerators.

BPP
LEARNING MEDIA

More generally

$$\frac{x}{d} + \frac{y}{d} = \frac{x+y}{d}$$

and by a similar logic

$$\frac{x}{d} - \frac{y}{d} = \frac{x-y}{d}$$

The main point for both addition and subtraction then is that we must firstly find this common denominator before we add or subtract fractions.

## Exercise 3

Work out all answers to four decimal places, using a calculator.

(a) $\dfrac{88+8}{12} + \dfrac{(29-11)}{2}$

(e) $\dfrac{7.6 \times 1.010}{10.1 \times 76,000}$

(b) $\dfrac{-36}{9-3} - \dfrac{84}{3-10} - \dfrac{-81}{3}$

(f) $\dfrac{-10.75 \times (-15.44)}{-14.25 \times 17.15} + \left(\dfrac{16.23}{8.4+3.002}\right)$

(c) $\dfrac{45.6 - 13.92 + 823.1}{14.3 \times 112.5}$

(g) $\dfrac{-7.366 \times 921.3}{10,493 - 2,422.8} + \left(\dfrac{8.4+3.002}{16.23}\right)$

(d) $\dfrac{303.3 + 7.06 \times 42.11}{1.03 \times 76,000}$

## 2.7 Decimals and percentages

### 2.7.1 Introduction

A fraction can be readily converted into a decimal by undertaking the division that it is equivalent to. Remember that $\dfrac{1}{2} \equiv 1 \div 2$ which equates to the decimal 0.5. Similarly $\dfrac{1}{4}$ = 0.25 and $\dfrac{1}{5}$ = 0.2.

These decimals can, in turn, be readily converted into percentages by multiplying the decimal value by 100%, hence a decimal value of 0.36 would equate to 0.36 × 100% = 36%.

Revisiting the above examples,

$\frac{1}{2}$ equates to a decimal of 0.50 and a percentage of 50%

$\frac{1}{4}$ equates to a decimal of 0.25 and a percentage of 25%

$\frac{1}{5}$ equates to a decimal of 0.20 and a percentage of 20%

However not all fractions reduce to a convenient decimal form.

For example, $\frac{1}{3}$ = 0.33333 recurring as a decimal, or 33.333333% recurring as a percentage. The difficulty with these decimal or percentage forms is that they run on indefinitely, they cannot be expressed in a finite number of decimal places. The usual mathematical notation for these is $0.\dot{3}$ as a decimal or $33.\dot{3}$% as a percentage.

## 2.7.2 Rounding decimal places

Obviously, dealing with numbers that have no finite limit is very difficult if not impossible. It is usual, therefore, to round such numbers to a specified number of decimal places by discarding all figures beyond that point. The usual approach to rounding is that if the first discarded figure is greater than or equal to five then the last retained figure is increased by one (rounding up). If, however, the first discarded figure is less than five then no adjustment is made (rounding down). As a quick illustration

49.28723 rounded to four decimal places is 49.2872 (rounded down)

49.28723 rounded to three decimal places is 49.287 (rounded down)

49.28723 rounded to two decimal places is 49.29 (rounded up)

49.28723 rounded to one decimal places is 49.3 (rounded up)

## Exercise 4

(a)     Round off the number 37,649 to one significant figure

(b)     Round off the number 0.073184 to one significant figure

(c)     Round off the number 0.0073184 to one significant figure

(d)     Work out the answer to 974 × 586 on a calculator and round off the answer to three significant figures

(e)     Work out the answer to 23 ÷ 946 on a calculator and round off the answer to three significant figures

# 3 POWERS AND ROOTS

## 3.1 Powers

When the same value is multiplied by itself several times it is described as being raised to the power, the power number indicating the number of values multiplied together. For example

| | | |
|---|---|---|
| $5^2 = 5 \times 5$ | $= 25$ | this is five squared |
| $5^3 = 5 \times 5 \times 5$ | $= 125$ | this is as five cubed |
| $5^4 = 5 \times 5 \times 5 \times 5$ | $= 625$ | this is five to the power of four |

## 3.2 Roots

A root is the reverse of a power.

Five squared is 25, hence the square root of 25 (designated as $\sqrt{25}$) is five

Five cubed is 125, hence the cubed root of 125 (designated as $\sqrt[3]{125}$) is five.

Five to the power of four is 625, hence the forth root of 625 (designated as $\sqrt[4]{625}$) is five.

## 3.3 Rules for powers

Based on these definitions we can now go on to develop some rules regarding the use of powers through a series of examples based on a variable, a.

### 3.3.1 Multiplying powers

$$a^3 \times a^2 = (a \times a \times a) \times (a \times a) = a \times a \times a \times a \times a = a^5 = a^{3+2}$$

That is, when we multiply powers of the same number we add the powers.

### 3.3.2 Dividing powers

Reversing the above example we have

$$a^5 \div a^2 = \frac{(a \times a \times a \times a \times a)}{(a \times a)} = (a \times a \times a) = a^3 = a^{5-2}$$

That is, when we divide powers of the same number we subtract the powers.

### 3.3.3 Raising powers to a power

We can take the multiplication rule further to consider powers of powers as follows.

$$(a^2)^3 = a^2 \times a^2 \times a^2 = a^6 = a^{2 \times 3}$$

So we can see that when we raise a power to a power we multiply the powers.

### 3.3.4 The power of zero

Extending the dividing powers idea we find

$$a^5 \div a^5 = a^{5-5} = a^0$$

However, by definition

$$a^5 \div a^5 = \frac{(a \times a \times a \times a \times a)}{(a \times a \times a \times a \times a)} = 1$$

As a result we have established the definition that for any value, a, $a^0 = 1$.

### 3.3.5 Negative powers

Extending this idea even further

$$a^3 \div a^5 = a^{3-5} = a^{-2}$$

but what does this actually represent? Based on first principles we get

$$a^3 \div a^5 = \frac{(a \times a \times a)}{(a \times a \times a \times a \times a)} = \frac{1}{(a \times a)} = \frac{1}{a^2}$$

hence

$$a^{-2} = \frac{1}{a^2}$$

More generally we have

$$a^{-n} = \frac{1}{a^n}$$

### 3.3.6 Fractional powers

One final question for us to consider is what does a fractional power mean, for example what is $a^{1/4}$. Applying the multiplication rule above we must have

$$a^{1/4} \times a^{1/4} \times a^{1/4} \times a^{1/4} = a$$

Hence $a^{1/4}$ is the forth root of a, or more generally $a^{1/n}$ is the $n^{th}$ root of a.

## Exercise 5

(a)     $(18.6)^{2.6}$

(b)     $(18.6)^{-2.6}$

(c)     $^{2.6}\sqrt{18.6}$

(d)     $(14.2)^4 \times (14.2)^{\frac{1}{4}}$

(e)     $(14.2)^4 + (14.2)^{-\frac{1}{4}}$

# 4 FUNCTIONS AND GRAPHS

## 4.1 Functions

A function is the specification of the mathematical relationship between variables. For example, if a business sells a product for £0.75 a unit then the total sales value achieved will be a function of (depend upon) the quantity of units sold. For this example we could specify the relationship between the sales value achieved and the quantity of units sold with the function

Sales value = £0.75 × Quantity sold

In this example we have just two variables

**Sales value** – which, in this example, would be referred to as the dependent variable since the sales value achieved depends on the number of units sold

**Quantity sold** – which, here, would be referred to as the independent variable since it is the number of units sold that drives the relationship

Where, like here, we have just two variables, it is usual to ease the notation by replacing the descriptive words by the variables x and y, where x is the independent variable (quantity sold) and y is the dependent variable (sales value). This reduces this equation to

$$y = £0.75 \times x$$

which may be stated even more simply as

$$y = 0.75x$$

This is a much easier form to manipulate mathematically, especially if it is just a small part of a much larger analysis.

## 4.2 Graphs

A graph is a diagrammatical representation of such a relationship in which, as a mathematical norm, the x variable is plotted along the horizontal axis and the y variable is plotted along the vertical axis as follows. Note that we are constraining ourselves to two dimensional graphs in this section.

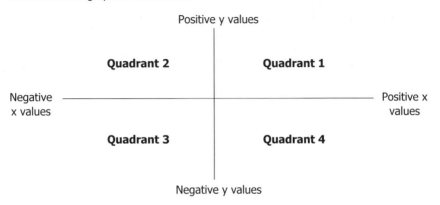

The two perpendicular axes divide the graph into four quadrants as indicated above, though many of the graphs we will be using will only show Quadrant I as the values we have will only be positive as in our Sales value v Quantity sold function above (we cannot sell a negative quantity).

The point where both x and y have the value zero is referred to as the origin, and any point on the graph may be referred to by its coordinates referenced from this point. A point's coordinates is the combination of x and y values that uniquely refer to that point, and the standard mathematical notation is (x value, y value).

For example, a point A with an x value of 3 and a y value of 2 would have the coordinates (3, 2) and would be plotted as follows.

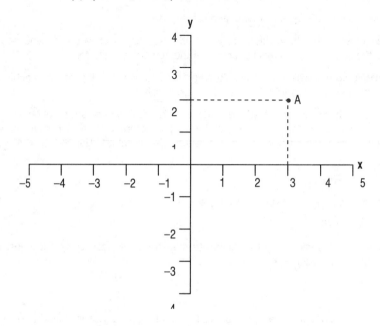

## Example

To illustrate this further we will plot three more points.

B, x value −3, y value 3, coordinates (−3, 3)

C, x value −5, y value −2, coordinates (−5, −2)

D, x value 5, y value −4, coordinates (5, −4)

## Solution

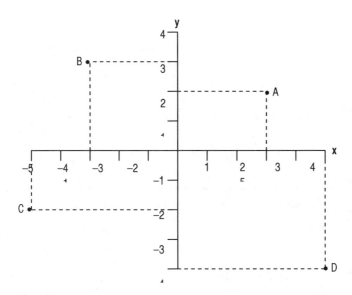

As we will see, graphs provide a very valuable tool for visualising how one variable relates to another.

Referring back to our functions example earlier, we had

$$y = 0.75x$$

where

y = Sales value

x = Quantity sold

As we have already noted, we can only have positive values for both x and y as we cannot sell a negative number of units. We could, therefore, plot the relationship as follows.

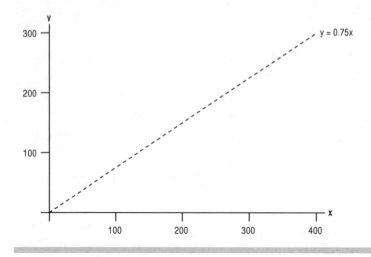

## 4.3 Constant functions

A constant function is a function where variable y takes the same value irrespective of the value of x. An example of a constant function is

y = 6

that would be represented graphically as

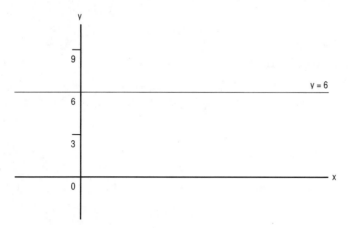

As described so far in this example, y takes the value of six for any x values, i.e. x values moving to infinity in either direction. However it may be that that y takes a value of six over just a certain range of values of x (referred to as a domain). If, for example, y takes a value of six for x values between zero and twenty then this would be stated as

y $= 6$ for $0 \le x \le 20$

$= 0$ elsewhere

BPP
LEARNING MEDIA

## 4.4 Linear functions

A linear function is one that gives a straight line when represented graphically. Our original function example

$$y = 0.75x$$

is an illustration of a linear function which we graphically represented earlier. Note that in this graphical representation we constrained ourselves to the domain $x \geq 0$, so strictly this should have been stated as

$$y \quad = 0.75x \text{ for } x \geq 0$$

$$= 0 \text{ elsewhere}$$

## 4.5 Function coefficients

To describe any linear equation requires just two pieces of information (two function coefficients) that the last two graphs have shown, specifically the

**Slope** – the change in the value of y per unit change in the value of x, or

$$\text{Slope} = \frac{\text{Change in y}}{\text{Change in x}}$$

**Intercept** – the value of y at which the line crosses the y axis

Considering the function

$$y = 0.75x$$

Evaluating two points on this function, if $x = 10$, $y = 7.5$; if $x = 20$, $y = 15$. Based on this we can assess the slope as

$$\text{Slope} = \frac{\text{Change in y}}{\text{Change in x}} = \frac{15 - 7.5}{20 - 10} = 0.75$$

We can see from this that the slope is the value by which x is multiplied within the function. Also we can see from the graph that the line passes through the origin (where $y = 0$), so the function has an intercept of zero.

Considering the constant function

$$y = 6$$

There is no increase or decrease in y, hence the function has a slope of zero. Also we can see from the graph that the line passes through the point $y = 6$, so the function has an intercept of 6, the constant function.

The general form of a linear function is

$$y = a + bx$$

where

a = intercept

b = slope

Graphically this would appear as follows.

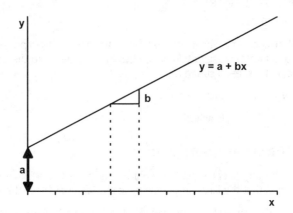

An example in this general form would be

$y = 0.5x + 4$

that would be represented graphically as

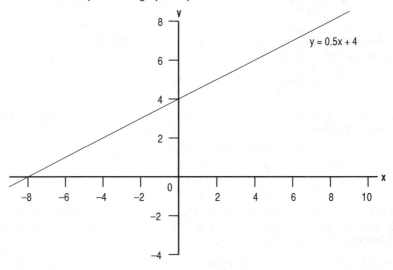

In this example, an increase in x results in an increase in y, As a result, this would be referred to as a positive function and described as having an upward slope. In addition, this function has a positive intercept of four.

Slopes and intercepts may, however, be either positive or negative. Any function where the value of y decreased as x increased would be referred to as a negative function having a downward slope. Any function where the line crosses the y axis below the origin has a negative intercept.

To illustrate this we have will plot the graphs of the following four functions

y = 0.5x + 4   (positive slope, positive intercept)

y = −0.2x + 2  (negative slope, positive intercept)

y = 0.3x − 5   (positive slope, negative intercept)

y = −0.1x − 1  (negative slope, negative intercept)

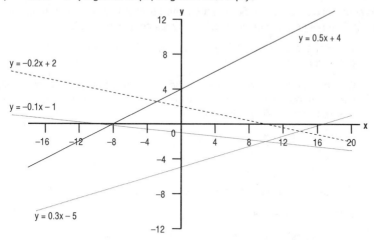

## Exercise 6

(a)    If y = 10 − x, the gradient = _____

(b)    If y = 10 − x, the gradient = _____

What is the intercept and gradient of the graph of 4y = 16x − 12?

|   | Intercept | Gradient |
|---|-----------|----------|
| A | −3 | +4 |
| B | −4 | +3 |
| C | +3 | −4 |
| D | +4 | −3 |

(c)    A company manufactures a product. The total fixed costs are £75 and the variable cost per unit is £5.

## Required

(i)     Find an expression for total costs (iii) in terms of q, the quantity produced.

(ii)    Use your answer to (i) to determine the total costs if 100 units are produced.

(iii)   Prepare a graph of the expression for total costs.

(iv)    Use your graph to determine the total cost if 75 units are produced.

## 4.6 Quadratic functions

Whereas a linear function is defined by two coefficients, a quadratic function requires three coefficients and takes the general form

$y = ax^2 + bx + c$

A quadratic function produces a curved relationship which may be either valley shaped or dome shaped and the coefficients are a little harder to define than those of the linear function. The points that influence/define the shape, however, are

- Whether the shape is a valley or domed and how tight or open the curve of that valley/dome is.

- Whether the trough of the valley (the minimum point) or peak of the dome (the maximum point) lies above or below the y axis. These points are collectively referred to as turning points.

- Where the line cuts the y axis (the intercept).

### 4.6.1 Function coefficients

The first of these characteristics is determined by the a coefficient as follows

- Valley or dome shaped

    – A positive a coefficient produces a valley shape
    – A negative a coefficient produces a dome shape

Positive a coefficient

Negative a coefficient

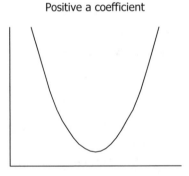
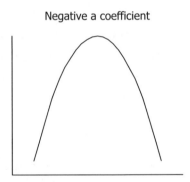

The curvature of the valley/dome is determined by the absolute value of a (i.e. the value ignoring the positive or negative sign). The higher the value of the a coefficient, the tighter the curve; the lower the value of the a coefficient, the more open the curve. Indeed when a = 0 there is zero curvature and the function becomes linear.

High value a coefficient

Low value a coefficient

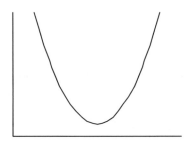
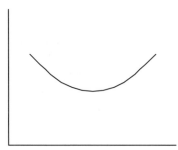

The second characteristic of this function, where the turning point lies in relation to the y axis, is determined by a combination of the a and b coefficients. If the product of these coefficients is positive, the turning point will be to the left of the y axis where the x value is negative. If the product of these coefficients is negative, the turning point will be to the right the y axis where the x value is positive.

The final characteristic of this function, the intercept, is given by the c coefficients. When $x = 0$, $y = c$.

### 4.6.2 Solving the quadratic

Under certain circumstances it may be important for us to determine the value of x at which the given quadratic function has a y value of zero (crosses the x axis). Not all quadratics will have a solution (or root), however. If a valley shaped function has a positive minimum value, or a dome shaped function has a negative maximum value then there will be no solution since the y values can never be zero.

Where a quadratic

$$y = ax^2 + bx + c$$

has a solution, we can determine this using the quadratic equation

$$x = \frac{-b \pm \sqrt{b^2 - 4ac}}{2a}$$

### Example

Solve

$$y = 4x^2 - 5x + 1$$

### Solution

Graphically, this looks as follows

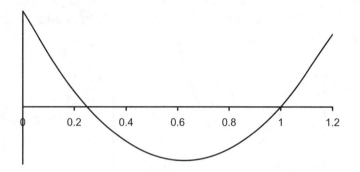

which allows us to estimate the solution, however if we wish to be accurate we must apply the quadratic.

In this example we have

a = 4

b = −5

c = 1

and applying the quadratic equation we get

$$x = \frac{-(-5) \pm \sqrt{(-5)^2 - 4 \times 4 \times 1}}{2 \times 4}$$

$$= \frac{5 \pm \sqrt{25 - 16}}{2 \times 4}$$

$$= \frac{5 \pm \sqrt{9}}{8}$$

$$= \frac{5 \pm 3}{8}$$

giving the two solutions

$$x = \frac{5 + 3}{8} = 1$$

and

$$x = \frac{5 - 3}{8} = 0.25$$

Note that, if it has any at all, we would normally expect two solutions to exists for a quadratic since if the curve passes up through the x axis at some point it must pass back down through it at another as we can see above. The only exception to this would be where the turning point just touches the x axis where we would have just one solution.

## Example

Solve

$$y = x^2 - 2x + 1$$

## Solution

Graphically, this looks as follows

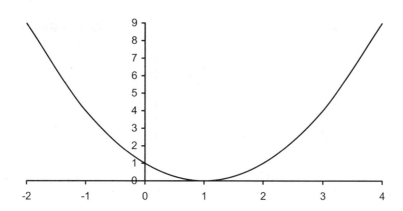

In this example we have

a = 1

b = −2

c = 1

and applying the quadratic equation we get

$$x = \frac{-(-2) \pm \sqrt{(-2)^2 - 4 \times 1 \times 1}}{2 \times 1}$$

$$= \frac{2 \pm \sqrt{4 - 4}}{2 \times 1}$$

$$= \frac{2 \pm \sqrt{0}}{2}$$

which has just one solution of

x = 1

## 4.7 Cubic and polynomial functions

A cubic function has the general form

$$y = ax^3 + bx^2 + cx + d$$

and has a more complex shape. Where a quadratic function has one turning point (maximum or minimum) a cubic function has up to two and may look like either

Positive a coefficient                    Negative a coefficient

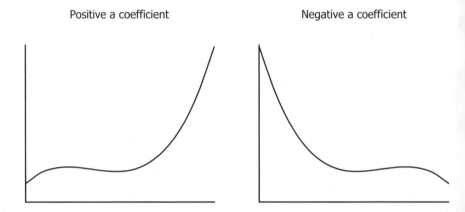

A polynomial function is one containing even higher powers of x such as

$$y = ax^4 + bx^3 + cx^2 + dx + e$$

The maximum number of turning points in such functions is determined by the maximum power of x in the function. The last function which goes to $x^4$ will have up to three turning points.

The one common feature in all of these different shapes is that the highest power is the deciding influence on the ultimate shape. This arises since as x gets larger $x^n$ will be much more significant than $x^{n-1}$ and any lower powers. The highest power will, therefore, dominate the value of y.

As a result of this, when coefficient a is positive, the value of $ax^n$ will be positive for all high positive values of x and the function will be increasing (rising to the right). Conversely if the a coefficient is negative the function will ultimately become a decreasing one at high positive values of x. For example, using the above polynomial

$$y = ax^4 + bx^3 + cx^2 + dx + e$$

we have

Positive a coefficient

Negative a coefficient

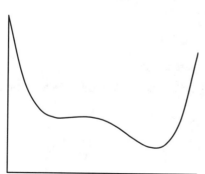
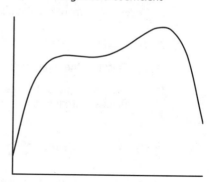

## 4.8 Exponential functions

One final case to consider is exponential functions. It is often said that certain variables grow or decay (shrink) exponentially. An exponential function is based on the exponential constant e (Euler's constant).

Exponential growth can be described by a function of the form

$$y = e^{ax}$$

For example, over the long term GDP growth follows an exponential trend and the world population is exhibiting exponential growth.

Exponential decay is described by the function

$$y = e^{-ax}$$

These two situations could be represented graphically as

Exponential growth $- y = e^{ax}$

Exponential decay $- y = e^{-ax}$

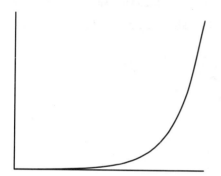
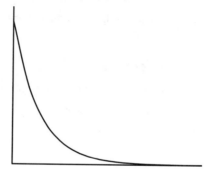

## Exercise 7

### Non linear graphs

A company manufactures a product, the total cost function for the product being given by $C = 25q - q^2$, where q is the quantity produced and C is in £.

### Required

(a)     Calculate the total cost if 15 units are produced.

(b)     Draw a graph of the total cost function and use it to calculate the total cost if 23 units are produced.

# 5   SIMULTANEOUS EQUATIONS

From time to time we may need to determine the point of intersection of two lines. When considering linear functions above, we plotted

$$y = 0.5x + 4$$

and

$$y = -0.2x + 2$$

We can see from the graph we considered at the time that these two lines cross or intersect but what are the coordinates of the point of intersection? Here we have two equations and we must find values for x and y which satisfy both at the same time (simultaneously).

There are a number of different approaches that can be used but perhaps the simplest one is

1.     If necessary, rearrange the first equation into the form $y = a + bx$.

2.     Substitute this value of y into the second equation giving an equation that only contains x values.

3.     Solve for x in this new second equation.

4.     Substitute this value back into the re-arranged first equation to establish y.

It may finally be worthwhile ensuring the derived values work in the second equation, as a check.

## Example

Find the values of x and y that satisfy both

$$y = 0.5x + 4$$

$$y = -0.2x + 2$$

## Solution

1.  **Rearrange first equation** – it is not necessary to rearrange the first equation in this example, it is already in the correct form

    $$y = 0.5x + 4$$

2.  **Substitute into second equation**

    $$y = -0.2x + 2$$

    giving

    $$0.5x + 4 = -0.2x + 2$$

3.  **Solve for x**

    $$0.5x + 4 = -0.2x + 2$$

    Adding 0.2x to both sides gives

    $$0.7x + 4 = 2$$

    Subtracting 4 from both sides gives

    $$0.7x = -2$$

    Dividing both sides by 0.7 gives

    $$x = -2.85714$$

4.  **Substitute into the rearranged first equation to solve for y**

    $$y = 0.5x + 4$$

    $$y = 0.5 \times (-2.85714) + 4 = 2.57143$$

**Checking the solution** – substituting this value of x into the second equation gives

$$y = -0.2x + 2$$

$$y = -0.2 \times (-2.85714) + 2 = 2.57143$$

The same value of y, hence the solution is correct

## Exercise 8

Solve the following simultaneous equation using algebra.

$$5x + 2y = 34$$

$$x + 3y = 25$$

# 6 ARITHMETIC AND GEOMETRIC PROGRESSION

## 6.1 Introduction

In many aspects of finance and finance theory we may need to consider not just a single number but a sequence of numbers. A sequence is an ordered list of numbers such as

5, 7, 9, 11, 13, 15, 17, 19

or

4, 8, 16, 32, 64, 128

Where it is possible to mathematically express what the value of any number in a sequence will be then we will refer to it as a series or progression.

## 6.2 Arithmetic progressions

An arithmetic progression is one where, following the first term, the difference between consecutive terms is constant. The first example above illustrates this, having a first term of five and a constant difference of two.

More generally, if the first term in the series is a and the constant difference is d then the successive terms in the arithmetic progression are

a, a + d, a + 2d, a + 3d, a + 4d ...

and there are two things we may wish to know

- What is the value of the $n^{th}$ term ($t_n$)
- What is the sum of all the terms in the series up to the $n^{th}$ term ($S_n$)

## 6.2.1 Value of the $n^{th}$ term

If we slightly rewrite the series as follows

a + 0d, a + 1d, a + 2d, a + 3d, a + 4d ...

the answer perhaps becomes a little clearer. Where we are considering the $n^{th}$ term we will have

$$t_n = a + (n - 1)d$$

## Example

Applying this to our original example, what should the $8^{th}$ term be?

## Solution

$$t_8 = 5 + (8 - 1) \times 2 = 5 + 14 = 19$$

which we know to be correct from the original example.

## 6.2.2 Sum up to and including the $n^{th}$ term

The sum of the terms in an arithmetic progression up to and including the $n^{th}$ term is given by

$$S_n = \frac{n}{2}(2a + (n-1)d)$$

## Example

Applying this to our original example, what is the sum of the first eight terms?

## Solution

$$S_8 = \frac{8}{2} \times (2 \times 5 + (8-1) \times 2) = 96$$

and checking by first principles shows

$$S_8 = 5 + 7 + 9 + 11 + 13 + 15 + 17 + 19 = 96$$

# 6.3 Geometric progressions

## 6.3.1 Introduction

A geometric progression is one where, following the first term, the ratio between consecutive terms is constant. The second example above illustrates this, having a first term of four and a constant ratio of two.

More generally, if the first term in the series is a and the constant ratio is r then the successive terms in the arithmetic progression are

$$a, ar, ar^2, ar^3, ar^4, ar^5, \ldots$$

and again there are two things we may wish to know

- What is the value of the $n^{th}$ term $(t_n)$
- What is the sum of all the terms in the series up to the $n^{th}$ term $(S_n)$

## 6.3.2 Value of the $n^{th}$ term

Once again we slightly rewrite the series as follows

$$ar^0, ar^1, ar^2, ar^3, ar^4, ar^5, \ldots$$

the answer perhaps becomes a little clearer. Where we are considering the $n^{th}$ term we will have

$$t_n = ar^{n-1}$$

## Example

Applying this to our original example, what should the value of the $8^{th}$ term be?

## Solution

$$T_8 = 4 \times 2^{(6-1)} = 4 \times 2^5 = 4 \times 32 = 128$$

which we know to be correct from the original example.

## 6.3.3 Sum up to and including the $n^{th}$ term

The sum of the terms in a geometric progression up to and including the $n^{th}$ term is given by

$$S_n = \frac{a(r^n - 1)}{r - 1}$$

## Example

Applying this to our original example, what is the sum of the first six terms?

## Solution

$$S_6 = \frac{4(2^6 - 1)}{2 - 1} = 4(2^6 - 1) = 4 \times 63 = 252$$

and checking by first principles shows

$$S_6 = 4 + 8 + 16 + 32 + 64 + 128 = 252$$

## Exercise 9

Calculate the value of the $9^{th}$ item and the sum up to and including the $9^{th}$ item of the

(a)     Arithmetic progression          5, 8, 11, 14, 17, 20...

(b)     Geometric progression          8, 24, 72, 216, 648, 1,944...

# 7 MATHEMATICAL RELATIONSHIPS SUMMARY

## 7.1 Mathematical precedence

Order of mathematical precedence is given by the mnemonic BIDMAS, ie

- **B**rackets
- **I**ndices (powers and roots)
- **D**ivision and **M**ultiplication
- **A**ddition and **S**ubtraction

## 7.2 Expanding brackets

For any three numbers or variables a, x and y

$a(x + y) \equiv (ax + ay)$

## 7.3 Negative numbers

### Addition and subtraction

- When we add a negative, we subtract.
- When we subtract a negative, we add.

### Multiplication and division

| Multiplication | Division |
|---|---|
| Positive × Positive = Positive | Positive ÷ Positive = Positive |
| Positive × Negative = Negative | Positive ÷ Negative = Negative |
| Negative × Positive = Negative | Negative ÷ Positive = Negative |
| Negative × Negative = Positive | Negative ÷ Negative = Positive |

Which could be summarised further as

- Same signs give a Positive
- Opposite signs give a Negative

## 7.4 Fractions

- $\text{Fraction} = \dfrac{\text{Numerator}}{\text{Denominator}}$

### Reciprocal

The reciprocal of a number, x, is 1 divided by that number, i.e. $\dfrac{1}{x}$

The reciprocal of a fraction, $\dfrac{a}{b}$, is $\dfrac{b}{a}$

Dividing is identical to multiplying by the reciprocal, ie

$x \div y = x \times \dfrac{1}{y}$

## Multiplication and division

$$\frac{a}{b} \times \frac{c}{d} = \frac{a \times c}{b \times d} = \frac{ac}{bd}$$

$$\frac{a}{b} \div \frac{c}{d} = \frac{a}{b} \times \frac{d}{c} = \frac{a \times d}{b \times c} = \frac{ad}{bc}$$

## Addition and subtraction

Firstly determine the common denominator, then

$$\frac{x}{d} + \frac{y}{d} = \frac{x + y}{d}$$

$$\frac{x}{d} - \frac{y}{d} = \frac{x - y}{d}$$

## 7.5 Powers and roots

- When we multiply powers of the same number we add the powers.
- When we divide powers of the same number we subtract the powers.
- When we raise a power to a power we multiply the powers.
- For any value, a, $a^0 = 1$.
- For negative powers, $a^{-n} = \dfrac{1}{a^n}$
- Fractional powers, $a^{1/n}$ is the $n^{th}$ root of a

## 7.6 Functions and graphs

### Graphs

Positive y values

**Quadrant 2**     |     **Quadrant 1**

Negative x values ——————————————— Positive x values

**Quadrant 3**     |     **Quadrant 4**

Negative y values

x = independent variable
y = dependent variable

## Linear functions

The general form of a linear function is

$$y = a + bx$$

where

$a$ = Intercept (value of $y$ when $x = 0$)

$$b = \text{Slope} = \frac{\text{Change in } y}{\text{Change in } x}$$

## Quadratic functions

The general form of a quadratic function is

$$y = ax^2 + bx + c$$

Which can be solved with the quadratic equation

$$x = \frac{-b \pm \sqrt{b^2 - 4ac}}{2a}$$

## Cubic and polynomial functions

The general form of a cubic function is

$$y = ax^3 + bx^2 + cx + d$$

Higher power polynomials contain higher powers of $x$, eg

$$y = ax^4 + bx^3 + cx^2 + dx + e$$

## Exponential functions

Exponential growth is described by the function

$$y = e^{ax}$$

Exponential decay is described by the function

$$y = e^{-ax}$$

## Simultaneous equations

1.  If necessary, rearrange the first equation into the form $y = a + bx$.

2.  Substitute this value of $y$ into the second equation giving an equation that only contains $x$ values.

3.  Solve for $x$ in this new second equation.

4.  Substitute this value back into the re-arranged first equation to establish $y$.

## 7.7 Arithmetic and geometric progression

### Arithmetic progression

Value of the $n^{th}$ term

$$t_n = a + (n - 1)d$$

Sum of the terms up to and including the $n^{th}$ term

$$S_n = \frac{n}{2}(2a + (n - 1)d)$$

### Geometric progressions

Value of the $n^{th}$ term

$$t_n = ar^{n-1}$$

Sum of the terms up to and including the $n^{th}$ term

$$S_n = \frac{a(r^n - 1)}{r - 1}$$

# 8 SOLUTIONS TO EXERCISES

1.  (a)  648.2565            (d)  11,985.6898

    (b)  30.0192             (e)  93.31

    (c)  0.4097              (f)  −102.79

2.  (a)  $64 - (-1) = 64 + 1 = 65$

    (b)  $-24 - (12) = -36$

3.  (a)  $8 + (-9) = -1$

    (b)  $-6 - (-12 - (-27)) = -6 + 12 + 27 = 33$

4.  (a)  40,000

    (b)  0.07

    (c)  0.0073

    (d)  $974 \times 586$ = 570,764
         = 571,000 (3 sf)

    (e)  $23 \div 946$ = 0.02431289641
         = 0.024 (3 dp)

5.  (a)  $(18.6)^{2.6} = 1,998.6358$

    (b)  $(18.6)^{2.6} = \left(\dfrac{1}{18.6}\right)^{2.6} = 0.0005$

    (c)  $\sqrt[2.6]{18.6} = 3.078$

    (d)  $(14.2)^4 \times (14.2)^{\frac{1}{4}} = (14.2)^{4.25} = 78,926.976$

    (e)  $(14.2)^4 + (14.2)^{\frac{1}{4}} = 40,658.6896 + 1.9412 = 40,660.6308$

6.  (a)  The gradient $= -1$

         If $y = 10 - x$, then $a = 10$ and $b = -1$ ($-1 \times x = -x$).

         Therefore gradient $= -1$

    (b)  $4y = 16x - 12$

         Equation must be in form $y = a + bx$

         $y = -3 + 4x$ (divide both sides by 4)

         Intercept $= a -3$

         Gradient $= b = 4$

         Therefore the correct answer is A.

If you selected option D, you have obviously confused the intercept and the gradient. Remember that with an equation in the form y = a + bx, a = intercept (ie where the line of the graph crosses the y axis) and b = the slope or gradient of the line.

(c)　(i)　　Let　　C = total costs
　　　　　　　　　C = total variable costs + total fixed costs
　　　　　　　　　C = 5q + 75

　　　(ii)　　If q = 100, C = (5 × 100) + 75 = £575

　　　(iii)　　If q = 0,　　　C = £75
　　　　　　　If q = 100,　　C = £575

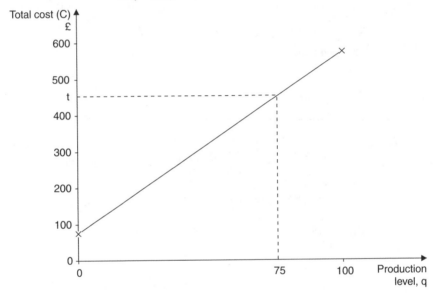

Total cost (C) £

　　　(iv)　　From the graph above, if q = 75, C = £450

7.　(a)　　C = 25q − q$^2$
　　　　　　If q = 15, C = (25 × 15) − 15$^2$ = 375 − 225 = £150

　　(b)

| q | C |
|---|---|
| 0 | 0 |
| 5.0 | 100.00 |
| 10.0 | 150.00 |
| 12.5 | 156.25 |
| 15.0 | 150.00 |
| 20.0 | 100.00 |
| 25.0 | 0 |

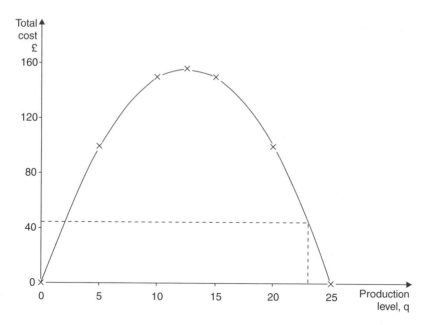

From the graph, if 23 units are produced the total cost is approximately £45

8.  $5x + 2y = 34$        (1)
    $x + 3y = 25$        (2)

Multiply (2) x 5:

$5x + 15y = 125$       (3)

Subtract (1) from (3):

$13y = 91$

  $y = 7$

Substitute into (2):

$x + \quad 21 = 25$

       $x = 25 - 21$

       $x = 4$

The solution is $x = 4$, $y = 7$

9. Arithmetic progression

$a + (n - 1)d$

$t_9 = = 5 + (9 - 1) \times 3 = 29$

$S_n = \dfrac{n}{2}(2a + (n - 1)d)$

$S_9 = \dfrac{9}{2}(2 \times 5 + (9 - 1) \times 3) = 153$

Geometric progression

$t_n = ar^{n-1}$

$t_9 = 8 \times 3^{9-1} = 52,488$

$S_n = \dfrac{a(r^n - 1)}{r - 1}$

$S_9 = \dfrac{8(3^9 - 1)}{3 - 1} = 78,728$

# APPENDIX – DERIVATION OF FORMULAE

## Quadratic equation proof

The solutions to the quadratic is

$$ax^2 + bx + c = 0$$

Dividing by a gives

$$x^2 + \frac{b}{a}x + \frac{c}{a} = 0$$

and subtracting $\frac{c}{a}$ from both sides gives

$$x^2 + \frac{b}{a}x = -\frac{c}{a}$$

Now, adding $\frac{b^2}{4a^2}$ to both sides gives

$$x^2 + \frac{b}{a}x + \frac{b^2}{4a^2} = \frac{b^2}{4a^2} - \frac{c}{a}$$

and we can rewrite the left hand side of this to give

$$\left(x + \frac{b}{2a}\right)^2 = \frac{b^2}{4a^2} - \frac{c}{a}$$

Restating the right hand side with a common denominator of $4a^2$ gives

$$\left(x + \frac{b}{2a}\right)^2 = \frac{b^2}{4a^2} - \frac{4ac}{4a^2}$$

or

$$\left(x + \frac{b}{2a}\right)^2 = \frac{(b^2 - 4ac)}{4a^2}$$

Now taking the square root of both sides gives

$$x + \frac{b}{2a} = \frac{\pm\sqrt{b^2 - 4ac}}{2a}$$

Hence

$$x = \frac{-b}{2a} + \frac{\pm\sqrt{b^2 - 4ac}}{2a}$$

or

$$x = \frac{-b \pm \sqrt{b^2 - 4ac}}{2a}$$

## The exponential

The definition of the exponential equation is

$$e^x = 1 + x + \frac{x^2}{2!} + \frac{x^3}{3!} + \frac{x^4}{4!} + \frac{x^5}{5!} + \ldots$$

or

$$e^x = \sum_{n=0}^{\infty} \frac{x^n}{n!}$$

The inverse function to the exponential is the natural logarithm, $\ln(x)$, ie

$$e^x \times \ln(x) = 1$$

The exponential constant is where $x = 1$, which gives

$$e^1 = 1 + 1 + \frac{1^2}{2!} + \frac{1^3}{3!} + \frac{1^4}{4!} + \frac{1^5}{5!} + \ldots = 2.718281828\ldots$$

## Arithmetic progression

The $n^{th}$ term of an arithmetic series is

$$t_n = a + (n - 1)d$$

Hence the sum of the first n terms of an arithmetic series is

$$S_n = a + (a + d) + (a + 2d) + \ldots + (a + (n - 2)d) + (a + (n - 1)d)$$

And if we simply reverse the order of the terms, which has no effect on its value, we will have

$$S_n = (a + (n - 1)d) + (a + (n - 2)d) + \ldots + (a + 2d) + (a + d) + a$$

Adding these equations term by term gives

$$2S_n = (2a + (n - 1)d) + (2a + (n - 1)d) + \ldots + (2a + (n - 1)d) + (2a + (n - 1)d)$$

or, since there are n terms

$$2S_n = n(2a + (n - 1)d)$$

and hence

$$S_n = \frac{n}{2}(2a + (n - 1)d)$$

## Geometric progressions

The $n^{th}$ term in a geometric series is

$$t_n = ar^{n-1}$$

Hence the sum of the first n terms of a geometric series is

$$S_n = a + ar + ar^2 + ar^3 + \ldots + ar^{n-2} + ar^{n-1},$$

Multiplying both sides by r gives

$$rS_n = ar + ar^2 + ar^3 + ar^4 + \ldots + ar^{n-1} + ar^n,$$

Subtracting the first equation from the second gives

$$rS_n - S_n = ar^n - a$$

Since on the right hand side all but the first term in the first equation and the last term in the second are common. Now rearranging both sides gives

$$S_n(r - 1) = a(r^n - 1)$$

Hence

$$S_n = \frac{a(r^n - 1)}{r - 1}$$

# 2  Calculus

## Contents

# 1 DIFFERENTIATION

## 1.1 Introduction

In the previous section we considered a variety of functions including linear, quadratic, cubic and polynomial. For all but the first of these we noted that their graphical representations were curved, possibly exhibiting one or more peaks (maximum points) and troughs (minimum points).

Imagine, for example, that we have constructed a mathematical model of how the profits of the company vary with sales levels, and have found this to be a dome shaped quadratic. We may wish to determine the sales level that will maximise profits. How can we achieve this? The solution is with the aid of differentiation as we will illustrate with the aid of the following example.

### Example

The profits of the company are described by the following equation

$$y = 100x - 0.0008x^2 - 300,000$$

where

y = Profit

x = Sales level

Plot a graph of profit against sales levels, determine the sales level that maximises profits and the level of those profits.

### Solution

If we plot a graph of the profit function we get

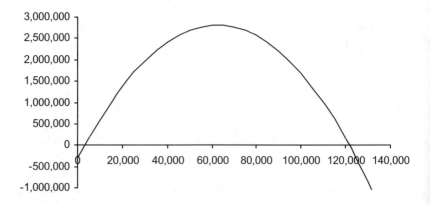

We can see from this graph that profits reach a peak at just over 60,000 units giving rise to a profit just under £3m.

But what if we wanted more accuracy than this? The answer is to recognise that profits are maximised when the slope of this function is zero. You will recall from the previous section that the slope, which may be referred to as the rate of change, can be calculated as

$$\text{Slope} = \frac{\text{Change in y}}{\text{Change in x}}$$

As x increases (a positive change in x)

- before the peak, y is increasing – a positive slope.

- after the peak, y is decreasing – a negative slope.

- at the peak, y is neither increasing or decreasing, the change in y is zero and the slope is zero.

What we need is a method that will allow us to determine the slope of the line at any point, and hence whether it is increasing or decreasing, which is what differentiation provides. What we will come to know as the first differential gives the slope of the line.

## 1.2 Theoretical development

### 1.2.1 Introduction

As we have already noted, the slope of a line can, in principle, be determined using

$$\text{Slope} = \frac{\text{Change in y}}{\text{Change in x}}$$

This is fine for linear relationships where the slope is constant, however we need to take some care for curves. If in the above example we take two values of x (say 30,000 and 40,000) determine the corresponding values of y (1.98m and 2.42m) and insert them in this equation we will get

$$\text{Slope} = \frac{2,420,000 - 1,980,000}{40,000 - 30,000} = 44$$

What this tells us is that the slope between x = 30,000 and x = 40,000 is 44 – a positive slope. What we have calculated is, effectively, the average slope over that range of x values. However, we don't want the average slope over a range of values of x, we want the instantaneous slope at any single value of x so that we can find the single value of x that maximises profits. How can we take this idea to achieve our objective?

To examine the theoretical development of differentiation we will consider an easier example

$$y = x^2$$

If we plot this, we get

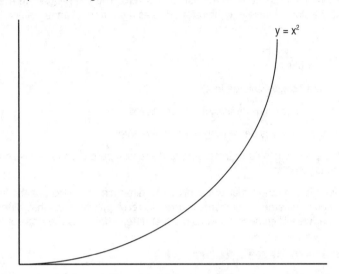

and the slope at point x would be the tangent at that point as illustrated below

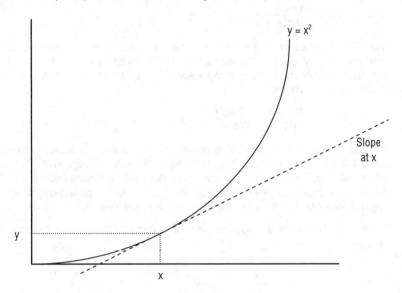

Now, if we wanted to work out the slope at x, we could pick a second higher x value, determine the corresponding y value and apply our slope formula, for example if we choose $x_1$ we will get

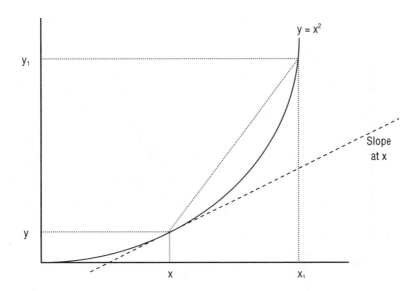

What we can see from the line connecting the points is that the slope between x and $x_1$ is steeper than the true slope at x. How can we get a closer approximation? We could try a closer second value in place of $x_1$, say $x_2$, which gives

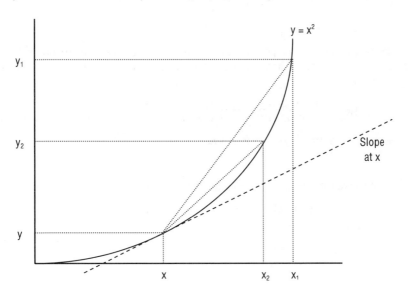

The slope between x and $x_2$ is clearly a closer match than that between x and $x_1$, however it is still not very accurate. However, if we choose a third closer value, $x_3$, we get even closer still.

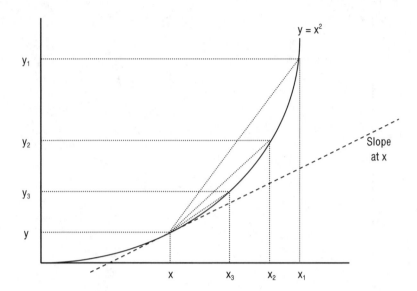

What is clear from this is that the closer together the two x values are, the better the match it is to the true slope. The idea behind differentiation is to consider smaller and smaller differences between the selected x values until we establish the true slope value.

## 1.3 First principles differentiation

Let us consider the two points $x$ and $x + \delta x$ (where $\delta x$ is a small change in the x value) which have corresponding y values of $y$ and $y + \delta y$. The slope between these points would be

$$\text{Slope} = \frac{\text{Change in y}}{\text{Change in x}} = \frac{(y + \delta y) - y}{(x + \delta x) - x} = \frac{\delta y}{\delta x}$$

Now, in our example here we are using

$$y = x^2$$

so when we move from $x$ to $x + \delta x$ we will have

$$y + \delta y = (x + \delta x)^2 = x^2 + 2x\delta x + \delta x^2$$

and subtracting

$$y = x^2$$

gives

$$\delta y = 2x\delta x + \delta x^2$$

So the slope will be

$$\text{Slope} = \frac{\delta y}{\delta x} = \frac{2x\delta x + \delta x^2}{\delta x} = 2x + \delta x$$

for any value of $x$ and $\delta x$.

What we know, however, is that to get an accurate measure of the slope we need to minimise the difference between the two points ($\delta x$), and in the limit as $\delta x$ tends to zero, the slope in this example simply becomes

$$\text{Slope} = \frac{dy}{dx} = 2x$$

Note, that we have changed $\frac{\delta y}{\delta x}$ to $\frac{dy}{dx}$ as an indication that we are considering this limiting situation and we may refer to this as the first differential of y with respect to x.

## 1.4 Mechanics

### 1.4.1 Basic mechanics

The above first principles approach may be applied to any functions we have. What we find, however, is that there are rules that we can apply to simplify any evaluations.

If we undertake a similar analysis for various powers of x we would find the following.

| y | $x^2$ | $x^3$ | $x^4$ | $x^5$ | $x^6$ | $x^7$ | $x^8$ |
|---|---|---|---|---|---|---|---|
| $\frac{dy}{dx}$ | $2x$ | $3x^2$ | $4x^3$ | $5x^4$ | $6x^5$ | $7x^6$ | $8x^7$ |

From this it appears that a general expression we could use is that if

$$y = x^n$$

then

$$\frac{dy}{dx} = nx^{n-1}$$

So **to differentiate** any power of x we **multiply by the power then subtract one from the power**.

Taking this a little further, consider

$$y = 6x^2$$

Now when we move from x to $x + \delta x$ we will have

$$y + \delta y = 6(x + \delta x)^2 = 6(x^2 + 2x\delta x + \delta x^2)$$

giving

$$\delta y = 6(2x\delta x + \delta x^2)$$

and so the slope will be

$$\text{Slope} = \frac{\delta y}{\delta x} = \frac{6(2x\delta x + \delta x^2)}{\delta x} = 6(2x + \delta x)$$

which, in the limit as $\delta x$ tends to zero, becomes

$$\text{Slope} = \frac{dy}{dx} = 6(2x) = 12x$$

More generally then, we have that when

$$y = ax^n$$

where a is a constant, then

$$\frac{dy}{dx} = anx^{n-1}$$

Which is, perhaps, the most general reflection of the relationship between y and $\frac{dy}{dx}$.

## 1.5 Constants

What if we have a constant in a function such as

$$y = 6x^2 + 4$$

When we move from x to x + $\delta$x we will have

$$y + \delta y = 6(x + \delta x)^2 + 4 = 6(x^2 + 2x\delta x + \delta x^2) + 4$$

and subtracting

$$y = 6x^2 + 4$$

gives

$$\delta y = 6(2x\delta x + \delta x^2)$$

so the slope will be

$$\text{Slope} = \frac{\delta y}{\delta x} = \frac{6(2x\delta x + \delta x^2)}{\delta x} = 6(2x + \delta x)$$

which, in the limit as $\delta$x tends to zero, becomes

$$\text{Slope} = \frac{dy}{dx} = 6(2x) = 12x$$

What we can see here is that the constant has disappeared in the differentiation process. This is because a constant function such as y = 4 has no slope so a constant makes no contribution to the slope of any function.

We could state this generally as if

$$y = ax^n + c$$

where a and c are constants, then

$$\frac{dy}{dx} = anx^{n-1}$$

## 1.6 Distributed functions

Can we apply these ideas to the differentiation of distributed functions, ie functions with several terms that are added together, such as

$$y = 6x^3 + 3x^2$$

First as a notation point, for convenience such functions may be abbreviated to the form

$$y = f(x)$$

and the first differential may be noted as

$$\frac{dy}{dx} = \frac{d}{dx} f(x)$$

the $\frac{d}{dx}$ notifying us that we are differentiating with respect to x.

Now, applying the first principles approach to this function, if we move to the point $x + \delta x$ (corresponding to a y value of $y + \delta y$), we get

$$y + \delta y = 6(x + \delta x)^3 + 3(x + \delta x)^2$$
$$= 6(x^3 + 3x^2\delta x + 3x\delta x^2 + \delta x^3) + 3(x^2 + 2x\delta x + \delta x^2)$$
$$= 6x^3 + 18x^2\delta x + 18x\delta x^2 + 6\delta x^3 + 3x^2 + 6x\delta x + 3\delta x^2$$

and subtracting $y = 6x^3 + 3x^2$ gives

$$\delta y = 18x^2\delta x + 18x\delta x^2 + 6\delta x^3 + 6x\delta x + 3\delta x^2$$

As a result, the slope here is

$$\text{Slope} = \frac{\delta y}{\delta x} = \frac{18x^2\delta x + 18x\delta x^2 + 6\delta x^3 + 6x\delta x + 3\delta x^2}{\delta x}$$
$$= 18x^2 + 18x\delta x + 6\delta x^2 + 6x + 3\delta x$$

which in the limit as $\delta x$ tends to zero gives

$$\text{Slope} = \frac{dy}{dx} = 18x^2 + 6x$$

So we have established from first principles that the first differential of

$$y = 6x^3 + 3x^2$$

is

$$\frac{dy}{dx} = 18x^2 + 6x$$

However, from what we have seen above, we know that the differential of $6x^3$ is $18x^2$ and the differential of $3x^2$ is $6x$, so if we had differentiated each of the two terms separately we would have arrived at the same result.

What this illustrates is that differentiation is distributive across addition (and subtraction – adding a negative), ie **to differentiate a distributed function we apply the rules to each term of the function in turn**.

We could state this as if

$$y = ax^n + bx^m$$

where a and b are a constants, then

$$\frac{dy}{dx} = anx^{n-1} + bmx^{m-1}$$

Alternatively, it may be stated as if

$$y = f(x) + g(x)$$

then

$$\frac{dy}{dx} = \frac{d}{dx} f(x) + \frac{d}{dx} g(x)$$

## Exercise 1

Differentiate with respect to x

(a)    $y = 15x^4 - 8x^2 + 5x - 3$

(b)    $y = 56x^8 + 14x^3$

(c)    $y = 13x^4 + 5x^6$

## 1.7 Multiplicative functions

What if our function is of the form

$$y = f(x) \times g(x) \text{sometimes abbreviated to as } y = uv$$

What is $\frac{dy}{dx}$ ?

Consider

$$y = 6x^3 \times 4x^2$$

Algebraically, this could be converted to

$$y = 24x^5$$

giving

$$\frac{dy}{dx} = 120x^4$$

Another way of getting to the same solution is to apply the following differentiation rule.

Where

$$y = uv$$

then

$$\frac{dy}{dx} = u\frac{dv}{dx} + v\frac{du}{dx}$$

Applying this idea to this example we have

$$u = 6x^3$$
$$v = 4x^2$$

so

$$\frac{du}{dx} = 18x^2$$

$$\frac{dv}{dx} = 8x$$

and

$$\frac{dy}{dx} = u\frac{dv}{dx} + v\frac{du}{dx} = 6x^3 \times 8x + 4x^2 \times 18x^2 = 48x^4 + 72x^4 = 120x^4$$

as before.

## Exercise 2

Differentiate

$$y = (2x^3 + 6x + 5)(3x^2 + 4x + 7)$$

## 1.8 Function of a function

How can we deal with a function such as

$$y = (x^2 - 1)^{\frac{1}{2}}$$

which cannot be easily expanded? The answer is to consider this as the differentiation of the function of a function, that is where

$$y = g(u)$$

and

$$u = f(x)$$

then

$$\frac{dy}{dx} = \frac{dy}{du} \times \frac{du}{dx}$$

So if we set

$$u = (x^2 - 1)$$

then

$$y = u^{\frac{1}{2}}$$

So

$$\frac{dy}{du} = \frac{1}{2}u^{-\frac{1}{2}}$$

or

$$\frac{dy}{du} = \frac{1}{2}(x^2 - 1)^{-\frac{1}{2}}$$

and

$$\frac{du}{dx} = 2x$$

hence

$$\frac{dy}{dx} = \frac{dy}{du} \times \frac{du}{dx} = \frac{1}{2}(x^2 - 1)^{-\frac{1}{2}} \times 2x = x(x^2 - 1)^{-\frac{1}{2}} \text{ or } \frac{x}{(x^2 - 1)^{\frac{1}{2}}}$$

## Exercise 3

Differentiate

$$y = (3x^2 + 2x + 5)^{1/4}$$

# 1.9 Some specific functions

Some specific functions that we may be interested in are the exponential function

$$y = e^x$$

and the natural logarithm function

$$y = \ln(x)$$

## 1.9.1 Exponential function

Now in the last section we introduced the definition of $e^x$ as

$$e^x = 1 + x + \frac{x^2}{2!} + \frac{x^3}{3!} + \frac{x^4}{4!} + \frac{x^5}{5!} + \dots$$

and, applying the above principles for distributive functions, gives

$$\frac{d}{dx} e^x = 0 + 1 + x + \frac{x^2}{2!} + \frac{x^3}{3!} + \frac{x^4}{4!} + \dots = e^x$$

ie

$$\frac{d}{dx} e^x = e^x$$

## 1.9.2 Natural logarithm

Now, consider the function

$$y = \ln(x)$$

Which is valid where $x > 0$. Then, taking the exponential of each side of this equation, we may say

$$e^y = e^{\ln(x)} = x$$

or

$$x = e^y$$

Now differentiating this with respect to y, applying what we derived above

$$\frac{dx}{dy} = e^y = x$$

and taking the reciprocal of each side this gives

$$\frac{dy}{dx} = \frac{1}{x}$$

So in conclusion, if

$$y = \ln(x)$$

then

$$\frac{dy}{dx} = \frac{1}{x}$$

# 1.10 Maximum points and minimum points

## 1.10.1 Determining the turning point

We have now considered all of the basic mechanical aspects of differentiate that we may need and we can move on to how we can apply the idea.

As we noted earlier in this section, the first differential of a function gives the slope of that function at a specific point. Where we may need to use this is in determining any turning points, ie where any functions are maximised or minimised.

The important characteristic of a turning point, as we noted earlier, is that the slope of the function at that point is zero, so to find the turning point we must equate the first differential to zero.

## Example

Referring back to the original example in this section, we had the profits of the company described by the function

$$y = 100x - 0.0008x^2 - 300,000$$

where

$$y = \text{Profit}$$

$$x = \text{Sales level}$$

Determine the sales level that maximises profits.

## Solution

Applying what we have covered above we get

$$\frac{dy}{dx} = 100 - 0.0016x$$

So for the maximum point, we need

$$100 - 0.0016x = 0$$

Now, adding 0.0016x to both sides gives

$$100 = 0.0016x$$

or

$0.0016x = 100$

and dividing both sides by 0.0016 gives

$x = 100 \div 0.0016 = 62,500$

Feeding this back into the original function

$y = 100x - 0.0008x^2 - 300,000$

gives

$y = 100 \times 62,500 - 0.0008 \times 62,500^2 - 300,000 = 2,825,000$

That is, profits are maximised at £2,825,000 when the output level is 62,500 units.

# 1.11 Determining whether it is a maximum point or a minimum point

## 1.11.1 Introduction

For the above equation we know from our graph that the turning point we have calculated is a maximum point but how can we tell whether we have calculated a maximum point or a minimum point in the absence of a graph.

The answer is through the aid of the second differential which involves differentiating the first differential and is designated $\frac{d^2y}{dx^2}$.

The first differential gives the rate of change of the y value, or slope of the line. The second differential gives the rate of change of the slope, or the curvature of the line, and

- A positive curvature implies an increasing slope as x increases,

- A negative curvature implies a decreasing slope as x increases.

As a result, the general shape at a turning point will be

Positive second differential                        Negative second differential

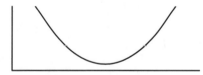 

As a result, at a turning point

- a positive differential implies a minimum point

- a negative differential implies a maximum point

## Example

Referring once more to the original example in this section, we had the profits of the company described by the function

$$y = 100x - 0.0008x^2 - 300{,}000$$

and had calculated the first differential as

$$\frac{dy}{dx} = 100 - 0.0016x$$

From which we determined the sales level that maximises profits as 62,500.

Show that this is a maximum point.

## Solution

Applying what we have covered above we get

$$\frac{d^2y}{dx^2} = -0.0016$$

a negative, hence the turning point is a maximum point.

## Conclusion

At any turning point

if $\frac{d^2y}{dx^2}$ is **positive** $\Rightarrow$ **minimum point**

if $\frac{d^2y}{dx^2}$ is **negative** $\Rightarrow$ **maximum point**

## 1.12 Partial differentiation

All of the functions we have considered so far have had one independent variable (x) and one dependent variable (y). It is quite possible, however, that there may be a number of independent variables that drive the dependent variable. For example, it may be that a company's profits are a function of

- *UK sales volumes* and the *sterling selling price*

- *European sales volumes*, the *Euro selling price* and the *exchange rate*

ie five different independent variables (italicised).

How could we establish the sales level that maximises profits in a situation like this?

The approach to apply here is partial differentiation, the mechanics of which is essentially the same as we have seen already along with a simultaneous equation problem.

The approach to a partial differentiation exercise is

1.  Differentiate the function with respect to each variable separately, assuming temporarily that all other independent variables are constant. This will produce a number of partial differentials, each one relating to one variable.

2.  For a turning point we need the differential with respect to any variable to be zero. For the turning points here we need the differentials with respect to all independent variables to equate to zero which we can solve through simultaneous equations – maximising the y value with respect to all input variables simultaneously.

Note, it is normal to designate the partial differential as $\frac{\partial y}{\partial x}$ rather than $\frac{dy}{dx}$ to highlight that it is a partial differential.

## Example

Consider the function

$$y = 4x^2 + 8xz + 5z^2 + 6x + 2z + 9$$

What values of x and z will maximise or minimise this function?

## Solution

1.  **Differentiating with respect to each independent variable**

    Differentiating

    $$y = 4x^2 + 8xz + 5z^2 + 6x + 2z + 9$$

    with respect to x, assuming that z remains constant, gives

    $$\frac{\partial y}{\partial x} = 8x + 8z + 6$$

    Differentiating

    $$y = 4x^2 + 8xz + 5z^2 + 6x + 2z + 9$$

    with respect to z, assuming that x remains constant, gives

    $$\frac{\partial y}{\partial z} = 8x + 10z + 2$$

2.  **Determining the turning point**

    For the turning point we need both of these partial differentials to equate to zero simultaneously, ie we need to solve simultaneously

    $$8x + 8z + 6 = 0$$

    and

    $$8x + 10z + 2 = 0$$

    Now, from the first equation

    $$8x = -8z - 6$$

or

x = −z − 0.75

Substituting this in the second equation gives

$$8(-z - 0.75) + 10z + 2 = 0$$

and expanding the brackets gives

$$-8z - 6 + 10z + 2 = 0$$

or

$$2z - 4 = 0$$

Adding 4 to both sides gives

$$2z = 4$$

and dividing both sides by 2 gives

$$z = 2$$

Substituting this back into the rearranged first equation

$$x = -z - 0.75$$

gives

$$x = -2 - 0.75 = -2.75$$

That is, y is at a turning point when x = − 2.75 and z = 2.

Substituting these x and z values into the original function

$$y = 4x^2 + 8xz + 5z^2 + 6x + 2z + 9$$

gives

$$y = 4 \times (-2.75)^2 + 8 \times (-2.75) \times 2 + 5 \times 2^2 + 6 \times (-2.75) + 2 \times 2 + 9$$
$$= 2.75$$

Hence, in this example the turning point is at x = −2.75, z = 2, corresponding to a y value of 2.75.

# 2 INTEGRATION

## 2.1 Introduction

For any function, differentiation allows us to determine the rate of change (or slope) of that function. What if we need to determine the original function when the rate of change is known? The answer is that we need to reverse the differentiation process, and this reverse process is called integration.

## 2.2 Theoretical development

### 2.2.1 Introduction

When

$$y = x^2$$

we had

$$\frac{dy}{dx} = 2x$$

So if we integrate 2x we should get back to $x^2$.

There is, however, one small issue to contend with. If we differentiate

$$y = x^2 + 4$$

we again get

$$\frac{dy}{dx} = 2x$$

since the constant in the original function has a zero rate of change and hence vanishes in the differentiation process. So, how can we get back to $x^2 + 4$ if we integrate 2x this time?

Since any constants vanish when we differentiate, they need to reappear when we integrate. When we integrate 2x, therefore, we should get

$$y = x^2 + c$$

where c is a constant whose value needs to be determined from the available data. If, for example, we know that when x = 2, y = 7 then we would have

$$
\begin{aligned}
7 &= 2^2 + c \\
7 &= 4 + c \\
c &= 3
\end{aligned}
$$

### 2.2.2 Notation

From the point of view of notation, for differentiation we had that where

$$y = f(x)$$

the first differential may be noted as

$$\frac{dy}{dx} = \frac{d}{dx} f(x)$$

the $\frac{d}{dx}$ notifying us that we are differentiating with respect to x.

If we wish to integrate a function f(x) in order to establish a mathematical equation fo this integral, the notation is

$$\int f(x)dx$$

the $\int$ symbol indicating that we are integrating, and the dx indicating that we are doing so with respect to x.

This may be referred to as an indefinite integral since we are leaving the solution as an equation rather than evaluating for certain values of x. When we are evaluating the integral at certain x values we may refer to the process as establishing the definite integral which we see later.

## 2.3 Mechanics

### 2.3.1 Introduction

The mechanical stages when we differentiate are

1.      multiply by the power
2.      subtract one from the power

with any constant in the original vanishing as part of that process.

The mechanics for integration, being the reverse of differentiation, is therefore

1.      Add one to the power
2.      Divide by the new power
3.      Add on a constant, c

And we can state this by the general expression that if

$$y = ax^n$$

then

$$\int y\,dx = \int ax^n\,dx = \frac{ax^{n+1}}{n+1} + c$$

for all values of n except n = −1, where

$$\int x^{-1}dx = \int \frac{1}{x}\,dx = \ln(x) + c$$

based on what we saw earlier when we differentiated the natural logarithm, ln(x).

### 2.3.2 Constants

Note, that we said this applies to all values of n except n = −1, so in particular it will apply to n = 0. For example, what is the integral of

$$y = a$$

where a is a constant. Based on the idea that for any number, x, $x^0 = 1$, we could rewrite this as

$$y = ax^0$$

And integrating this applying the above rules gives

$$\int y\,dx = \int ax^0\,dx = ax^1 \qquad \text{or more simply} \qquad ax$$

### 2.3.3 Distributed functions

Now we saw earlier that differentiation was distributive over addition and subtraction, ie if

$$y = f(x) + g(x)$$

then

$$\frac{dy}{dx} = \frac{d}{dx}f(x) + \frac{d}{dx}g(x)$$

Since integration is simply the reverse of differentiation, it follows that integration is also distributive over addition and subtraction, which we could state as

$$\int(f(x) + g(x))dx = \int f(x)dx + \int g(x)dx$$

What this means is that if there are several terms in a function we can deal with each one separately.

### Example

Integrate

$$y = 8x^3 + 12x^2 - 6x - 5$$

with respect to x.

### Solution

$$\int y\,dx = \int(8x^3 + 12x^2 - 6x - 5)\,dx$$

$$= \int 8x^3\,dx + \int 12x^2\,dx - \int 6x\,dx - \int 5\,dx$$

$$= \int 8x^3\,dx + \int 12x^2\,dx - \int 6x\,dx - \int 5x^0\,dx$$

$$= \frac{8x^4}{4} + \frac{12x^3}{3} - \frac{6x^2}{2} - \frac{5x^1}{1} + c$$

$$= 2x^4 + 4x^3 - 3x^2 - 5x + c$$

### Exercise 4

Integrate $y = 6x^2 + 12x + 3$

### Application

Though we have introduced integration as the reverse process of differentiation, it ca be viewed as serving a second purpose.

Consider the line $y = 3$, what will be the area under that line from the origin to a point x?

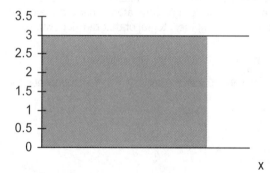

Since this is a rectangle, the area will be

Area = Height × Width = 3x

Now, if we integrate the line y = 3 we get

$$\int y\,dx = \int 3\,dx = \int 3x^0\,dx = 3x + c$$

Which, when c = 0, corresponds to the area.

Consider, alternatively, the line y = 2x, what will be the area under that line from the origin to a point x?

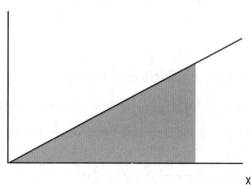

Since this is a triangle, the area will be

Area = ½ Base × Height = ½ × x × y = ½ × x × 2x = $x^2$

Now, if we integrate the line y = 2x we get

$$\int y\,dx = \int 2x\,dx = x^2 + c$$

Which again, when c = 0, corresponds to the area.

Note that when we are calculating the area from the origin to point x, when x = 0 the area is zero, so it must be that c = 0.

A similar analysis could be undertaken for any functions of x and the same result would be found. That is, we can find the area under a curve or function from the origin to any selected x value using the integral of that function with c = 0.

## Example

Calculate the area under the curve $y = 6x^2 + 2x$ between the points x = 4 and x = 8.

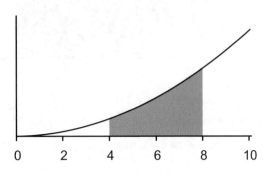

## Solution

Integrating $y = 6x^2 + 2x$ and evaluating that integral over the range from x = 4 to x = 8. This may be referred to as determining the definite integral and would be noted as

$$\int_{4}^{8} y \, dx$$

So undertaking the integration mechanics gives

$$\int y \, dx = \int (6x^2 + 2x) \, dx = \int 6x^2 \, dx + \int 2x \, dx = 2x^3 + x^2 + c$$

Hence, setting c = 0, the area under the curve from the origin to any point x is

Area = $2x^3 + x^2$

So, the area between the origin and x = 4 is

Area = $2x^3 + x^2 = 2 \times 4^3 + 4^2 = 144$

and the area between the origin and x = 8 is

Area = $2x^3 + x^2 = 2 \times 8^3 + 8^2 = 1,088$

So the area under the curve between x = 4 and x = 8 is

Area = $1,088 - 144 = 944$

## Conclusion

Integration is the opposite process to differentiation which can be used to either

- Determine the original function from the rate of change
- Determine the area under a curve between two points

The second of these applications will be seen when we examine probability distributions later on this book.

## Exercise 5

Calculate the area under the curve

$$y = 6x^2 + 6x$$

between $x = 5$ and $x = 8$

# 3 CALCULUS SUMMARY

## 3.1 Differentiation

### 3.1.1 Basic rules

The mechanical steps are

- Multiply by the power
- Subtract one from the new power

Where

$$y = ax^n$$

then

$$\frac{dy}{dx} = anx^{n-1}$$

### 3.1.2 Constants

Any constants disappear in this differentiation process, ie if

$$y = ax^n + c$$

then

$$\frac{dy}{dx} = anx^{n-1}$$

### 3.1.3 Distributed functions

To differentiate a distributed function we apply the rules to each term of the function in turn, ie if

$$y = ax^n + bx^m \quad \text{or} \quad y = f(x) + g(x)$$

then

$$\frac{dy}{dx} = anx^{n-1} + bmx^{m-1} \quad \text{or} \quad \frac{dy}{dx} = \frac{d}{dx}f(x) + \frac{d}{dx}g(x)$$

### 3.1.4 Multiplicative functions

Where

$$y = uv$$

then

$$\frac{dy}{dx} = u\frac{dv}{dx} + v\frac{du}{dx}$$

### 3.1.5 Function of a function

Where

$$y = g(u) \text{ and } u = f(x)$$

then

$$\frac{dy}{dx} = \frac{dy}{du} \times \frac{du}{dx}$$

### 3.1.6 Specific functions

#### Exponential function

$$e^x = 1 + x + \frac{x^2}{2!} + \frac{x^3}{3!} + \frac{x^4}{4!} + \frac{x^5}{5!} + \dots$$

then

$$\frac{d}{dx}e^x = e^x$$

#### Natural logarithm function

$$y = \ln(x)$$

then

$$\frac{dy}{dx} = \frac{1}{x}$$

### 3.1.7 Maximum points and minimum points

At any turning point

if $\dfrac{d^2y}{dx^2}$ is **positive** $\Rightarrow$ **minimum point**

if $\dfrac{d^2y}{dx^2}$ is **negative** $\Rightarrow$ **maximum point**

## 3.2 Partial differentiation

Differentiate the function with respect to each variable separately, assuming temporarily that all other independent variables are constant. This will produce a number of partial differentials, each one relating to one variable.

For a turning point we need the differential with respect to any variable to be zero. For the turning points here we need the differentials with respect to all independent variables to equate to zero which we can solve through simultaneous equations – maximising the y value with respect to all input variables simultaneously.

## 3.3 Integration

Integration is the opposite process to differentiation, hence the mechanical steps are

1.      Add one to the power

2.      Divide by the new power

3.      Add on a constant, c

So if

   $y = ax^n$

then

$$\int y\,dx = \int ax^n\,dx = \frac{ax^{n+1}}{n+1} + c$$

for all values of n except n = −1, where

$$\int x^{-1}dx = \int \frac{1}{x}\,dx = \ln(x) + c$$

Integration can be used to either

–       Determine the original function from the rate of change

–       Determine the area under a curve between two points

# 4 SOLUTIONS TO EXERCISES

1. (a) $y = 15x^4 - 8x^2 + 5x - 3$

$$\frac{dy}{dx} = 60x^3 - 16x + 5$$

(b) $y = 56x^8 - 14x^3$

$$\frac{dy}{dx} = 478x^7 + 42x^2$$

(c) $y = 13x^4 + 5x^6$

$$\frac{dy}{dx} = 52x^3 + 30x^5$$

2. $y = (2x^3 + 6x + 5)(3x^2 + 4x + 7)$

When $y = uv$ (where u and v are functions of x)

$$\frac{dy}{dx} = u\frac{dv}{dx} + v\frac{du}{dx}$$

Here $u = 2x^3 + 6x + 5$

so $v\dfrac{du}{dx} = 6x + 6$

Also $v = 3x^2 + 4x + 7$

so $\dfrac{dv}{dx} = 6x + 4$

And hence

$$\frac{dy}{dx} = (2x^3 + 6x + 5)(6x + 4) + (3x^2 + 4x + 7)(6x + 6)$$

3. $y = (3x^2 + 2x + 5)^{1/4}$

or

$y = u^{1/4}$

Where $u = 3x^2 + 2x + 5$

Here $\dfrac{dy}{dx} = \dfrac{dy}{du} \times \dfrac{du}{dx}$

$$\frac{dy}{du} = \frac{1}{4}u^{-3/4} = \frac{1}{4}(3x^2 + 2x + 5)^{-3/4}$$

$$\frac{du}{dx} = 6x + 2$$

so

$$\frac{dy}{dx} = \frac{1}{4}(3x^2 + 2x + 5)^{-3/4} \times (6x + 2)$$

4.  $y = 6x^2 + 12x + 3$

$$\int y\,dx = \int (6x^2 + 12x + 3)\,dx$$

$$\int 6x^2 dx + \int 6x^2\,dx + \int 12x\,dx + \int 3dx$$

$$= 2x^3 + 6x^2 + 3x + c$$

5.  $y = 6x^2 + 6x$

$$\int_5^8 y\,dx = \int_5^8 (6x^2 + 6x)\,dx$$

$$= \int_5^8 6x^2\,dx + \int_5^8 6x\,dx$$

$$= 2x^3 + 3x^2 \quad \text{to be evaluated at } x = 5 \text{ and } x = 8$$

$X = 8,\ 2x^3 + 3x^2 \qquad = 1{,}216$

$X = 5,\ 2x^3 + 3x^2 \qquad = \underline{\ 325}$

Area $\qquad\qquad\qquad = \underline{\ 891}$

# 3

# Data and data presentation

## Contents

## Introduction

Analysing investment opportunities involves the collection, assimilation and presentation of a large amount of information regarding the security under consideration. This is true regardless of whether the investment manager is using fundamental analysis, technical analysis or quantitative analysis, though differing types and levels of information would be required for each.

For example, a technical analyst studying equities would require detailed information regarding the past price movements of a share, and he would wish to be able to appreciate the information as easily as possible. Clearly, he could obtain a list of the values the share has taken each day for, say, the last five years, however this is unlikely to be the most convenient form. Some kind of chart, plotting share prices against time, would obviously be much more suitable from the point of view of showing trends, and hence much more useful.

A fundamental analyst would probably wish to appreciate the changes in the fundamental factors that influence the performance of the company and hence the value of its shares. He would perhaps wish to study any changes that have taken place in a wide range of economic variables such as inflation rates, interest rates, exchange rates, etc. Again it is important to be able to appreciate the information contained within such data, hence again perhaps a chart, plotting these factors and how they have moved over time, may be the most appropriate.

Our considerations here are

- How do we collect data, i.e. what sources are available?
- What different types of data could we collect and what unique factors may they have?
- How can these data be presented in the most convenient and useful form?

# 1 DEFINITIONS

## 1.1 Sources of data

### 1.1.1 Primary data

The collection or generation of new data in relation to a specific project or task is referred to as collection of **primary data**. Primary data may be obtained through the use of such techniques as

- Scientific investigation/research.
- Observation.
- Discussion.
- Questionnaires/Market research.

Clearly, since it is produced as a result of research into a specific project or task, it is relatively time-consuming and hence expensive to obtain.

## 1.1.2 Secondary data

There are many companies and government agencies whose role is to collect and distribute/sell information. Such existing data are referred to as **secondary data**. Clearly, for those who originally collected the data it was primary data, however, its use by others would not require any new original investigations, hence they would regard it as secondary data.

In the financial markets in particular there are an extensive amount of secondary data sources available, both in written publications and on computer databases. These will probably provide the initial source of any analyst's data due to their immediate availability and relatively low cost, however, this may need to be followed up by some original research of the form described above.

### Published data sources

The following are frequently used sources of published secondary data.

- Government publications such as
    - The *Annual Abstract of Statistics* and the *Monthly Digest of Statistics* which provide general statistical information regarding the economy covering such factors as population, employment, production, transport, energy, etc.
    - Monthly *Economic Trends* and monthly *Financial Statistics* which provide more detailed economic data such as money supply information, interest rates, balance of payments figures, etc.
    - *Regional Trends* and *Social Trends*, both annual publications, which provide more specialist regional and social data regarding population trends, employment, etc.
    - The *Employment Gazette*, providing detailed labour market data such as employment, unemployment, earnings, etc.

- *Bank of England Quarterly Bulletin*, showing a variety of different economic indicators such as interest rates, inflation rates, etc.

- *Federal Reserve Bulletin*, produced monthly by the US Federal Reserve showing similar information in relation to the US.

- International Monetary Fund's International Financial Statistics.

- The Bank for International Settlement publishes data regarding international banking cash flows.

- The World Bank and OECD (Organisation for Economic Cooperation and Development) provide a range of international economic data.

### Computerised sources of data

The following are examples of frequently used computerised sources of secondary data

- *Datastream, Reuters, Blomberg, FT Profile*, which all provide historical data regarding securities' prices and a range of other economic variables.

- *Extel Financial*, which provides summarised data and statistics such as PE ratios obtained from company accounts.

## 1.2 Sampling and populations

### 1.2.1 Introduction

When we are gathering information it is important to appreciate the distinction between a sample and the full population. Have we asked only a few people their opinion or have we asked everyone? The terms are fairly easy to understand when we are talking about, say, an election where the whole population can vote. The terms are, however, used more broadly in relation to data gathering.

### 1.2.2 Population

The **population** represents all the members of a specifically defined group. When undertaking some investigation it is important to clearly define the population you are considering. It may, for example, be

- Everyone of voting age in the UK.

- Everyone living in London - clearly this is a subset of the above population, however, if we are only interested in people living in London (e.g. local elections) then they would represent our *full* population and the views of someone who did not live in London would be irrelevant.

- Everyone living in a particular street if we were interested in views regarding parking restrictions in that street, say.

- All UK companies.

- All UK listed companies - clearly a subset of the above.

- All FTSE 100 companies - again clearly a subset of the above.

The important point is that we must be able to clearly define the group of items that we are interested in, and any item that falls within that definition will be a member of the population.

### 1.2.3 Sample

We may wish to consider every item in the population, e.g. the population of voters at a general election. However, due to the costs involved in investigating the full population, it is more common to investigate a sample.

A sample represents a subset of the full population that has been selected for investigation. For example, in establishing the CPI, the prices of a sample of items are investigated rather than all goods available. The CPI is, however, taken to be representative of all goods, i.e. we investigate a sample to provide information regarding the full population.

## Reasons for taking a sample rather than examining the whole population

- **Testing to destruction** – for example, testing matches. If a tester checked that all the matches worked, there would be none left to sell.

- **Physical impossibility** – it may not be possible or practicable to test the whole population, e.g. the height of all human beings in the world.

- **Cost and time** – even if it is possible to test the whole population, it may be time-consuming or expensive.

- **Adequacy of the sample** – the sample may give highly reliable results, even if it only represents a small portion of the overall population, if selected properly.

# 1.3 Sample selection

## 1.3.1 Introduction

If we are going to select a sample which we hope will enable us to draw some conclusions about the full population, then it clearly must be representative of the full population. We will, therefore, need to take great care in the selection of our sample and the size of our sample. With regard to sample selection, this may be either

- Random; or
- Non-random.

## 1.3.2 Random

A random sample is one where every item in the population has an equal chance of being selected. If such a sample is large enough it should be representative of the population. Indeed, the margin for error can be statistically evaluated when such a technique is used correctly.

The difficulty lies in achieving a purely random sample. Clearly, if we wished to establish voting intentions we would need to select people from everywhere in the UK. Simply conducting a survey in the centre of a few large cities will probably exclude the possibility of obtaining the views of a substantial part of the population. As a result, though we may randomly test the city dwellers by this method, it is not a pure random sample.

## 1.3.3 Non-random

The example above clearly illustrates the difficulty, in certain circumstances, of obtaining a good random sample. We may, therefore, need to select a sample on another basis which, by definition, will mean that we are excluding some of the population.

## Quota sampling

Quota sampling is where a sample is selected which it is believed will be representative of the full population. Help with this may be obtained from such sources as census information which will enable us to get a picture of the proportion of the population displaying a range of characteristics. A sample can then be selected which displays these characteristics, and hence should be reasonably representative. This is the typical approach utilised in market research.

## Panelling

Panelling is where a, hopefully, representative sample is selected to provide continuous information over a period of time. TV viewing figures are obtained in this way, where a panel of individuals report on their viewing habits - the TV companies do not know what everyone is watching all the time!

## Postal or telephone surveys

We may try to achieve a random sample by undertaking a postal or telephone survey enabling us to obtain very large coverage of the population. This will not turn out to be a random sample, however, since not everyone has a telephone (hence they cannot be selected) and not everyone would choose to respond to a postal survey. Indeed there is a reasonable chance of obtaining an atypical response since the 'average' person may not reply and only those with strong or extreme views do.

### 1.3.4 Sample size

The larger the sample is, the more likely it will be to represent the full population; if we continue to extend a sample we will ultimately test the full population.

Conversely, the smaller the sample, the less representative it is likely to be. Clearly, asking just one person their opinion at general election time will provide very little useful information from the point of view of assessing the likely voting patterns and election result.

# 2  MEASUREMENT OF DATA

The data that we utilise may be obtained from various sources and may represent either a sample or the full population. They may also take a variety of forms.

## 2.1 Types of data

### 2.1.1 Continuous data

Continuous data are data that can take any value whatsoever. Real life statistics such as height, weight, temperature, etc. fall within this category.

### 2.1.2 Discrete data

Discrete data are data that can only take certain specific values such as whole numbers. In the financial markets data are most frequently of this form as money changes hands in whole units.

## 2.2 Levels of measurement of data

### 2.2.1 Categorical or nominal data

Categorical or nominal data are data that have been classified into a number of distinct categories. The collection of this type of data is seen on census forms and market research questionnaires, where a box is ticked in response to such questions as 'which of the following newspapers do you read?' (followed by a list of popular dailies), 'do you drive a car?', 'did you vote at the last election?', etc.

To process such data on a computer we may assign a number to each of the bands, however, this number does not convey any other information and cannot be used to calculate such statistics as the standard deviation (covered later). This measure is inappropriate for categorical data. Such data can only be used as a simple statistic such as 30% of people drive cars.

### 2.2.2 Ordinal

Ordinal data are data that have been classified into a number of distinct *ranked* categories. The star system for hotel ratings is an example of such a system, or the classification of degrees into firsts, seconds and thirds.

When assigning numbers to this type of data for processing, care should again be taken in trying to draw statistical conclusions. Once more, the calculation of, say, a standard deviation (covered later) would be inappropriate and only such measures which are based on the position within the order, such as the median (also covered later), should be considered.

# 3    DATA PRESENTATION

## 3.1 Introduction

Having gathered our data, we now need to find a way of presenting them in a useful form for analysis.

### Example 1

We have gathered the following data regarding the weekly sales volumes of packets of cornflakes from 200 shops.

| | | | | | | | | | | | | | | | | | | | |
|---|---|---|---|---|---|---|---|---|---|---|---|---|---|---|---|---|---|---|---|
| 26 | 59 | 51 | 41 | 27 | 33 | 39 | 28 | 47 | 30 | 41 | 51 | 44 | 41 | 30 | 48 | 31 | 35 | 27 | 22 |
| 42 | 39 | 48 | 32 | 42 | 45 | 38 | 56 | 22 | 55 | 52 | 25 | 41 | 34 | 36 | 52 | 40 | 42 | 37 | 34 |
| 33 | 36 | 38 | 28 | 34 | 32 | 42 | 43 | 36 | 31 | 29 | 38 | 34 | 39 | 28 | 43 | 47 | 39 | 41 | 30 |
| 58 | 32 | 42 | 35 | 40 | 50 | 26 | 22 | 31 | 47 | 36 | 32 | 38 | 20 | 21 | 44 | 50 | 33 | 37 | 42 |
| 46 | 45 | 31 | 38 | 39 | 52 | 25 | 39 | 34 | 41 | 37 | 37 | 35 | 44 | 32 | 51 | 39 | 36 | 24 | 38 |
| 51 | 41 | 27 | 35 | 31 | 48 | 30 | 41 | 44 | 22 | 59 | 26 | 47 | 28 | 39 | 33 | 27 | 41 | 51 | 30 |
| 25 | 52 | 37 | 42 | 40 | 52 | 36 | 34 | 41 | 34 | 39 | 42 | 22 | 56 | 38 | 45 | 42 | 32 | 48 | 55 |
| 38 | 29 | 41 | 39 | 47 | 43 | 28 | 39 | 34 | 30 | 36 | 33 | 36 | 43 | 42 | 32 | 34 | 28 | 38 | 31 |
| 32 | 36 | 37 | 33 | 50 | 44 | 21 | 20 | 38 | 42 | 32 | 58 | 31 | 22 | 26 | 50 | 40 | 35 | 42 | 47 |
| 37 | 37 | 24 | 36 | 39 | 51 | 32 | 44 | 35 | 38 | 45 | 46 | 34 | 39 | 25 | 52 | 39 | 38 | 31 | 41 |

Clearly this just looks like a list of random numbers, hence how can it be presented in a useful form?

## 3.2 Tables

### 3.2.1 Introduction

The tabulation of data provides a means of summarising the raw data in a more convenient and usable form, whilst retaining the detailed content, i.e. values involved.

### 3.2.2 Frequency distribution

A **frequency distribution** groups the data into bands of specific values and displays the frequency of occurrence of each band.

Tabulating into a frequency distribution represents a very powerful way of presenting and summarising data, though care needs to be taken in the selection of the size of the bands, as illustrated by the following tabulations of the above data.

### Solution 1

**Version 1 - band size of 1**

One potential frequency distribution for the above data would be to group them by each possible value, giving (where $f$ represents the frequency of observation)

| Sales | f | Sales | f | Sales | f | Sales | f |
|-------|---|-------|---|-------|---|-------|---|
| 20 | 2 | 30 | 6 | 40 | 4 | 50 | 4 |
| 21 | 4 | 31 | 10 | 41 | 12 | 51 | 6 |
| 22 | 4 | 32 | 8 | 42 | 12 | 52 | 6 |
| 23 | 0 | 33 | 8 | 43 | 4 | 53 | 0 |
| 24 | 2 | 34 | 8 | 44 | 6 | 54 | 0 |
| 25 | 4 | 35 | 6 | 45 | 4 | 55 | 2 |
| 26 | 4 | 36 | 10 | 46 | 2 | 56 | 2 |
| 27 | 4 | 37 | 8 | 47 | 6 | 57 | 0 |
| 28 | 6 | 38 | 12 | 48 | 4 | 58 | 2 |
| 29 | 2 | 39 | 14 | 49 | 0 | 59 | 2 |

This does not appear to provide a particular improvement over the raw data.

**Version 2 - band size of 4**

An alternative, and perhaps more useful, presentation would be to group these data into bands 4 wide as follows.

| Sales Range | f | Units Sold |
|-------------|---|------------|
| 20 - 23 | 10 | 212 |
| 24 - 27 | 14 | 360 |
| 28 - 31 | 24 | 716 |
| 32 - 35 | 30 | 1,002 |
| 36 - 39 | 44 | 1,658 |
| 40 - 43 | 32 | 1,328 |
| 44 - 47 | 18 | 818 |
| 48 - 51 | 14 | 698 |
| 52 - 55 | 8 | 422 |
| 56 - 59 | 6 | 346 |
| | 200 | 7,560 |

This tabulation is clearly more manageable and usable. We can now easily see a trend in the figures which was far from apparent in the raw data or the original frequency distribution.

**Version 3 - band size of 10**

Summarising into bands 10 wide produces the following.

| Sales Range | f | Units Sold |
|---|---|---|
| 20 - 29 | 32 | 798 |
| 30 - 39 | 90 | 3,150 |
| 40 - 49 | 54 | 2,338 |
| 50 - 59 | 24 | 1,274 |
| | 200 | 7,560 |

Clearly, in this last case a lot of trend information is lost and if we enlarged the bands further the situation would become worse.

## 3.2.3 Relative frequency distribution

A *relative frequency distribution* displays the same data as a percentage of the sample or population size, rather than as actual observed frequencies.

A relative frequency distribution would possibly be more appropriate where a more direct comparison between bandings is desired or where the sample size has been exceptionally large, hence the scale of the numbers may obscure their understanding.

## Solution 2

The second alternative above could be represented as a relative frequency distribution as follows.

| Sales Range | f % | Units Sold % |
|---|---|---|
| 20 - 23 | 5 | 2.81 |
| 24 - 27 | 7 | 4.76 |
| 28 - 31 | 12 | 9.47 |
| 32 - 35 | 15 | 13.25 |
| 36 - 39 | 22 | 21.93 |
| 40 - 43 | 16 | 17.57 |
| 44 - 47 | 9 | 10.82 |
| 48 - 51 | 7 | 9.23 |
| 52 - 55 | 4 | 5.58 |
| 56 - 59 | 3 | 4.58 |
| | 100% | 100.00% |

We can now easily see that 15% of stores achieve sales of between 32 and 35 packets a week which represented 13.25% of the total sales volume.

## Exercise 1

The distribution of firms' turnover in a particular industrial sector is as follows.

| £ million | % |
|---|---|
| 0.0 - 0.5 | 21 |
| 0.6 - 1.0 | 19 |
| 1.1 - 2.0 | 10 |
| 2.1 - 5.0 | 20 |
| 5.1 - 10.0 | 14 |
| 10.1 - 50.0 | 12 |
| 51+ | 4 |

If there are 20 firms with a turnover of less than £500,000 or greater than £51m, how many firms have a turnover between £1.1m and £5m?

## Exercise 2

The proportion of employees in various salary ranges within a major bank is given below. If 150 people earned less than £17,000, how many earned £24,000 and more?

| | |
|---|---|
| £12,000 - £14,000 | 0.12 |
| £15,000 - £17,000 | 0.18 |
| £18,000 - £20,000 | 0.17 |
| £21,000 - £23,000 | 0.28 |
| £24,000 and more | 0.25 |

## 3.2.4 Cumulative frequency distribution

An extension of the above ideas would be to prepare a **cumulative frequency distribution**. This could be used as an adjunct to either the frequency distribution or the relative frequency distribution and would show the number/percentage of a sample or population with a value less than or equal to a given figure.

## Solution

Illustrating this idea in connection to the relative distribution established above gives

| Sales Range | f | | Units Sold | |
|---|---|---|---|---|
| | % | Cum % | % | Cum % |
| 20 - 23 | 5 | 5 | 2.81 | 2.81 |
| 24 - 27 | 7 | 12 | 4.76 | 7.57 |
| 28 - 31 | 12 | 24 | 9.47 | 17.04 |
| 32 - 35 | 15 | 39 | 13.25 | 30.29 |
| 36 - 39 | 22 | 61 | 21.93 | 52.22 |
| 40 - 43 | 16 | 77 | 17.57 | 69.79 |
| 44 - 47 | 9 | 86 | 10.82 | 80.61 |
| 48 - 51 | 7 | 93 | 9.23 | 89.84 |
| 52 - 55 | 4 | 97 | 5.58 | 95.42 |
| 56 - 59 | 3 | 100 | 4.58 | 100.00 |
| | 100% | | 100.00% | |

We can now easily see 39% of stores achieved sales of 35 units or less and contributed just 30.29% of the total sales volume.

## 3.2.5 Data interval/band width

As we said at the outset, frequency distributions (basic, relative or cumulative) provide a very powerful way of presenting data. However, the selection of the data interval or band width is essential to the meaningfulness and usefulness of the data presented and needs to be done with great care on the basis of the individual data being considered. There are no rules regarding this aspect of data presentation.

This is perhaps an even more acute problem when we are considering continuous data where we must be very careful to ensure that all items are included within a band but only within one band. For continuous data, bands will need to be described as, for example

- Greater than or equal to 20 but less than 24.
- Greater than or equal to 24 but less than 28.
- Greater than or equal to 28 but less than 32, etc.

# 3.3 Graphs and charts

## 3.3.1 Introduction

Tables provide a useful way of presenting information and retaining the detailed values, though sometimes the detail in the numbers may obscure the understanding a little. It is possible that the same level of information can be conveyed more easily and intuitively by the use of charts.

There are a variety of different methods of producing charts which are each suited to different applications. We consider below some of the more fundamental types.

## 3.3.2 Lorenz curve

A **Lorenz curve** is a visual representation of the two cumulative frequency distributions against each other. It shows the proportion of items which contribute a proportion of values.

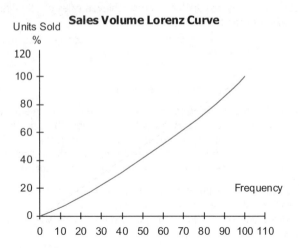

If this represents the norm then any divergence from this line would indicate an unusual change/move from the trend.

If the line was a straight $45^o$ line then it would imply all stores sold the same amount. Any divergence in this $45^o$ line implies some bias or weighting in the population.

### 3.3.3 Pie charts

A pie chart provides an alternative way of representing relative frequencies by dividing a circle (the pie) into sections (slices) whose area is proportional to the relative frequency.

Since a circle spans $360^o$ and we wish this to represent the full sample/population (i.e. 100%), then we will use $3.6^o$ to represent each 1%, e.g. 22% = 22 × 3.6 = $79.2^o$ on the chart.

A pie chart for the above relative frequency distribution would appear as follows.

**Sales Volume Pie Chart**

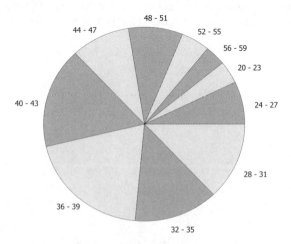

### 3.3.4 Bar charts

A **bar chart** represents through the *height* of a bar the number or percentage of items displaying a particular characteristic.

## Example

Suppose our sales volume data can be subanalysed into the following cross tabulation showing the number of stores and their volumes by region.

| Volume | North | South | East | West | Total |
|--------|-------|-------|------|------|-------|
| 20 - 29 | 8 | 8 | 9 | 7 | 32 |
| 30 - 39 | 22 | 23 | 25 | 20 | 90 |
| 40 - 49 | 11 | 15 | 15 | 13 | 54 |
| 50 - 59 | 4 | 5 | 9 | 6 | 24 |
|  | 45 | 51 | 58 | 46 | 200 |

We could construct the following bar chart to illustrate the number of stores by region.

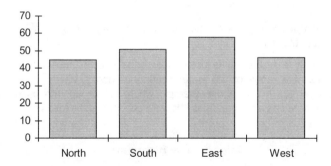

**Stores by Region**

If we wished to use this graph to convey some further information we could construct a **component bar chart** breaking down the number of stores by region and by sales volume as follows.

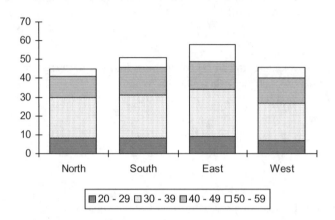

Stores by Region and Sales Volume

## 3.3.5 Histograms

A *histogram* displays the number or percentage of items falling within a given band through the *area* of a bar.

Generally a histogram is used to describe circumstances where one bar is used to represent a range of values for continuous data. Where discrete data are grouped, however (as in the above example where we group into bands 4 wide), it may be represented as a histogram as if it were continuous, as follows.

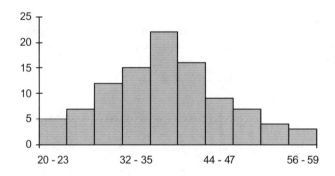

Sales Volume Histogram

One problem that may arise in relation to a histogram is where the extreme bands are simply described as greater than something or less than something (e.g. if the extreme bands in the above example were simply described as ≤23 and ≥56), i.e. they are not bounded. How do we decide what width to make the band?

There are no strict rules regarding this and it will require a degree of judgement on behalf of the researcher. If a definite upper and lower limit are known then these will provide obvious bounds. If they are not, a bound will need to be assumed since the histogram cannot be drawn unless all areas are bounded.

One consequence of this, however, is how tall do we make the band? In completing the histogram, one thing that we will need to bear in mind is that if any bands are wider than any others, their heights will have to be scaled down proportionally to ensure that the **area** of that band still reflects the number of items. This problem is most likely to arise in the context of the extreme bands, however, it may also be applicable to other bands of differing widths.

For example, if three bands each contain 24 items but the bands are one, two and three units wide, respectively then their heights will be 24, 12, 8, respectively so that they each have an area of 24.

## 3.3.6 Graphs and scatter graphs

### Introduction - basic graphs

One of the most effective ways to demonstrate the relationship between two items is to plot them on a graph where the values of one of the factors is plotted along the horizontal axis (the x-axis) and the corresponding values of the other factor are plotted along the vertical axis (the y-axis). We may then be able to use this graph to try to make some predictions.

### Independent versus dependent

By convention, the variable thought to be responsible for causing the change (the **independent variable**) is plotted along the x-axis, and the variable whose value is driven by this x value and whose change we are seeking to predict (the **dependent variable**) is plotted up the y-axis.

A frequent requirement is to plot how something has changed with **time**. In this situation the item alters *with time*, i.e. the item is the dependent variable, time is the independent one. Time cannot be altered, i.e. time could never be the dependent variable. Hence we plot time along the x-axis and the item along the y-axis.

### Example

The sales achieved by a company over the last ten years have been

| Year | £'000 |
|------|-------|
| 1999 | 1,000 |
| 2000 | 1,210 |
| 2001 | 1,450 |
| 2002 | 1,730 |
| 2003 | 2,080 |
| 2004 | 2,490 |
| 2005 | 2,990 |
| 2006 | 3,590 |
| 2007 | 4,300 |
| 2008 | 5,160 |

Plot these data on a graph.

## Solution

Clearly, the sales vary with time, i.e. sales is the dependent variable, time is the independent one (we clearly could not make time go faster by selling more units!). Hence we plot time along the x-axis and sales along the y-axis, giving the following scatter graph.

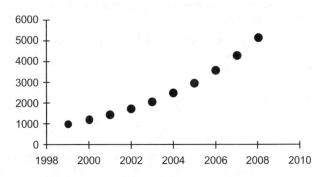

**Scatter Graph of Sales by Year**

Alternatively, the data may be represented by a graph in which those points are joined by a smooth line as follows.

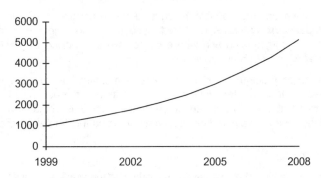

**Graph of Sales by Year**

This graph shows a trend of rising sales values which is clearly very positive for the company.

Unfortunately, curves do not lend themselves well to extrapolation, or predicting forward, hence this may not be the preferred presentation and we may find the semi-logarithmic graph described below more useful.

## Axis values

When drawing a graph, the selection of the y-axis values is of fundamental importance. Clearly we should select y-axis values that are representative of the data being graphed. It would be fairly stupid in our example above to show the y-axis going up to, say, £600m as the data will hardly appear at all.

## Axis scale - rates of change and semi-logarithmic graphs

Of equal importance to the usefulness of a graph is the selection of the scale. The illustration above shows a trend of accelerating growth in sales. When we are in the position that we wish to establish the rate of change, it may be more appropriate to utilise a semi-logarithmic scale, effectively plotting the log of the value instead of the value itself on the y-axis.

On such a graph, if something is growing at a constant rate it will appear as a straight line which will be much more useful for prediction purposes. In addition, any move away from steady growth would be highlighted by this graph. If the item's growth rate increased then the graph would become steeper. Conversely, if the growth rate slowed the graph would become flatter.

If we plot the above figures on a semi-logarithmic graph we obtain the following.

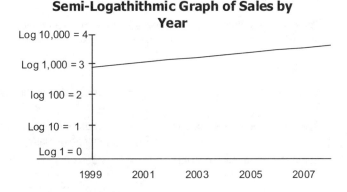

What we can see on this graph is that a ten-fold increase in value is represented by the same vertical distance, hence its appropriateness for illustrating constant growth which compounds in this way.

# 4 SUMMARY

## 4.1 Sources of data

- Primary data     =     Collection/generation of new data
- Secondary data     =     Use of existing data

## 4.2 Samples

- Random sample     =     where every item in a population has an equal chance of being selected

- Quota sample     =     where sample selected is believed to be representative of the population

- Panelling     =     sample selected to provide continuous data over a period

## 4.3 Data types

- Continuous     =     Can take any value
- Discrete     =     Can only take certain values, eg integer values

## 4.4 Data levels

- Categorical/nominal     =     classified into distinct categories
- Ordinal     =     classified into ranked categories

## 4.5 Tables

- Frequency distribution     =     Group data into bands, table frequency for each band

- Relative frequency distribution     =     Group data into bands, table relative percentage data

- Cumulative frequency distribution     =     Group data into bands, table cumulative frequency from first band to selected band

## 4.6 Graphs/charts

- Lorenz curve     =     visual representation of two cumulative frequency curves against each other

- Pie chart     =     circular representation of relative frequency

- Bar chart     =     bar height related to frequency/relative frequency

- Histogram     =     bar area related to frequency/relative frequency

- Independent variable     =     driving variable causing a change
- Dependent variable     =     driven variable

# 5 SOLUTIONS TO EXERCISES

1.  Turnover < £0.5m =   21%

    Turnover > £51m =    4%

    ———

    25% of companies

    ———

    25% = 20 companies

    ⇒ 100% = 80 companies

    30% of companies have turnover in the range of £1.1m to £5m

    ⇒ 30% × 80 = 24 companies

2.  150 people represent 30% (0.30 = 0.12 + 0.18) of total.  Those earning over £24,000 represents 25% (0.25), i.e. 125 individuals $\left( 150 \times \dfrac{25}{30} \right)$

# 4 Location and dispersion

## Contents

# 1 INTRODUCTION

## 1.1 Aim of location and dispersion measures

In a certain world we would always know what is going to happen, e.g. what dividend return a share is going to offer or how the stock market in general is going to perform. As a result we would be able to make perfect investment decisions.

In a more realistic world we will not know such factors for certain. We may be able to make an estimate based on technical analysis of previous performance or fundamental analysis of relevant factors, however, we would have to accept that this forecast is likely to be incorrect and that the true position may vary away from this estimate.

In performing our technical analysis we would review past returns and how these have varied, hoping that these may give us some guide to the future, though bearing in mind the dangers of making this link. It is in this context that location and dispersion measures may be of use to the investment manager.

The purpose of location and dispersion measures is to indicate the

- Central/long run average value/return achieved – *Location*.
- The variability or spread of values around this point - *Dispersion*.

In the context of, say, shares these measures will provide us with an indication of

- The expected future returns from the share (all other things being equal).

- The risk we are facing (the potential variability of the returns about this expected return value) in holding the shares.

## 1.2 Considerations

There are a number of different measures outlined individually below which each have their own advantages and disadvantages.

The main consideration when undertaking any calculations is the way in which the data are presented. There are three possibilities that we may be faced with.

- Raw data.
- Tabulated data.
- Grouped data.

We will provide examples of each of these and show how the location and dispersion measures may be calculated for each.

### 1.2.1 Raw data

Raw data are presented as a simple list of figures or values which may or may not be ordered.

## Example

The example we will use is the following *ordered* series of raw data.

1, 2, 3, 3, 4, 5, 5, 5, 6, 7, 8, 9, 20.

## 1.2.2 Tabulated data

Tabulating data is a useful method for summarising large volumes of discrete data (i.e. data that can only take certain values, e.g. whole numbers).

## Example

The example we will use to illustrate this form of data presentation is

| Value | Frequency |
|-------|-----------|
|       | *f*       |
| 1     | 20        |
| 2     | 40        |
| 3     | 60        |
| 4     | 50        |
| 5     | 10        |
|       | 180       |

## 1.2.3 Grouped data

Grouping data is a convenient way to summarise continuous data (i.e. data that can take any value within a range).

## Example

The example we will use to illustrate this form of data presentation is

| Range | | | Frequency |
|-------|----|--------|-----------|
|       |    |        | *f*       |
| 0     | to | 4.9˙%  | 30        |
| 5     | to | 9.9˙%  | 50        |
| 10    | to | 14.9˙% | 40        |
| 15    | to | 19.9˙% | 10        |
|       |    |        | 130       |

*Note*: 4.9˙ represents 4.9999.... (four point nine recurring), and hence the first range represents any number in the range greater than or equal to zero to less than five. Sometimes people may use 4.9 to end such a range. They are not intending to exclude any items between 4.9 and 5.0, rather they are using 4.9 to indicate any number less than 5.

# 2 LOCATION/CENTRAL MEASURES

## 2.1 Introduction

There are four location measures that we need to be familiar with, specifically

- Arithmetic mean.
- Median.
- Mode.
- Geometric mean.

## 2.2 Arithmetic mean

### 2.2.1 Calculation

The arithmetic mean is the simple average that we are probably all used to. It is calculated by adding up (arithmetically) the observed values and dividing by the number of observed values. Again the only difficulties arise in the way in which the data are presented.

### Raw data

The calculation of the arithmetic mean can be mathematically expressed as

$$\bar{x} = \frac{\sum x_i}{n}$$

where

$\bar{x}$ = the mean;

$x_i$ = the observed values;

$\sum$ represents the summation of those following values;

n = number of values.

This could alternatively be shown as (and will certainly be calculated as)

$$\bar{x} = \frac{x_1 + x_2 + x_3 + \ldots + x_n}{n}$$

although the initial formula is the one we will be stating.

### Solution

$$\bar{x} = \frac{\sum x_i}{n} = \frac{1+2+3+3+4+5+5+5+6+7+8+9+20}{13} = \frac{78}{13} = 6$$

## Tabulated data

With tabulated data we will have many items with the same value (in the same band). If an item appears, say, 20 times then rather than adding it in 20 times to the numerator of the fraction, we simply add 20× the value as one figure.

The calculation of the arithmetic mean for tabulated data can thus be achieved using

$$\overline{x} = \frac{\sum f_i x_i}{n}$$

where

$\overline{x}$ = the mean;

$x_i$ = the observed values;

$f_i$ = the frequency with which those values have been observed;

$\sum$ represents the summation of those following values;

n = number of values.

## Solution

| Value<br>x | Frequency<br>f | Frequency<br>fx |
|:---:|:---:|:---:|
| 1 | 20 | 20 |
| 2 | 40 | 80 |
| 3 | 60 | 180 |
| 4 | 50 | 200 |
| 5 | 10 | 50 |
| | n = 180 | $\sum f_i x_i = 530$ |

Hence

$$\overline{x} = \frac{\sum f_i x_i}{n} = \frac{530}{180} = 2.94$$

## Grouped data

The calculation for grouped data requires us to make the assumption that values are evenly spread within each range and we can, therefore, evaluate each range based on its midpoint. Having done this, the calculation is identical to the calculation for tabulated data.

The calculation of the mean for grouped data is

$$\overline{x} = \frac{\sum f_i m_i}{n}$$

where

$\bar{x}$ = the mean;

$m_i$ = the midpoint of the range;

$f_i$ = the frequency with which values in the ranges have been observed;

$\Sigma$ represents the summation of those following values;

$n$ = number of values.

## Solution

| Range | | | Midpoint<br>$m$ | Frequency<br>$f$ | Frequency<br>$fm$ |
|---|---|---|---|---|---|
| 0 | to | 4.9% | 2.5 | 30 | 75 |
| 5 | to | 9.9% | 7.5 | 50 | 375 |
| 10 | to | 14.9% | 12.5 | 40 | 500 |
| 15 | to | 19.9% | 17.5 | 10 | 175 |
| | | | | $n = 130$ | $\Sigma f_i m_i = 1{,}125$ |

Hence

$$\bar{x} = \frac{\Sigma f_i m_i}{n} = \frac{1{,}125}{130} = 8.65$$

## 2.2.2 Comments

We should note in relation to the arithmetic mean that the calculated *mean is not necessarily one of the possible values.* This can be seen easily from the raw data example and the tabulated data example.

In addition, since all observed values are considered, this measure can *be severely distorted by extreme values.*

### Example

Suppose in our raw data example the last observed item had been 100 rather than 20. The mean would then be

$$\bar{x} = \frac{\Sigma x_i}{n} = \frac{1+2+3+3+4+5+5+5+6+7+8+9+100}{13} = \frac{158}{13} = 12.15$$

when clearly the majority of observed values are less than nine.

## 2.2.3 Summary of mean

### Raw data

$$\bar{x} = \frac{\sum x_i}{n} = \frac{x_1 + x_2 + x_3 + \ldots + x_n}{n}$$

### Tabulated data

$$\bar{x} = \frac{\sum f_i x_i}{n}$$

### Grouped data

$$\bar{x} = \frac{\sum f_i m_i}{n}$$

# 2.3 Median

## 2.3.1 Calculation

The median is the value of the middle item in an ordered arrangement of the observed data. The item number to consider will be given by

$$n_m = \frac{n+1}{2}$$

i.e. if we had 5 observed values, the median would be the value of item number

$$n_m = \frac{5+1}{2} = \frac{6}{2} = 3$$

in an ordered arrangement.

Clearly, if there are an even number of items this calculation will not produce a whole number. In this case the median will be a simple average of the middle two values either side of this point. For example, if we had six items then this formula would produce

$$n_m = \frac{n+1}{2} = \frac{6+1}{2} = \frac{7}{2} = 3.5$$

hence we would take a simple average of the value of the third and fourth items.

### Raw data

### Solution

Our raw data example had 13 values, hence the median would be item number

$$n_m = \frac{13+1}{2} = \frac{14}{2} = 7$$

If we look to the ordered list of values{1, 2, 3, 3, 4, 5, **5**, 5, 6, 7, 8, 9, 20}, the seventh item is the second five, hence

Median = 5

## Tabulated data

For tabulated data we would again need to find the value of the middle item which would turn out to be the value associated with one of the rows.

## Solution

The item to consider is given by

$$n_m = \frac{n+1}{2} = \frac{180+1}{2} = \frac{181}{2} = 90.5$$

| Value x | Frequency f | Cumulative f |
|---------|-------------|--------------|
| 1 | 20 | 20 |
| 2 | 40 | 60 |
| 3 | 60 | 120 |
| 4 | 50 | 170 |
| 5 | 10 | 180 |
| | n = 180 | |

There are 20 items of value one and 40 items of value 2, hence we have seen 60 items before we see an item valued at 3. There are 60 items valued at 3, taking us up to a cumulative total of 120 items. Hence the 90.5th item is one of these, i.e. the median item has a value of 3.

## Grouped data

## Solution

The median for this example is item number

$$n_m = \frac{n+1}{2} = \frac{130+1}{2} = \frac{131}{2} = 65.5$$

| Range | | | Frequency f | Cumulative f |
|---|---|---|---|---|
| 0 | to | 4.9% | 30 | 30 |
| 5 | to | 9.9% | 50 | 80 |
| 10 | to | 14.9% | 40 | 120 |
| 15 | to | 19.9% | 10 | 130 |
| | | | 130 | |

If we look at the cumulative frequency above we see that we have seen 30 items by the end of the 0 to 4.9 band and 80 by the end of the 5 to 9.9 band. The 65.5th item therefore falls within the range 5 to 9.9˙ (5 to 10), indeed it should be the 35.5th (65.5 – 30.0) item in that band. On the assumption that the items are evenly spread throughout this range, the median will be given $\dfrac{35.5}{50}$ into this 5 to 10 range, i.e.

$$\text{Median} = 5 + \frac{35.5}{50} \times (10 - 5) = 8.55$$

### 2.3.2 Comments

The median will *either be one of the actual observed values* (if there are an odd number if items), *or a simple average of the mid two items* (if there are an even number).

Unlike the mean, the median will *not be affected by extreme values* since it only ever considers the most central values in the ordered list.

### Exercise 1

The distribution of daily share price changes for a sample of 1,000 UK stocks is as follows.

| Interval | | | Number of Shares f |
|---|---|---|---|
| −10.0 | to | −0.1 | 130 |
| 0.0 | to | 9.9 | 470 |
| 10.0 | to | 19.9 | 270 |
| 20.9 | to | 29.9 | 130 |

What is the median price change?

### Exercise 2

A sample of 300 share price changes over one year was distributed as follows.

| % Change | | | Number of Shares f |
|---|---|---|---|
| −20 | to | −10.1 | 52 |
| −10 | to | 0.1 | 27 |
| 1 | to | 9.99 | 101 |
| 10 | to | 19.9 | 80 |
| 20 | to | 29.9 | 40 |

What is the lower quartile price change?

## 2.4 Mode

### 2.4.1 Calculation

The mode is the most frequently occurring item in the observed data on the basis that the more central items should occur most frequently in a *normal* distribution.

## Raw data

### Solution

Based on our example above, the mode is 5 since this occurs three times in the range

1, 2, 3, 3, 4, **5, 5, 5**, 6, 7, 8, 9, 20.

## Tabulated data

When we consider the tabulated data

| Value | Frequency |
|-------|-----------|
|       | f |
| 1 | 20 |
| 2 | 40 |
| 3 | 60 |
| 4 | 50 |
| 5 | 10 |
|   | 180 |

we can see that the most frequently occurring value is, again, three, i.e.

Mode = 3

## Grouped data

For the following grouped data the mode falls within the range 5 to 9.9˙ as there are 50 items in this range.

| Range | | | Frequency |
|-------|-----|-------|-----------|
|       |     |       | f |
| 0 | to | 4.9% | 30 |
| 5 | to | 9.9% | 50 |
| 10 | to | 14.9% | 40 |
| 15 | to | 19.9% | 10 |
|   |   |   | 130 |

This is the limit of the accuracy we can achieve, i.e.

Modal Range = 5 to 9.9˙

We cannot establish a single value within this range since we assume that the items are evenly distributed throughout the range, hence all are equally likely/occur as frequently as each other.

### 2.4.2 Comments

By definition, the mode *must be one of the actually occurring items* (like the median but unlike the mean). In addition, it is *not affected by extreme values.*

The unfortunate problem with this measure is that *there may be several modes* if number of items occur with equal frequency. For example, if there were a third '3' instead of a '4' in the raw data example then there would be three 3's and three 5's, an hence there would be two modes, 3 and 5. If we had the following data: 1, 6, 7, 8, 36, each would be a mode since each only appears once. As a result, the mode may be of limited value as a central measure since, in extreme cases as above, it gives little or no indication of central tendency.

Since it is the most frequently occurring item, by definition it is *unaffected by extremes*.

## 2.5 Geometric mean

### 2.5.1 Calculation

The geometric mean is calculated by taking the nth root of the product of the n observed values. Again the only difficulties arise in the way in which we present the data.

**Raw data**

$$\bar{x} = \sqrt[n]{x_1 \times x_2 \times x_3 \times .... \times x_n}$$

where

$\bar{x}$ = the mean;

$x_i$ = the observed values (i going from 1 to n);

n = number of values.

**Solution**

$$\bar{x} = \sqrt[n]{x_1 \times x_2 \times x_3 \times .... \times x_n}$$

$$= \sqrt[13]{1 \times 2 \times 3 \times 3 \times 4 \times 5 \times 5 \times 5 \times 6 \times 7 \times 8 \times 9 \times 20}$$

$$= \sqrt[13]{544,320,000} = 4.70$$

**Tabulated data**

The calculation for tabulated data simply extends this idea. If, when we look in the band with a value of three, we observe 60 items, then we must multiply 60 3's together (which can be calculated as $3^{60}$). We need to consider both the observed value *and* its frequency in a similar way to the way we multiplied 3 by 60 to calculate the arithmetic mean. Hence the geometric mean is

$$\bar{x} = \sqrt[n]{x_1^{n1} \times x_2^{n2} \times x_3^{n3} \times ... \times x_n^{nn}}$$

where

$\bar{x}$ = the mean;

$x_i$ = the observed value for band i (i going from 1 to m);

$n_i$ = number of values in band (i going from 1 to m);

n = total number of values ($n_1 + n_2 + n_3 + \cdots + n_n$).

## Solution

$$\bar{x} = \sqrt[n]{x_1^{n1} \times x_2^{n2} \times x_3^{n3} \times .... \times x_n^{nn}}$$

$$= \sqrt[180]{1^{20} \times 2^{40} \times 3^{60} \times 4^{50} \times 5^{10}}$$

$$= \sqrt[18]{1^2 \times 2^4 \times 3^6 \times 4^5 \times 5^1}$$

$$= \sqrt[18]{59,719,680} = 2.70$$

## Grouped data

The calculation for grouped data would be as for tabulated data, using the midpoint of the group as the observed value, i.e.

$$\bar{x} = \sqrt[n]{m_1^{n1} \times m_2^{n2} \times m_3^{n3} \times ... \times m_n^{nn}}$$

where

$\bar{x}$ = the mean;

$m_i$ = the mid values of group i (i going from 1 to m);

$n_i$ = number of values in band i (i going from 1 to m);

n = total number of values ($n_1 + n_2 + n_3 + \cdots + n_n$).

## Solution

$$\bar{x} = \sqrt[n]{m_1^{n1} \times m_2^{n2} \times m_3^{n3} \times .... \times m_n^{nn}}$$

$$= \sqrt[130]{2.5^{30} \times 7.5^{50} \times 12.5^{40} \times 17.5^{10}}$$

$$= \sqrt[13]{2.5^3 \times 7.5^5 \times 12.5^4 \times 17.5^1}$$

$$= \sqrt[13]{158,417,967,359} = 7.27$$

## 2.5.2 Comments

### Usefulness

The geometric mean may be most appropriate as a central measure when we are considering growth or inflation which compounds each year (i.e. builds on top of the previous years rather than simply adding to it).

### Example

A share price rises by the following amounts each month over a six month period.

+5%, +4%, +2%, –3%, –1%, +3%

What is the average growth per month over that period?

### Solution

To appreciate the solution we need to consider the value at the end of six months of each £1 invested at the start of the period.

After the first month this £1 will have grown by 5% to £1.05, i.e.

New value = £1 × 1.05 = £1.05

This £1.05 will then grow in the next month by 4% to £1.092, i.e.

New value = £1 × 1.05 × 1.04 = £1.092

By the end of the six months the value will have grown to

New value = £1 × 1.05 × 1.04 × 1.02 × 0.97 × 0.99 × 1.03 = £1.1017

*Note*: the general term we are using to compound up the values each period (the Compound Factor) is given by

$$CF = (1 + r)$$

where r = the growth rate expressed as a decimal, i.e. +5% = +0.05 giving.

$$CF = (1 + 0.05) = 1.05$$

and –3% = –0.03 giving

$$CF = (1 - 0.03) = 0.97$$

If we now wished to work out the average growth rate, then it would be

$$\bar{x} = \sqrt[6]{1.1017} = 1.0163$$

i.e. an average growth rate of 1.63% per month.

### Relationship to arithmetic mean

The geometric mean *will understate average growth/returns, etc. compared to the arithmetic mean* as a comparison of the results of the above examples demonstrates.

This fact can most easily be appreciated by considering the impact of an extreme item with an observed value of zero. The arithmetic mean, which works by adding the values together, will have a value so long as there are other non-zero values observed. Since the geometric mean works by multiplying together all the relevant items, if any one of them is zero them the product and hence the geometric mean will be zero.

## 2.6 Relationship between mean, median and mode

### 2.6.1 Introduction

In a perfectly symmetrical population, with the mean being the most commonly occurring item, the mean, median and mode would have the same value, as

- The average (mean) would be the midpoint (the median).
- The mean would be the most frequently occurring item (the mode).

We could represent such a distribution as

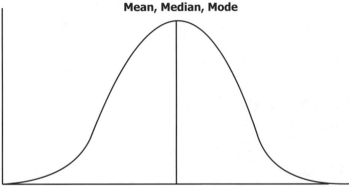

**Mean, Median, Mode**

If, however, we added just one extremely high value in this otherwise symmetrical distribution, then

- The mode would be unaltered - the most commonly occurring item is unaltered.

- The median would now be slightly higher since there is now one more item.

- The mean could be significantly higher depending on how extreme the additional item is.

If we extend this idea to consider a number of unsymmetrical items, producing a *positively skewed* distribution (i.e. one where the more extreme items lie above the mode) we would find the relationship between the three measures to be

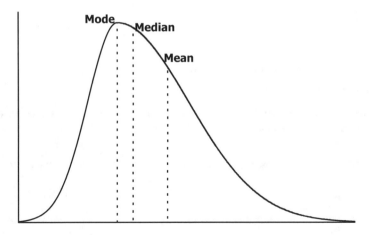

i.e. *mode < median < mean*

Similarly, for a *negatively skewed* distribution (one where the more extreme items fell below the mode) we would find

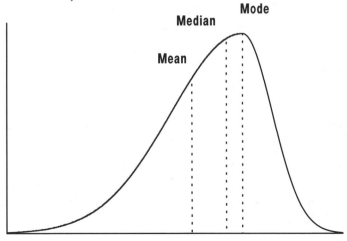

Mean  Median  Mode

i.e. *mean < median < mode*

## 2.6.2 Measuring skewness

It is possible to measure skew using the following formula.

$$\text{Skewness } (S_k) = \frac{n}{(n-1)(n-2)} \times \frac{\sum (x - \bar{x})^3}{s^3}$$

where

n = sample size

s = sample standard deviation (see below)

$\bar{x}$ = sample mean

You will notice that we are taking the **cube of the deviations** around the mean in the numerator. This is because the cube preserves the sign of the original deviation. For example, $-4^3 = -64$.

The cubing process also **exaggerates** large deviations compared to small deviations.

## Example

Say a sample had three items with values of 1, 5 and 6. Calculate relative skewness for the sample.

## Solution

The mean of the sample is 4.

The deviations around the mean are −3, +1 and +2.

The sum of the cubed deviations is −27 + 8 = −18

The negative deviation is further from the mean and has a greater effect on the calculation. As a result, the relative skewness measure will be negative, indicating a **negatively skewed** sample.

For the above sample, the sample standard deviation is 2.65 (check this yourself after the next section) and the skewness measure is

$$\text{Skewness } (S_k) = \frac{3}{(3-1)(3-2)} \times \frac{-18}{2.65^3} = -1.45$$

If the sample is **symmetrical**, the skewness measure will give a value of **zero**.

# 3 DISPERSION MEASURES

## 3.1 Introduction

Dispersion measures aim to tell us how broadly spread a range of values are around the observed central point. For, say, the returns offered by a share the location may provide the expected return and the dispersion may provide a measure of risk.

Different measures are appropriate depending on how the central point has been calculated. The measures that we need to be aware of are

| Location Measure | Related Dispersion Measures |
|---|---|
| Arithmetic Mean | Standard Deviation |
| | Variance |
| Median | Range |
| | Interquartile Range |
| | Percentiles |
| Mode | N/A |
| Geometric Mean | N/A |

# 3.2 Standard deviation and variance

## 3.2.1 Calculation

The standard deviation, as we noted above, is a dispersion measure that is related to the arithmetic mean. The idea behind the calculation is to establish how far each observed value falls from the mean, the standard deviation being a function of this divergence, and the variance being the square of the standard deviation.

The greater the divergence of the observed values from the mean, the greater the standard deviation (or risk).

## 3.2.2 Population

When we are considering the total population of values with no omissions, the approach, as for location measures, varies slightly depending on how the data are presented, although in outline the calculation of the standard deviation is as follows.

- Calculate the mean $\bar{x}$.

- Calculate the divergence of each observed value from the mean $(x - \bar{x})$, the sum of which must be zero since some items lie above the mean and have positive values and some below the mean and have negative values.

- Square the divergences to remove the negative signs from those lying below the mean, i.e. we are now considering just the value (or square of the value) of the divergences, ignoring whether they lie above or below the mean.

- Sum these squared divergences.

- Calculate the average of these squared divergences by dividing by the number of observed values.

- Take the square root of this average to cancel the effects of our earlier squaring up.

Since we square the divergences up then later take the square root, the units of the standard deviation will be the same as those for the mean, i.e. if the mean is, say, the average number of miles travelled in several journeys, the standard deviation will also be in miles.

## Raw data

Stating the above as a mathematical expression for the calculation of the standard deviation for raw data gives

$$\sigma = \sqrt{\frac{\Sigma(x - \bar{x})^2}{n}}$$

and the calculation of the variance is

Variance = $\sigma^2$

## Solution

We calculated earlier that the mean of this population was $\bar{x} = 6$. To calculate the standard deviation it would be most convenient to tabulate the data as follows.

| $X$ | $(x - \bar{x})$ | $(x - \bar{x})^2$ |
|---|---|---|
| 1 | −5 | 25 |
| 2 | −4 | 16 |
| 3 | −3 | 9 |
| 3 | −3 | 9 |
| 4 | −2 | 4 |
| 5 | −1 | 1 |
| 5 | −1 | 1 |
| 5 | −1 | 1 |
| 6 | 0 | 0 |
| 7 | 1 | 1 |
| 8 | 2 | 4 |
| 9 | 3 | 9 |
| 20 | 14 | 196 |
| | $\overline{\overline{0}}$ | $\overline{276}$ |

This gives

$$\sigma = \sqrt{\frac{\Sigma(x - \bar{x})^2}{n}} = \sqrt{\frac{276}{13}} = \sqrt{21.23} = 4.61$$

and

Variance = $\sigma^2 = 4.61^2 = 21.23$

## Tabulated data

The calculation for tabulated data must take account of the frequency of each observed value within each band, and hence the frequency of each observed divergence, by multiplying the square of the divergence for the band by the number of items in that band. Thus the standard deviation can be calculated as follows.

| | |
|---|---|
| MarketPlace | : Biblio |
| Order Number | : 2384534 |
| Ship Method | : Standard |
| Order Date | : 2014-02-05 |
| Email | : insaneinthemembrane@live.co.uk |

**Items : 1**

| Qty | Item | Locator |
|---|---|---|
| 1 | City Essentials - Introduction to Financial Mathem | HOL-1-LD-207-05-12 |
| | ISBN : 0751753939 | RY |

RCode: ||||||||||||||||||||||||||||||||||||||||||||||||

## Please note:

Items are dispatched individually. If you have ordered multiple books they will

arrive in separate packages

We hope that you are completely satisfied with your purchase and ask you to leave positive feedback accordingly.

However, if you are unsatisfied with your order, please contact us by telephone or email. We will do whatever it takes to resolve the issue.

Mulberry House, Woods Way, Goring By Sea, West Sussex, BN12 4QY. Tel:+44(0)1903 507544
Email: sales@worldofbooks.com | Twitter: @WorldofBooksltd | Web: www.worldofbooks.com

$$\sigma = \sqrt{\frac{\sum f(x - \bar{x})^2}{n}}$$

The calculation of the variance is

Variance $= \sigma^2$

This can easily be illustrated by correctly banding our raw data above as follows.

| x | Frequency | $(x - \bar{x})$ | $f(x - \bar{x})^2$ |
|---|---|---|---|
| | f | | |
| 1 | 1 | −5 | 25 |
| 2 | 1 | −4 | 16 |
| 3 | 2 | −3 | 18 |
| 4 | 1 | −2 | 4 |
| 5 | 3 | −1 | 3 |
| 6 | 1 | 0 | 0 |
| 7 | 1 | 1 | 1 |
| 8 | 1 | 2 | 4 |
| 9 | 1 | 3 | 9 |
| 20 | 1 | 14 | 196 |
| | 13 | | 276 |

The sum of the squared divergences again adding up to 276.

## Solution

In the previous part to this example we calculated the mean as 2.94, which we show again below. Our full calculation of both the mean and the standard deviation could be laid out as follows.

| x | f | fx | $(x - \bar{x})$ | $f(x - \bar{x})^2$ |
|---|---|---|---|---|
| 1 | 20 | 20 | −1.94 | 75.272 |
| 2 | 40 | 80 | −0.94 | 35.344 |
| 3 | 60 | 180 | 0.06 | 0.216 |
| 4 | 50 | 200 | 1.06 | 56.180 |
| 5 | 10 | 50 | 2.06 | 42.436 |
| | n = 180 | $\sum f_i x_i = 530$ | $\sum f(x - \bar{x})^2$ | = 209.448 |

Hence

$$\bar{x} = \frac{\sum f_i x_i}{n} = \frac{530}{180} = 2.94$$

$$\sigma = \sqrt{\frac{\sum f(x - \bar{x})^2}{n}} = \sqrt{\frac{209.448}{180}} = \sqrt{1.1636} = 1.079$$

and

Variance $= \sigma^2 = 1.079^2 = 1.1636$

## Grouped data

The calculations for tabulated and grouped data are almost identical except we use the group midpoint as the observed value as for location measures above.

## Solution

Our full calculation of both the mean and the standard deviation for the grouped data example could be laid out as follows.

| Range | | m | f | fm | $(m - \bar{m})$ | $f(m - \bar{m})^2$ |
|---|---|---|---|---|---|---|
| 0 to 4.9% | | 2.5 | 30 | 75 | −6.15 | 1,134.675 |
| 5 to 9.9% | | 7.5 | 50 | 375 | −1.15 | 66.125 |
| 10 to 14.9% | | 12.5 | 40 | 500 | 3.85 | 592.900 |
| 15 to 19.9% | | 17.5 | 10 | 175 | 8.85 | 783.225 |
| | | | n = 130 | $\sum f_i m_i = 1{,}125$ | | $\sum f(m - \bar{m})^2 = 2{,}576.925$ |

Hence

$$\bar{x} = \frac{\sum f_i m_i}{n} = \frac{1{,}125}{130} = 8.65$$

$$\sigma = \sqrt{\frac{\sum f(m - \bar{m})^2}{n}} = \sqrt{\frac{2{,}576.925}{130}} = \sqrt{19.8225} = 4.45$$

and

Variance = $\sigma^2 = 4.45^2 = 19.8225$

## 3.2.3 Population summary

### Raw data

$$\sigma = \sqrt{\frac{\sum(x - \bar{x})^2}{n}}$$

### Tabulated data

$$\sigma = \sqrt{\frac{\sum(x - \bar{x})^2}{n}}$$

### Grouped data

$$\sigma = \sqrt{\frac{\sum f(m - \bar{m})^2}{n}}$$

## 3.2.4 Sample

When calculating the standard deviation based only on a sample of the values, the calculation described above is unlikely to give a realistic measure since it may not consider a representative sample of variations. To give an extreme example, if a sample of one item is selected from a population then it will not be possible to calculate a standard deviation, since this item, being the only one observed, will be the mean and hence there will be no divergence of observed items from this mean.

Clearly, therefore, we cannot calculate the standard deviation when we only consider one value. Similarly, the standard deviation for small sized samples are likely to underestimate the true standard deviation, since the values chosen may not be representative (it is unlikely that we will select the extremes in a small sample).

As a result it is most usual to use Bessels approximation in the calculation of the standard deviation, that is divide down by n − 1, rather than n. This ensures that

- No standard deviation can be calculated when the sample size is one since that would involve dividing by zero.

- Calculated standard deviations are slightly enlarged, since division by n − 1 produces a larger value than division by n (e.g. 16 ÷ 4 = 4, 16 ÷ 5 = 3.2).

- As the size of the sample is increased towards the size of the full population, deducting one from the denominator will have increasingly insignificant effect until the standard deviation is (approximately) identical to that calculated using the above equations for the full population.

The calculations therefore become

### Raw data

$$\sigma = \sqrt{\frac{\Sigma(x - \bar{x})^2}{n-1}}$$

### Tabulated data

$$\sigma = \sqrt{\frac{\Sigma(x - \bar{x})^2}{n-1}}$$

### Grouped data

$$\sigma = \sqrt{\frac{\Sigma f(m - \bar{m})^2}{n-1}}$$

### 3.2.5 Alternative calculation

In order to establish the standard deviation we need to undertake a tabular calculation to assess the sum of squared deviations $(\sum f(x - \bar{x})^2)$ for the numerator of the fraction. *Note*, it is the same numerator for both the population standard deviation and for the sample standard deviation. An alternative, slightly quicker, calculation can be found via an algebraic rearrangement of this sum of squared deviations formula, as follows.

$$\sum f(x - \bar{x})^2 = \sum f(x^2 - 2x\bar{x} + \bar{x}^2)$$

$$= \sum fx^2 - 2\sum fx\bar{x} + \sum f\bar{x}^2$$

Now: $\bar{x} = \dfrac{\sum fx}{n}$

hence: $\sum fx = n\bar{x}$

giving: $\sum f(x - \bar{x})^2 \quad = \sum fx^2 - 2n\bar{x}^2 + n\bar{x}^2$

$$= \sum fx^2 - n\bar{x}^2$$

or $\qquad\qquad\qquad = \text{Sum of squared values} - n\bar{x}^2$

Hence the standard deviation formula becomes

$$\sigma = \sqrt{\dfrac{\sum fx^2 - n\bar{x}^2}{n}}$$

The advantage of this formula is that it reduces the amount of calculation required as there is no need to calculate $x - \bar{x}$ for each value. Illustrating this for the above tabulated data example gives

| x | f | fx | fx² |
|---|---|----|-----|
| 1 | 20 | 20 | 20 |
| 2 | 40 | 80 | 160 |
| 3 | 60 | 180 | 540 |
| 4 | 50 | 200 | 800 |
| 5 | 10 | 50 | 250 |
|   | $\sum n = 180$ | $\sum fx = 530$ | $\sum fx^2 = 1,770$ |

Hence

$$\bar{x} = \frac{\sum fx}{n} = \frac{530}{180} = 2.9444$$

$$\sigma = \sqrt{\frac{\sum fx^2 - n\bar{x}^2}{n}} = \sqrt{\frac{1,770 - 180 \times 2.9444^2}{180}} = \sqrt{\frac{209.4}{180}} = 1.079$$

and

Variance $= \sigma^2 = 1.079^2 = 1.1636$

## Exercise 3

The probability distribution of annual returns from investing in company A is given below.

| Return % | Probability |
|----------|-------------|
| 10 | 0.1 |
| 20 | 0.7 |
| 30 | 0.2 |

What is the mean and standard deviation of the annual rate of return on this investment?

## Exercise 4

The probability distribution of annual returns from investing in a company is given below.

| Return % | Probability |
|----------|-------------|
| 10 | 0.4 |
| 15 | 0.4 |
| 5 | 0.2 |

What is the standard deviation of the annual rates of return on this investment?

# 3.3 Coefficient of variation

## 3.3.1 Introduction

The mean and standard deviation are absolute value measures which may make comparisons difficult if we are trying to assess the relative risk of two or more items which have different means.

The coefficient of variation provides a way of overcoming this potential problem, producing a relative risk measure. The coefficient of variation is the standard deviation of the data divided by the mean, i.e.

$$\text{Coefficient of variation} = \frac{\sigma}{\overline{x}}$$

## Example

Using the raw data example above we calculated

$$\overline{x} = 6$$

$$\sigma = 4.61$$

Hence

$$\text{Coefficient of variation} = \frac{\sigma}{\overline{x}} = \frac{4.61}{6} = 0.7683$$

## 3.4 Semi-deviation and semi-variance

One criticism of the standard deviation is that it does not differentiate between what people may consider to be positive variations and what they may consider negative. The standard deviation and variance assess the average deviation from the mean, considering variations both above and below the mean.

Arguably, however, for most investors an above average return would be welcomed and they are only concerned by the prospects of a below average return which is where the semi-deviation and semi-variance come in. These are calculated in the same way as a standard deviation and variance, except that only the observations that fall below the mean return and the extent to which they fall below this mean return are included, i.e. this ratio uses the standard deviation of the below-average returns and is sometimes referred to as downside standard deviation.

### Example

Using the following economic forecast in which a security offered the following returns

| Probability | Return |
|---|---|
| 0.25 | 0% |
| 0.45 | 10% |
| 0.30 | 20% |

We assessed this security as offering an expected return of 10.5% at a standard deviation of 7.399%. We now wish to calculate its semi-deviation.

### Solution

The approach is as above but only considering the returns falling below 10.5%, giving

| Probability (p) | Return ($r_i$) (%) | $r_i - \bar{r}_i$ | $\left(r_i - \bar{r}_i\right)^2$ | $p\left(r_i - \bar{r}_i\right)^2$ |
|---|---|---|---|---|
| 0.25 | 0 | −10.5 | 110.25 | 27.5625 |
| 0.45 | 10 | −0.5 | 0.25 | 0.1125 |
| | | | Semi-variance = | 27.6750 |

Semi-deviation = $\sqrt{27.6750}$ = 5.26%

*Note*: this 5.26% semi-deviation should not be compared in any way to the 7.399% standard deviation. When comparing risks it is essential to compare like for like, ie compare one standard deviation to another, or compare one semi-deviation to another. Consistency is all important here.

### Exercise 5

In the summer of 2008, a portfolio manager considers that the outlook for the UK equity market for 2009 will depend crucially on exchange rate and interest rate developments. In particular, he identifies three possible states of the world with their associated probabilities of occurrence and equity market returns.

| State of the World | Probability | Rate of Return (%) |
|---|---|---|
| No change | 0.2 | 8 |
| ERM realignment | 0.4 | 26 |
| £ leaves ERM | 0.4 | 15 |

Calculate the expected return, standard deviation and coefficient of variation of the return on the UK equity market for 2009.

## Exercise 6

A monetarist economist believes he knows the relationship between monetary growth and subsequent inflation. In addition, he has views on the likelihood of different monetary regimes in the next year. The table below summarises his views.

| Monetary Growth | Probability | Rate of Inflation (%) |
|---|---|---|
| Non-existent | 0.2 | 1 |
| Moderate | 0.4 | 5 |
| Fast | 0.4 | 12 |

Calculate the expected inflation rate, the standard deviation and coefficient of variation of the inflation rate given his views.

# 3.5 Range and interquartile range

## 3.5.1 Introduction

As we noted above, the range and interquartile range are measures of dispersion most frequently associated with the median.

## 3.5.2 Range

The range is the distance between the highest and lowest observed values.

It may be expressed as

Range = Highest − Lowest

As such, it is *completely* dependent on (and sensitive to) the two most extreme values, and takes no account of the frequency of occurrence of any items or the values of any of the other items. As a result, it may be of little use in determining most likely variations. We now consider each of our three initial examples in turn.

### Raw data

Our series of raw data was 1, 2, 3, 3, 4, 5, 5, 5, 6, 7, 8, 9, 20.

### Solution

The range will be

Range = 20 − 1 = 19

## Tabulated data

Our tabulated data had five values from one to five.

## Solution

The range will therefore be

Range = 5 − 1 = 4

*Note*: this is unaffected by the frequency of occurrence of the two extreme values, it is simply the difference between them.

## Grouped data

To calculate the range for the grouped data we, again, need to make the assumption that values within the range are evenly spread throughout that range, hence the lowest value in any range will be the value marking the bottom of that range and the highest value will be the value marking the top of the range.

Our grouped example had four groupings, the extreme ends being 0 and 20 (19.9˙).

## Solution

As such the range is

Range = 20 − 0 = 20

## 3.5.3 Interquartile range

The interquartile range tries to give a measure of spread that is more representative of the observed values. It is calculated by placing the values in ascending order, dividing them into four quarters or *quartiles* each containing the same number of items, and measuring the difference between the top of the first quartile and the top of the third. Hence it measures the range over the central 50% of the population and should, therefore, be a more representative measure since extremes are excluded (i.e. it is insensitive to extremes).

The median itself, being the mid item in an ordered list, marks the top of the second quartile.

To calculate which items we need to consider we use item numbers

- $n_1 = \dfrac{1}{4}(n + 1)$     to give the item marking the top of the first quartile.

- $n_2 = \dfrac{2}{4}(n + 1)$     to give the item marking the top of the second quartile i.e. the median item.

BPP
LEARNING MEDIA

- $n_3 = \dfrac{3}{4}(n + 1)$      to give the item marking the top of the third quartile.

The median and interquartile range are given by

Median = $x_2$

Interquartile Range = $x_3 - x_1$

where

$x_1$ is the value associated with item $n_1$
$x_2$ is the value associated with item $n_2$
$x_3$ is the value associated with item $n_3$

## Raw data

## Solution

There are 13 items, therefore

- $n_1 = \dfrac{1}{4}(13 + 1) = \dfrac{14}{4} = 3.5$th item.

  We therefore need to take the average of the third and fourth items, which are both three, hence $x_1 = 3$.

- $n_2 = \dfrac{2}{4}(13 + 1) = \dfrac{28}{4} = 7$th item.

  The median is therefore the seventh item, hence $x_2 = 5$.

- $n_3 = \dfrac{3}{4}(13 + 1) = \dfrac{42}{4} = 10.5$th item.

  We therefore need to take the average of the tenth and eleventh items, which are 7 and 8, hence $x_3 = 7.5$.

Thus

Median = 5

Interquartile range = $7.5 - 3 = 4.5$

## Tabulated data

With tabulated data we need to calculate which bands the quartiles fall in as these give the appropriate values (since all items in a band have the same value).

## Solution

Given our tabulated data

| Value<br>x | Frequency<br>f | Cumulative<br>f |
|---|---|---|
| 1 | 20 | 20 |
| 2 | 40 | 60 |
| 3 | 60 | 120 |
| 4 | 50 | 170 |
| 5 | 10 | 180 |
| | n = 180 | |

the items that we need to consider are

- $n_1 = \dfrac{1}{4}(180 + 1) = \dfrac{181}{4} = 45.25$th item.

  This falls in the second band which has a value of 2, hence $x_1 = 2$.

- $n_2 = \dfrac{2}{4}(180 + 1) = \dfrac{362}{4} = 90.5$th item.

  This falls in the third band which has a value of 3, hence $x_2 = 3$.

- $n_3 = \dfrac{3}{4}(180 + 1) = \dfrac{543}{4} = 135.75$th item.

  This falls in the fourth band which has a value of 4, hence $x_3 = 4$.

Thus

Median = 3

Interquartile range = 4 − 2 = 2

## Grouped data

Given our grouped data

| Range | | | Frequency<br>f | Cumulative<br>f |
|---|---|---|---|---|
| 0 | to | 4.9 | 30 | 30 |
| 5 | to | 9.9 | 50 | 80 |
| 10 | to | 14.9 | 40 | 120 |
| 15 | to | 19.9 | 10 | 130 |
| | | | 130 | |

## Solution

The items we need to consider are

- $n_1 = \dfrac{1}{4}(130 + 1) = \dfrac{131}{4} = 32.75$th item.

  This falls 2.75 into the second range which contains 50 items between 5 and 10. We would therefore ascribe a value of

  $x_1 = 5 + \dfrac{2.75}{50} \times (10 - 5) = 5.275.$

- $n_2 = \dfrac{2}{4}(130 + 1) = \dfrac{262}{4} = 65.5$th item.

  This falls 35.5 into the second range which contains 50 items between 5 and 10. We would therefore ascribe a value of

  $x_2 = 5 + \dfrac{35.5}{50} \times (10 - 5) = 8.550.$

- $n_3 = \dfrac{3}{4}(130 + 1) = \dfrac{393}{4} = 98.25$th item.

  This falls 18.25 into the third range which contains 40 items between 10 and 15. We would therefore ascribe a value of

  $x_3 = 10 + \dfrac{18.25}{40} \times (15 - 10) = 12.281.$

Thus

Median = 8.550

Interquartile range = 12.281 – 5.275 = 7.006

## Exercise 7

A sample of 200 share price changes over a year was as follows.

| % Change | Number of Shares |
|----------|------------------|
| 0 - 4.9 | 37 |
| 5 - 9.9 | 29 |
| 10 - 14.9 | 55 |
| 15 - 19.9 | 41 |
| 20 - 24.9 | 38 |

What is the upper quartile price change?

### 3.5.4 Percentiles

Percentiles are calculated in a similar way to quartiles, indeed a quartile is just a specific instance of a percentile. Quartiles calculate the spread from the ¼ point (or *25th percentile*) to the ¾ point (or *75th percentile*). In a similar way we could calculate the spread over any selected range where the percentile indicates how far through the population we are looking.

# 4 SUMMARY

There are a number of formulae to remember, however, they are all similar which should aid their memorising. The main points are summarised as follows.

## 4.1 Mean, standard deviation and variance

### Calculation

|  | *Raw Data* | *Tabulated Data* | *Grouped Data* |
|---|---|---|---|
| $\bar{x} =$ | $\dfrac{\sum x_i}{n}$ | $\dfrac{\sum f_i x_i}{n}$ | $\dfrac{\sum f_i m_i}{n}$ |
| Population $\sigma =$ | $\sqrt{\dfrac{\sum(x-\bar{x})^2}{n}}$ | $\sqrt{\dfrac{\sum f(x-\bar{x})^2}{n}}$ | $\sqrt{\dfrac{\sum f(m-\bar{m})^2}{n}}$ |
| Sample $\sigma =$ | $\sqrt{\dfrac{\sum(x-\bar{x})^2}{n-1}}$ | $\sqrt{\dfrac{\sum f(x-\bar{x})}{n-1}}$ | $\sqrt{\dfrac{\sum f(m-\bar{m})^2}{n-1}}$ |

It is perhaps easiest to remember the tabulated data version for the full population only (highlighted). These are the most general ones since

- For raw data $f_i = 1$ for each item.
- For grouped data remember to use the mid points.
- Sample $\sigma$'s divide by $n-1$ rather than n.

### Comments

The measures are

- Not necessarily one of the observed values.
- Greatly affected by extremes.

## 4.2 Coefficient of variation

### Calculation

$$\text{Coefficient of variation} = \frac{\sigma}{\bar{x}}$$

## 4.3 Median, range, interquartile range, percentile

### Calculation and comments

Items to consider for median and interquartile range (and associated values) are

- $n_1 = \dfrac{1}{4}(n + 1)$      value = $x_1$

- $n_2 = \dfrac{2}{4}(n + 1)$      value = $x_2$

- $n_3 = \dfrac{3}{4}(n + 1)$      value = $x_3$.

The measures are given by

| | |
|---|---|
| Median = $x_2$ | – Unaffected by extremes. |
| Range = Highest – lowest | – Considers only extremes. |
| Interquartile range = $x_3 - x_1$ | – Unaffected by extremes. |
| Percentile = percentage point through pop'n. | – Unaffected by extremes. |

## 4.4 Mode

### Calculation

The most frequently occurring item (or range for grouped data).

### Comments

There may be several modes, hence it may not provide a useful measure.

## 4.5 Geometric mean

### Calculation

$$\bar{x} = \sqrt[n]{x_1^{n1} \times x_2^{n2} \times x_3^{n3} \times \ldots \times x_n^{nn}} \quad \text{where } n = n1 + n2 + n3 + \cdots + nn.$$

### Comments

- Useful for averaging compounding effects such as growth and inflation.
- Understates the mean compared to the arithmetic mean.

# 5 SOLUTIONS TO EXERCISES

1.

| Interval | | | Number | Cumulative |
|---|---|---|---|---|
| − 10.0 | to | −0.1 | 130 | 130 |
| 0.0 | to | 9.9 | 470 | 600 |
| 10.0 | to | 19.9 | 270 | 870 |
| 20.9 | to | 29.9 | 130 | 1,000 |
| | | | 1,000 | |

Median item = $\dfrac{n+1}{2}$ = 500.5$^{th}$ item, i.e. 370.5$^{th}$ item of the 470 in the 0.0 to 9.9 band giving

Median = 0.0 + $\dfrac{370.5}{470}$ × 9.9 = 7.8%

2. Number of shares = 52 + 27 + 101 + 80 + 40 = 300

Lower quartile limit = $\dfrac{n+1}{4}$ = $\dfrac{300+1}{4}$ = 75.25$^{th}$

This is 23.25 (75.25 − 52) into the −10 to −0.1 band which contains 27 items in total, hence is 23.25/27 (or 86.11%) from the start of that band, i.e. 10 × 86.11% = 8.611 into the band.

Hence lower quartile price change is −10 + 8.611 = −1.389

3.

| $p$ | $r$ % | $pr$ | $r - \bar{r}$ | $(r - \bar{r})^2$ | $p(r - \bar{r})^2$ |
|---|---|---|---|---|---|
| 0.1 | 10 | 1 | −11 | 121 | 12.1 |
| 0.7 | 20 | 14 | −1 | 1 | 0.7 |
| 0.2 | 30 | 6 | 9 | 81 | 16.2 |
| | $\bar{r} =$ | 21 | | $\sigma^2 =$ | 29.0 |

$\bar{r}$ = 21

$\sigma = \sqrt{29}$ = 5.39

4.

| State of World | $p$ | $r$ | $pr$ | $(r - \bar{r})^2$ | $p(r - \bar{r})^2$ |
|---|---|---|---|---|---|
| No change | 0.2 | 8 | 1.6 | 100 | 20.0 |
| ERM realignment | 0.4 | 26 | 10.4 | 64 | 25.6 |
| £ leaves ERM | 0.4 | 15 | 6.0 | 9 | 3.6 |
| | | $\bar{r} =$ | 18.0 | $\sigma_2 =$ | 49.2 |

Expected return = $\bar{r}$ = 18%

Standard deviation of return, $\sigma = \sqrt{49.2}$ = 7%

Coefficient of variation = $\dfrac{\sigma}{\bar{r}}$ = $\dfrac{7}{18}$ = 0.389

5.

| $p$ | $r$ | $pr$ | $r - \bar{r}$ | $(r - \bar{r})^2$ | $p(r - \bar{r})^2$ |
|---|---|---|---|---|---|
| 0.4 | 10 | 4 | −1 | 1 | 0.4 |
| 0.4 | 15 | 6 | 4 | 16 | 6.4 |
| 0.2 | 5 | 1 | −6 | 36 | 7.2 |
| $\bar{r} =$ | | 11 | | $\sigma^2 =$ | 14.0 |
| | | | | $\sigma =$ | 3.74% |

6.

| $p$ | $i$ | $pi$ | $\left(i - \bar{i}\right)$ | $\left(i - \bar{i}\right)^2$ | $p\left(i - \bar{i}\right)^2$ |
|---|---|---|---|---|---|
| 0.2 | 1 | 0.2 | −6 | 36 | 7.2 |
| 0.4 | 5 | 2.0 | −2 | 4 | 1.6 |
| 0.4 | 12 | 4.8 | 5 | 25 | 10.0 |
| $\bar{i} =$ | | 7.0 | | $\sigma^2 =$ | 18.8 |

$$\sigma = 4.34$$

Coefficient of variation $= \dfrac{\sigma}{\bar{r}} = \dfrac{4.34}{7.00} = 0.62$

7.

| Change | Number | Cumulative |
|---|---|---|
| 0 - 4.9 | 37 | 37 |
| 5 - 9.9 | 29 | 66 |
| 10 - 14.9 | 55 | 121 |
| 15 - 19.9 | 41 | 162 |
| 20 - 24.9 | 38 | 200 |
| | 200 | |

Upper quartile item $= \dfrac{3(N+1)}{4} = \dfrac{3(200+1)}{4} = 150.75^{th}$ item, i.e. 29.75 (150.75 − 121) into the 15 to 19.9 band which contains 41 items. Assuming an even spread within the band

Upper quartile $= 15 + \dfrac{29.75}{40} \times 5 = 18.63$

# 5 Probability theory

## Contents

## Introduction

Very few things in life are absolutely certain, which frequently makes it impossible to determine exactly what will happen. For example, when you set off for work you never know exactly (to the second) how long it will take to get in, or when you toss an unbiased coin you will never know which way it will fall.

Investment returns clearly fall into this same category, i.e. are subject to uncertainty. It is unlikely that we will know for sure what return a particular share will provide over the next year. This may make it somewhat difficult to decide which share should be selected for a portfolio whose performance is assessed annually.

Probability theory aims to provide a means of assessing the various possible outcomes or *events* in order to facilitate decision making under such circumstances. Probability theory provides a basis for the assessment of risk in many contexts, such as the insurance industry, though our primary concern here is in the assessment of risk and expected return in investment appraisal.

Probability theory was first developed in relation to gambling and many of our examples are based on the use of coins, dice, cards, etc. because of their familiarity to people. Our ultimate aim is, however, to apply the ideas to more practical business decisions.

# 1 DEFINITION

## 1.1 Basic definition

The probability of a particular *event*, E, occurring as a result of undertaking a *test* or *trial* could be defined as

$$P(E) = \frac{\text{The number of ways E can occur}}{\text{Total number of equally likely outcomes}}$$

This definition is relatively easy to appreciate with some fairly simple and logical examples.

## Example 1

An unbiased coin is tossed, what is the probability of it coming up heads?

## Solution 1

Applying the above relationship, there are a total of two equally likely possible outcomes (heads or tails) of which only one (heads) would be considered a success, hence

$P(\text{Heads}) = \frac{1}{2} = 0.5$ or 50%

## Example 2

An unbiased dice is rolled, what is the probability of throwing a six?

## Solution 2

Applying the above relationship once more, there are a total of six equally likely possible outcomes (1, 2, 3, 4, 5, 6) of which only one (6) would be considered a success, hence

$$P(6) = \tfrac{1}{6} = 0.1667 \text{ or } 16.67\%$$

## Example 3

A card is selected at random from a pack, what is the probability of it being a spade?

## Solution 3

Once again applying the above relationship, there are a total of four equally likely possible outcomes (hearts, diamonds, clubs, spades) of which only one (spades) would be considered a success, hence

$$P(\text{Spade}) = \tfrac{1}{4} = 0.25 \text{ or } 25\%$$

## 1.2 Extending the definition

One problem with the above definition is that it requires complete knowledge of all possible outcomes in particular circumstances. Clearly, this is not always going to be the case. For example, what is the probability that a particular individual will crash his car this year?

The only approach that can be adopted here is to ascertain the frequency of occurrence in the past and assume that the same frequency will continue into the future, i.e.

$$P(E) = \frac{\text{The number of observed occurrences of E}}{\text{Total number of observed occurrences}}$$

It can be seen that this is not dissimilar to the initial definition above, and all insurance policies are based upon this type of probability calculation, as are investment projections.

## Example

A share price has fallen on seven days out of ten, what is the probability that the share price will rise on any day?

## Solution

Applying the above relationship, in a ten day period the price will rise on three days, hence

$$P(\text{Rise on one day}) = \frac{3}{10} = 0.30 \text{ or } 30\%$$

# 1.3 Probability values

## 1.3.1 Basic values

Probabilities are generally expressed as a fraction, decimal or a percentage as above, though throughout this section we utilise fractions and decimals.

From the above definition it is evident that the probability of a particular event occurring lies between 0 and 1 (or 100%) and these two extremes can be viewed as follows.

- If it is certain that the event (E) *will not* occur, then the number of occurrences will always be zero, hence probability of it occurring is zero, $P(E) = 0$.

- If it is certain that the event (E) *will* definitely occur then the number of occurrences will always equal the number of trials, hence the probability of it occurring is one, $P(E) = 1$.

Clearly, all events lie somewhere between absolutely no chance and a dead certainty, hence the probabilities lie between 0 and 1 as noted above.

## 1.3.2 Sum of probabilities

Extending this idea, the sum of the probabilities of all possible outcomes must equal one since it is certain that one of them will occur.

## Example 1

Earlier we established that when we toss an unbiased coin

$$P(\text{Heads}) = \frac{1}{2}$$

similarly

$$P(\text{Tails}) = \frac{1}{2}$$

and, since these represent all the possibilities, we can see

$$P(\text{Heads}) + P(\text{Tails}) = \frac{1}{2} + \frac{1}{2} = 1$$

## Example 2

Again, we established earlier that when we select a card from a pack

$$P(\text{Spades}) = \frac{1}{4}$$

similarly

$$P(\text{Hearts}) = P(\text{Diamonds}) = P(\text{Clubs}) = \frac{1}{4}$$

and, since these represent all the possibilities, we can see

P(Spades) + P(Hearts) + P(Diamonds) + P(Clubs)

$$= \frac{1}{4} + \frac{1}{4} + \frac{1}{4} + \frac{1}{4} = 1$$

### 1.3.3 The concept of NOT

Continuing this last example enables us to illustrate the concept of NOT. If we do not select a spade then we select a heart, diamond or club, hence

$$P(\text{NOT Spades}) = P(\text{Hearts}) + P(\text{Diamonds}) + P(\text{Clubs}) = \frac{3}{4}$$

Now

P(Spades) + P(Hearts) + P(Diamonds) + P(Clubs) = 1

from which it follows that

P(Spades) + P(NOT Spades) = 1

and hence

P(Spades) = 1 – P(NOT Spades)

In this context, this seems obvious but superfluous. The idea can be seen to have some attractions, however, in the following example.

## Example

What is the probability of finding two or more misprinted pages in 500?

## Solution

We do not have the information to actually evaluate this problem, although we can, at least, consider the approach. There are two possible approaches we could adopt to the calculation.

**Alternative 1**

P(2 or more) = P(2) + P(3) + P(4) + ····· + P(500)

**Alternative 2**

$$P(2 \text{ or more}) = 1 - P(\text{NOT } 2 \text{ or more})$$
$$= 1 - [P(0) + P(1)]$$

which will be a lot easier to evaluate.

# 2 MORE COMPLEX APPLICATIONS

## 2.1 Introduction

So far we have considered relatively easy examples where we are looking at just one test (one toss of the coin, one throw of the dice, one day's observation) and determining the probability of just one event or outcome (a head, a six, a price rise). The problems that arise in relation to probabilities are

■ The ways that events are related and the implications of this on the performance of the trials.

■ The ways that events may be combined when more than one is considered.

## 2.2 Relationships between events

When we undertake a test or series of tests we will find that the possible outcomes may be either

■ **Independent** – i.e. the outcome of one has no effect on the outcome of the others; or
■ **Dependent** – i.e. the outcome of one test *does* affect the subsequent ones.

When we consider the possible outcomes from any one test they may be either

■ **Mutually exclusive** – i.e. they may *not* occur simultaneously; or
■ **Not mutually exclusive** – i.e. they may occur together.

The impact of these relationships is considered below.

# 2.3 Combining events

## 2.3.1 Introduction

In certain types of tests there are several ways of viewing the events. In our example above involving the selection of a card from a pack we ascertained the probability of selecting a spade. We could equally have calculated the probability of selecting a card with a specific value.

## Example

A card is selected at random from a pack, what is the probability of it being an ace?

## Solution

There are a total of 13 possible outcomes (Ace, 2, 3, 4, 5, 6, 7, 8, 9, 10, J, Q, K) of which only one (Ace) we would consider a success, hence

$$P(Ace) = \frac{1}{13}$$

What we are seeing are different ways of viewing the outcomes, i.e. two different *events* arising from the same test, and there are two ways that we could consider combining these events

- What is the probability of a particular suit AND a particular value?
- What is the probability of a particular suit OR a particular value?

## 2.3.2 AND – the multiplication law

### Independent events

What if, in our cards example, we wanted to establish the probability of selecting a card that is both a particular suit *and* a particular value (e.g. the ace of spades). Clearly, the suit and the value of the card are independent of each other since all four suits have all 13 values, hence we are combining independent events. The relationship that can be used to establish this probability is

$P(A \text{ AND } B) = P(A) \times P(B)$

## Example

A card is selected at random from a pack, what is the probability of it being both a spade and an ace (i.e. the ace of spades)?

## Solution

There are two possible approaches to this question, use either

- First principles; or
- The multiplication law.

The purpose of this example is clearly to illustrate the latter, though in this situation the former is more obvious. The former can be seen as a proof of the multiplication law.

**First principles**

There are a total of 52 possible outcomes (52 different cards in a pack) of which only one (the ace of spades) would be considered a success, hence

$$P(\text{Ace of Spades}) = \frac{1}{52}$$

**Multiplication law**

We established above that:

$$P(\text{Ace}) = \frac{1}{13}$$

$$P(\text{Spade}) = \frac{1}{4}$$

The probability of both occurring, i.e. the probability of selecting the ace of spades, can be found by using

P(A AND B) = P(A) × P(B)

giving

P(Ace AND Spade) = P(Ace) × P(Spade)

$$= \frac{1}{13} \times \frac{1}{4} = \frac{1}{52}$$

## Dependent events

If two events are such that the outcome of one is in some way influenced by the other then this above relationship needs to be modified. The calculations involve the consideration of *conditional probabilities*. The relationship that we need to apply is

P(A AND B) = P(A) × P(B|A)

Where P(B|A) means the probability of B occurring given that A has occurred, a *conditional probability*.

## Example

45% of the population of 100,000 are male and 55% female. In addition, 60% of men and 40% of women drink beer. If a person is selected at random, what is the probability of selecting a beer drinking man?

## Solution

Again there are two possible approaches to this particular question

- First principles.
- The multiplication law.

**First principles**

To apply our first principles we need to establish the total number of beer drinking men in the population. Since 45% of the population are men, then there are 45,000 men. Since 60% of them drink beer there will be 27,000 beer drinking men. Hence

$$P(\text{Beer drinking man}) = \frac{27,000}{100,000} = 0.27$$

**Multiplication law**

The multiplication law is simply a formalised consideration of the above, being

$$P(A \text{ AND } B) = P(A) \times P(B|A)$$

where P(B|A) means the probability of B occurring given that A already has.

Hence

$$P(\text{Beer drinking man}) = P(\text{Male}) \times P(\text{Drinks beer}|\text{Male})$$
$$= 0.45 \times 0.60 = 0.27$$

## Conclusion

If we wish to establish the probability of two events occurring we can use the **general expression**:

$$P(A \text{ AND } B) = P(A) \times P(B|A)$$

Where P(B|A) means the probability of B occurring given that A has occurred (a *conditional probability*).

If A and B are two **independent** events then P(B|A) = P(B) and this expression reduces to

$$P(A \text{ AND } B) = P(A) \times P(B)$$

*Note:* we consider some alternative (easier) ways of tackling conditional probability problems below.

## 2.3.3 OR – the addition law

## Mutually exclusive events

What if, returning to our cards example, we wished to establish the probability of selecting a card that is either a spade *or* a heart. These are two mutually exclusive events since a card cannot be both a spade and a heart simultaneously. The relationship that can be used to establish the probability in this situation is

$$P(A \text{ OR } B) = P(A) + P(B)$$

## Example

A card is selected at random from a pack, what is the probability of it being either a spade or a heart?

## Solution

Again, there are two possible approaches to this question, use either

- First principles; or
- The addition law.

Once more the purpose of this example is to illustrate the latter, though the former is used as a proof of the addition law.

### First principles

There are a total of 52 possible outcomes (52 different cards in a pack) of which 26 (thirteen spades and thirteen hearts) would be considered a success, hence

$$P(\text{Spade OR Heart}) = \frac{26}{52} = 0.50$$

### Addition law

We established above that

$$P(\text{Spade}) = P(\text{Hearts}) = \frac{1}{4}$$

The probability of either occurring in this situation may be found by using

$$P(A \text{ OR } B) = P(A) + P(B)$$

giving

$$P(\text{Spade OR Heart}) = P(\text{Spade}) + P(\text{Heart})$$

$$= \frac{1}{4} + \frac{1}{4} = \frac{1}{2}$$

## Not mutually exclusive events

If two events are not mutually exclusive then we need to modify this relationship otherwise we may overestimate the probability. The relationship that we need to use is

$$P(A \text{ OR } B) = P(A) + P(B) - P(A \text{ AND } B)$$

where the last term is subtracted to prevent double counting as we explain below.

## Example

A card is selected from a pack of 30 cards numbered 1 to 30. What is the probabilit that the value on the card will be divisible by either three or five?

## Solution

As for the above examples, there are two possible approaches to this question, use either

- First principles; or
- The addition law.

### First principles

In order to approach this question from first principles we need to establish all the numbers between 1 and 30 that are divisible by either 3 or 5, i.e.

3, 5, 6, 9, 10, 12, 15, 18, 20, 21, 24, 25, 27, 30  =  14 cards in total

Hence

$$P(\text{Divisible by 3 OR 5}) = \frac{14}{30}$$

### Addition law

In order to apply the addition law we need to break down the cards into those that are

- Divisible by 3 = 3, 6, 9, 12, 15, 18, 21, 24, 27, 30  =  10 cards
- Divisible by 5 = 5, 10, 15, 20, 25, 30  =  6 cards

and ascertain

$$P(\text{Divisible by 3}) = \frac{10}{30}$$

$$P(\text{Divisible by 5}) = \frac{6}{30}$$

If we simply applied the earlier formula

$$P(A \text{ OR } B) = P(A) + P(B)$$

we would get

$$P(\text{Divisible by 3 OR 5}) = \frac{10}{30} + \frac{6}{30} = \frac{16}{30}$$

which is clearly too high. It appears to imply that there are 16 numbers that satisfy the required condition when we know that there are only 14. The reason for this is that an element of double counting has occurred. The numbers 15 and 30 appear in both sets, i.e. those divisible by 3 and those divisible by 5, and this double counting must be eliminated by subtracting the number of numbers divisible by both 3 AND 5 so that they are only counted once.

As we noted above the probability of either occurring in this situation may be found by using

$$P(A \text{ OR } B) = P(A) + P(B) - P(A \text{ AND } B)$$

giving

$$P(\text{Divisible by 3 OR 5}) = \frac{10}{30} + \frac{6}{30} - \left(\frac{10}{30} \times \frac{6}{30}\right)$$

$$= \frac{10}{30} + \frac{6}{30} - \frac{2}{30} = \frac{14}{30}$$

## Conclusion

If we wish to establish the probability of either of two events occurring, we can use the **general expression**

$$P(A \text{ OR } B) = P(A) + P(B) - P(A \text{ AND } B)$$

If A and B are two **mutually exclusive** events then P(A AND B) = 0 and this reduces to

$$P(A \text{ OR } B) = P(A) + P(B)$$

# 2.4 A practical approach to problems

## 2.4.1 Introduction

The probability laws are fine to an extent but rapidly become unwieldy as problems become more complex. Probability tables and probability trees provide a practical method for combining the probabilities of a series of events which are either independent or dependent, although their use is most effective in solving particularly intricate conditional probability problems.

We will illustrate the use of both a probability table and a probability tree using the same example below. We will also solve the same example using probability laws in order to illustrate that

- They all provide the same result as we would hope.
- The table and tree are quite intuitive, whereas the probability laws are not.

## Example 1

45% of the population of 100,000 are male and 55% female. In addition, 60% of men and 40% of women drink. If a person is selected at random what is the probability of selecting a man who drinks? And what is the probability of a drinker being female?

## Example 2

A further study of the drinking habits of the individuals identified in example 1 above reveals that they drink either beer, lager or wine. The exact proportions are as follows.

- Male drinkers - 60% beer, 20% lager, 20% wine.
- Female drinkers - 40% beer, 30% lager, 30% wine.

What is the probability of a person selected at random being a lager drinker, and what is the probability of a beer drinker being female?

## 2.4.2 Probability table

## Solution 1

The table below illustrates all the information that we can ascertain from the question that was provided. It has been constructed as follows.

- The bottom right hand figure, the total of the total column, is set to one.

- The total of males and total of females can then be ascertained based on the proportionate breakdown of the population.

- The proportion of male drinkers and female drinkers can then be ascertained by multiplying the male and female totals by the proportion of males and females who drink, respectively.

- The proportion of non-drinkers are then balancing figures in the male and female columns.

- The total of drinkers and non-drinkers is the sum of the male and female ones.

|  | Male | Female | Total |
|---|---|---|---|
| Drinkers | 0.27 | 0.22 | 0.49 |
| Non-drinkers | ×60%  0.18 | ×40%  0.33 | 0.51 |
| Total | 0.45 | 0.55 | 1.00 |
| Total | ×45% | ×55% | |

We can then determine from this that

$$P(\text{Drinking man}) = \frac{0.27}{1.00} = 0.27$$

$$P(\text{Drinker being female}) = \frac{0.22}{0.49} = 0.449$$

Note that in the second part of this question we are only sampling the drinkers and trying to find out how many of them are female. As a result, the total number of possible outcomes is 0.49 of which 0.22 represents the number of females.

## Solution 2

This table can be extended to deal with the further breakdown required in this example, although its extension is perhaps less flexible than the extension of a probability tree.

The following table has been constructed from the information requested in the question and provides all the data necessary for solving the problems asked.

| | | *Male* | | *Female* | *Total* |
|---|---|---|---|---|---|
| Beer | ×60% → | 0.162 | ×40% → | 0.088 | 0.250 |
| Lager | ×20% → | 0.054 | ×30% → | 0.066 | 0.120 |
| Wine | ×20% → | 0.054 | ×30% → | 0.066 | 0.120 |
| Drinkers | | 0.270 | | 0.220 | 0.490 |
| Non-drinkers | | 0.180 | | 0.330 | 0.510 |
| Total | | 0.450 | | 0.550 | 1.000 |

We can then determine from this that

$$P(\text{Lager drinker}) = \frac{0.12}{1.00} = 0.12$$

$$P(\text{Beer drinker being female}) = \frac{0.088}{0.250} = 0.352$$

Once again in dealing with the last part of this question we need to realise that we are only considering the beer drinkers and trying to determine what proportion of them are female. As a result, the total number of possible outcomes is 0.25 and the total possible ways of achieving the desired outcome, i.e. a female, is 0.088.

## Exercise 1

A recent survey of a large number of fund managers revealed that 35% of them used 'quant' techniques. It also transpired that if they worked for US owned fund management groups this proportion rose to 70%. 20% of those interviewed worked for US owned groups. What is the probability that a fund manager drawn at random used quantitative techniques and worked for a US fund management group?

## Exercise 2

The probability of a revaluation of the Swiss Franc in 2008 is put at 0.7 by a consensus of City commentators. The same group believes that such a revaluation would lead to a sharp fall in UK interest rates with probability 0.3, a moderate fall with probability 0.5 and no change with probability 0.2. On the other hand, if the Mark is not revalued then the commentators foresee no change in UK interest rates. What is the probability that there will not be a sharp fall in UK interest rates?

## Exercise 3

It has been observed that 60% of City economists have been trained at Oxbridge, and of those trained at Oxbridge 65% work on the 'international side'. What is the probability that an economist selected at random does not work on the 'international side' and was trained at Oxbridge?

### 2.4.3 Probability tree

Probability trees provide an alternative graphical way of viewing the same information and will, as one would expect, give exactly the same results.

The idea is that the various branches of the tree break the scenario down into more and more levels of detail as we can see with the two examples.

## Solution 1

In this example whether an individual is a drinker or not is dependent on whether they are male or female. We therefore need to break the population down firstly into males and females and then break each of these in turn into drinkers and non-drinkers. Noting various comments and related probabilities alongside the various branches will enable us to quickly calculate the probability of winding up at the tip of one of those branches. For example, the probability of being a male drinker can be read straight from the tree as 0.27.

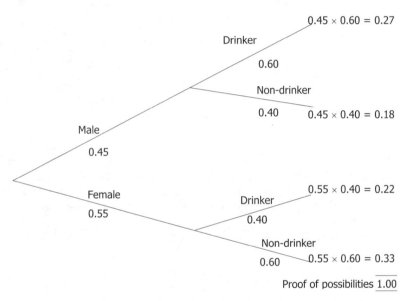

You will notice that the probabilities noted at the ends of each branch are identical to those in the probability table above, we are simply analysing the same problem in a slightly different way. Once again we can determine from this that

$$P(\text{Male drinker}) = \frac{0.27}{1.00} = 0.27$$

$$P(\text{Drinker being female}) = \frac{0.22}{0.22 + 0.27} = 0.449$$

You will also note in the above probability tree that we have added up the probabilities arising at the end of each branch and found that it comes to 1. This is the situation that we would expect, since the sum of the probabilities of all possible outcomes must add up to 1 as we noted earlier. This calculation therefore represents a proof of our workings to an extent.

## Solution 2

This tree can now be extended to break down the drinkers, either male or female, into those who drink beer, those who drink lager, and those who drink wine. When the relevant probabilities are attached to each of these sub-branches we can calculate the probability of arriving at the end of each of these.

Once more to prove the calculated end probabilities we have added them up to ensure that they total up to 1. This extended tree now looks as follows.

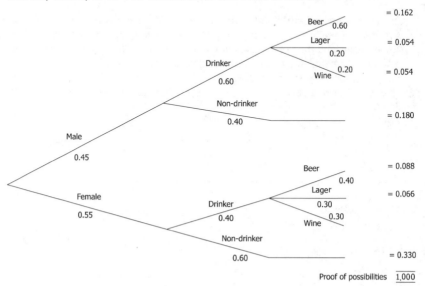

Once more you will notice that the probabilities noted at the ends of each branch are identical to those in the probability table above, we are simply analysing the same problem in a slightly different way. Again we can determine from this that

$$P(\text{Lager drinker}) = \frac{0.054 + 0.066}{1.00} = 0.12$$

$$P(\text{Beer drinker being female}) = \frac{0.088}{0.162 + 0.088} = 0.352$$

In using this table to calculate the probability of being a lager drinker we have had to appreciate that there are both male and female lager drinkers, and hence the total number of individuals who satisfy this criteria is the sum of these two.

To calculate the probability of a beer drinker being female we must remember that we are only sampling from the population of beer drinkers, both male and female. The probability of a beer drinker being female is then the proportionate number of beer drinking females over the total number of beer drinkers.

## 2.4.4 Probability laws

Using the probability laws is doing exactly the same thing as constructing a probability table or probability tree. The difference is that it is far less intuitive than either of the above two alternatives and therefore much more prone to error. The solutions below illustrate how the probability laws could be used for these two examples although you will quickly appreciate how involved they become and we certainly do not recommend this method.

## Solution 1

### Part 1

To answer the first part of this question we need to determine

$$P(\text{Drinking man}) = P(\text{Male AND Drinker})$$
$$= P(\text{Male}) \times P(\text{Drinker|Male})$$
$$= 0.45 \times 0.60$$
$$= 0.27$$

### Part 2

To answer the second part of this question we need to determine

$$P(\text{Drinker is female}) = P(\text{Female|Drinker})$$

$$= \frac{P(\text{Female AND Drinker})}{P(\text{Drinker})}$$

$$= \frac{P(\text{Female AND Drinker})}{P[(\text{Female AND Drinker}) \text{ OR } (\text{Male AND Drinker})]}$$

$$= \frac{P(\text{Female AND Drinker})}{P(\text{Female AND Drinker}) + P(\text{Male AND Drinker})}$$

Now

$$P(\text{Female AND Drinker}) = P(\text{Female}) \times P(\text{Drinker|Female})$$
$$= 0.55 \times 0.40$$
$$= 0.22$$

Hence

$$P(\text{Drinker is female}) = \frac{P(\text{Female AND Drinker})}{P(\text{Female AND Drinker}) + P(\text{Male AND Drinker})}$$

$$= \frac{0.22}{0.22 + 0.27}$$

$$= 0.449$$

As you can see, there has been a lot more involved in using these formulae than there was in constructing either the probability table or probability tree. The end result is the same although, as example 2 shows, the application and extension of the ideas becomes very difficult.

## Solution 2

### Part 1

To answer the first part of this question we need to determine

P(Lager drinker) = P[(Female AND Lager drinker) OR (Male AND Lager drinker)]

= P(Female AND Lager drinker) + P(Male AND Lager drinker)

Now

P(Female AND Lager drinker) = P(Female) × P(Lager drinker|Female)

= P(Female) × P(Drinker|Female) × P(Lager|Female drinker)

= 0.55 × 0.40 × 0.30 = 0.066

and

P(Male AND Lager drinker) = P(Male) × P(Lager drinker|Male)

= P(Male) × P(Drinker|Male) × P(Lager|Male drinker)

= 0.45 × 0.60 × 0.20 = 0.054

Hence

P(Lager drinker) = P(Female AND Lager drinker) + P(Male AND Lager drinker)

= 0.066 + 0.054 = 0.120

### Part 2

To answer the second part of this question we need to determine

$$P(\text{Beer drinker is female}) = P(\text{Female|Beer drinker}) = \frac{P(\text{Female AND Beer drinker})}{P(\text{Beer drinker})}$$

As a starting point we can calculate

P(Beer drinker) = P[(Female AND Beer drinker) OR (Male AND Beer drinker)]

= P(Female AND Beer drinker) + P(Male AND Beer drinker)

now

P(Female AND Beer drinker) = P(Female) × P(Beer drinker|Female)

= P(Female) × P(Drinker|Female) × P(Beer |Female drinker)

= 0.55 × 0.40 × 0.40 = 0.088

and

P(Male AND Beer drinker) = P(Male) × P(Beer drinker|Male)

   = P(Male) × P(Drinker|Male) × P(Beer |Male drinker)

   = 0.45 × 0.60  × 0.60  =  0.162

Hence

P(Beer drinker)   = P(Female AND Beer drinker)  +  P(Male AND Beer drinker)

   = 0.088 + 0.162 = 0.250

P(Female|beer drinker)   $= \dfrac{\text{P(Female AND Beer drinker)}}{\text{P(Beer drinker)}}$

$= \dfrac{0.088}{0.250}$

= 0.352

Once more the results we have obtained are identical to those that we obtained using either the probability table or probability tree above.  The levels of calculations have, however, become much more involved, clearly indicating the difficulty in extending these ideas too far.

## 2.4.5 Conclusion

As we can see from the above, the probability tree represents what is most likely to be the most flexible method for calculating more extensive problems, especially those involving conditional probabilities.  The probability table is fine so long as there are only two variables (e.g. male/female, drinkers/non-drinkers) although it becomes difficult to extend and subanalyse the categories as the second example showed.  Either of these methods are considered reasonably practical.

As we noted above, we would strongly recommend against trying to apply the probability laws in the form of mathematical equations.  Their application becomes very awkward in extended examples.

# 3 SUMMARY

## 3.1 Introduction

Probability theory provides a means of establishing the likelihood of an event occurring. The major facts to be familiar and comfortable with are

## 3.2 Probability theory

### Probability of a single event

$$P(E) = \frac{\text{The number of ways E can occur}}{\text{Total number of equally likely outcomes}}$$

or

$$P(E) = \frac{\text{The number of observed occurrences of E}}{\text{Total number of observed occurrences}}$$

### Addition law

$$P(A \text{ OR } B) = P(A) + P(B) - P(A \text{ AND } B) \text{ - generally}$$
$$= P(A) + P(B) \text{ - if A and B are mutually exclusive}$$

### Multiplication law

$$P(A \text{ AND } B) = P(A) \times P(B|A) \quad \text{- generally}$$
$$P(A \text{ AND } B) = P(A) \times P(B) \quad \text{- if A and B are independent}$$

**Not**

$$P(\text{NOT } A) = 1 - P(A)$$

### Conditional probabilities

Conditional probability problems are best tackled through the use of either

- Distribution trees; or
- Distribution tables.

# 4 SOLUTIONS TO EXERCISES

1.

|  |  | US | Non-US | Total |
|---|---|---|---|---|
| Quant | (0.20 × 70%) | 0.14 | 0.21 | 0.35 |
| Non-quant | (Bal) | 0.06 | 0.59 | 0.65 |
| Total |  | 0.20 | 0.80 | 1.00 |

P(US AND Quant) = 0.14

2.

|  |  | Revaluation | No Revaluation | Total |
|---|---|---|---|---|
| Sharp fall | (0.70 × 30%) | 0.21 | 0.00 | 0.21 |
| Moderate fall | (0.70 × 50%) | 0.35 | 0.00 | 0.35 |
| No change | (0.70 × 20%) | 0.14 | 0.30 | 0.44 |
| Total |  | 0.70 | 0.30 | 1.00 |

P(Not a sharp fall)   = 1 − P(Sharp fall)

= 1 − 0.21 = 0.79

3.

|  |  | Oxbridge | Non-Oxbridge | Total |
|---|---|---|---|---|
| International | (0.60 × 65%) | 0.39 |  |  |
| Non-int. | (Bal) | 0.21 |  |  |
| Total |  | 0.60 | 0.40 | 1.00 |

P(Non-int. AND Oxbridge) = 0.21

# 6 Probability distributions

## Contents

## Introduction

Probability trees and probability tables provide us with the means for considering all the various possible outcomes and the probabilities associated with them. Probability distributions provide an alternative way of considering the full set of possibilities and of calculating the related probabilities.

There are two different types of distribution that we shall consider.

- The binomial distribution.
- The normal distribution.

It is important that you are aware under what circumstances these distributions may be useful.

# 1   BINOMIAL DISTRIBUTION

## 1.1 Introduction

The binomial distribution extends our basic probability ideas to aid calculations which involve large samples of independent trials with two possible outcomes. We will illustrate this idea with the following example.

### Example

If three cards are chosen at random from a normal pack, the previously selected card being replaced and the pack shuffled between selections to ensure independence, what is the probability that two are hearts?

We will first solve this question from first principles and then introduce the binomial expression and show how it could have been solved much more quickly.

### Solution

In this situation there are only two possible outcomes for any selection, specifically

- We have selected a heart (H) - probability 0.25.
- We have not selected a heart (N) - probability 0.75.

If we now consider all the possible outcomes from selecting three cards we get the following.

| Outcomes | Probability Calculation | Probability |
|---|---|---|
| *All Hearts* | | |
| H AND H AND H | $0.25 \times 0.25 \times 0.25 = 0.015625$ | 0.015625 |
| *Two Hearts* | | |
| H AND H AND N | $0.25 \times 0.25 \times 0.75 = 0.046875$ | |
| H AND N AND H | $0.25 \times 0.75 \times 0.25 = 0.046875$ | 0.140625 |
| N AND H AND H | $0.75 \times 0.25 \times 0.25 = 0.046875$ | |
| *One Heart* | | |
| H AND N AND N | $0.25 \times 0.75 \times 0.75 = 0.140625$ | |
| N AND H AND N | $0.75 \times 0.25 \times 0.75 = 0.140625$ | 0.421875 |
| N AND N AND H | $0.75 \times 0.75 \times 0.25 = 0.140625$ | |
| *No Hearts* | | |
| N AND N AND N | $0.75 \times 0.75 \times 0.75 = 0.421875$ | 0.421875 |
| | | 1.000000 |

What we can see from this example is that there are a number of different ways of achieving any one result (e.g. three ways of selecting two hearts), although each way has an equal probability.

Thus the probability of selecting two hearts in three cards is 0.140625.

## 1.2 Binomial expression

The binomial expression gives us a means to calculate any of these probabilities directly without listing all of the alternatives.

Given two possible outcomes, one of which is considered a success (with probability p) and one of which is considered a failure (with probability $1 - p$), then the probability of r successes in n trials is given by

$$P(r) = \frac{n!}{r!(n-r)!} \times p^r \times (1-p)^{n-r}$$

where

$\dfrac{n!}{r_r!(n-r)!}$ = the number of possible combinations of r successes and $n - r$ failures in n trials;

$p \times (1-p)^{n-r}$ = the probability of any single combination of r successes and $n - r$ failures in any one trial.

## Solution

Applying this binomial expression to the above example we can calculate that the probability of two hearts (a success) in three cards is given by

$$P(2) = \frac{3!}{2!-1!} \times 0.25^2 \times 0.75^1$$
$$= 3 \times 0.0625 \times 0.75$$
$$= 0.140625$$

## 1.3 Use of the expression

The real use of the binomial expression comes when we consider more complex problems such as the following one.

### Example

The probability of passing a driving test is 0.3. If ten people take the driving test what is the probability that at least two will pass?

### Solution

P(At least two) = P(Two or more)

and

$$P(\text{Two or more}) = 1 - P(0 \text{ OR } 1)$$
$$= 1 - [P(0) + P(1)]$$

Now

$$P(0) = \frac{10!}{0! - 10!} \times 0.3^0 \times 0.7^{10} = 1 \times 1 \times 0.0282 = 0.0282$$

and

$$P(1) = \frac{10!}{1! - 9!} \times 0.3^1 \times 0.7^9 = 10 \times 0.3 \times 0.0404 = 0.1211$$

hence

$$P(\text{At least two}) = 1 - [P(0) + P(1)]$$
$$= 1 - [0.0282 + 0.1211]$$
$$= 1 - 0.1493$$
$$= 0.8507$$

### Exercise 1

During the recent prolonged rise in the value of the yen against the dollar, the yen rose on two days out of three. What is the probability that it rose on seven days or less out of any ten-day period?

### Exercise 2

During a recent bull market, bond prices rose on two days out of three. What is the probability that prices fell on at least four days out of a five-day period?

## Exercise 3

Over the last year, the pound has fallen against the euro on two out of three days. What is the probability that the euro has fallen against the pound on less than two days in any five-day period?

# 1.4 Binomial distribution

If we were to plot a histogram of probability against number of possible successes we would be constructing the binomial distribution. Whether this distribution is symmetrical or skewed is dependent upon the probability of achieving a success.

In general the binomial distribution is a histogram which shows

▪ All the possible outcomes along the x axis.

▪ The probabilities of the y axis, the height of each histogram bar being calculated using the above binomial expression.

As a result, the area of the histogram will be proportional to the frequency of the occurrences of the various events and the total area underneath the histogram must be 1, since the sum of all probabilities is 1.

## 1.4.1 Symmetrical

If, in the above driving test example, the probability of passing the driving test was 0.5, then the probabilities of ten people passing the binomial distribution would appear symmetrical as follows.

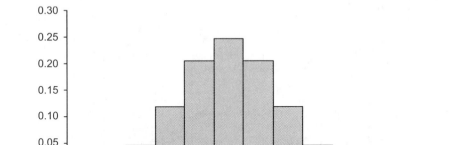

## 1.4.1.1 Skewed

## Positively skewed

If we use the probability of passing the driving test of 0.3, as in the example above, calculate the probability of all possible numbers of successes between 0 and 10 and plot these on a histogram, we would obtain a positively skewed distribution as illustrated below. A positively skewed distribution is one where more items lie above the most frequently occurring one than lie below it. In this example we can see that the most frequently occurring event is three which we could have expected since, on average, three in ten pass.

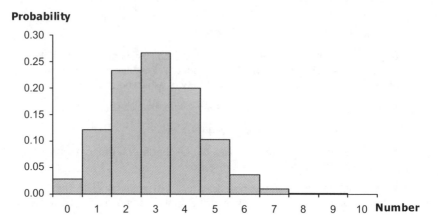

## Negatively skewed

Similarly, if the probability of a success in the driving test was 0.7 then the most likely number of successes in 10 trials would be 7 and we would have a negatively skewed distribution as illustrated below.

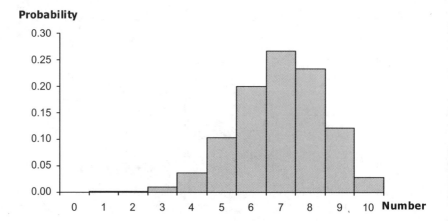

# 2 STANDARD NORMAL DISTRIBUTION

## 2.1 Introduction

The binomial distribution deals with discrete data (e.g. whole numbers of people passing a driving test), and enables us to calculate the probability of certain outcomes.

The normal distribution enables us to perform similar calculations on continuous data, i.e. data that do not just take whole values (e.g. heights, weights, growth rates).

The normal distribution appears very similar to the symmetrical binomial distribution and may be used as an approximation to the binomial distribution where there are a very large number of items as we outline below.

As for the binomial distribution the area under the curve between any two points represents the probability of observing a value between those two points and the total area under the curve is 1 (the total of all probabilities of all possible outcomes). The area under the curve between two points could be established mathematically by solving the equation

$$P(\text{Between } x_1 \text{ and } x_2) = \int_{x_1}^{x_2} \frac{1}{\sigma\sqrt{2\pi}} e^{-\frac{(x-\mu)^2}{2\sigma^2}} dx$$

although it is much more convenient to utilise the normal distribution tables which are included as an appendix to this session.

## 2.2 Characteristics of the distribution

### 2.2.1 Graphically

Graphically the normal distribution appears as follows.

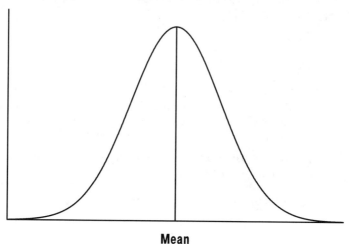

**Mean**

## 2.2.2 Characteristics

The characteristics of this distribution are as follows.

- It is bell-shaped.

- It is symmetrical, i.e. there is an equal probability of being either above or below the central point and, as a result, the normal distribution tables can be used on both sides of the mean as we will illustrate below.

- The mean equals the highest central point, i.e. the mode (since it is symmetrical).

- It is asymptotic, i.e. neither tail ever reaches the x axis.

- The total area under the curve equals 1.

- The area under the curve between two points gives the probability of observing an item lying within that range.

- There is a measure of spread, the standard deviation of the distribution, which determines how wide the distribution is.

All normal distributions are defined by two measures, the

- **Mean**, the central and most frequently occurring value; and

- **Standard deviation**, an indication of the spread of values about that mean or central point.

## 2.3 Uses of the normal distribution

### 2.3.1 Introduction

Where a population is normally distributed we can calculate the probability of observing a value in a particular range, or the range of values corresponding to a given probability using just two things.

- Z value

$$Z = \frac{X - \mu}{\sigma}$$

  i.e. the distance of the observed value x from the mean $\mu$ expressed as multiple of the standard deviation $\sigma$. *NB.* the sign of the Z value may be ignored when looking it up in the normal distribution tables as we illustrate below.

- **Normal distribution tables** which provide the area of the curve beyond point, hence the probability of observing a value beyond that point when moving away from the mean (i.e. above that value if the value lies above the mean, below it if the value lies below the mean).

## 2.3.2 Calculating probabilities given values

### Approach

What we must do to calculate probabilities associated with particular ranges of values is

■ Draw up the curve and establish the area that we are interested in, a quick sketch to highlight the relevant points is essential.

■ Determine how we can construct just this area by either

− Adding together non-overlapping areas which make it up;
− Deducting the areas that are not wanted from others.

At the end of the day it is a simple problem of addition and/or subtraction.

### Relating the approach to probability theory

In adding areas together we are saying that the value lies in one area or the other. The justification for this, in terms of probability theory, is that as long as they are not overlapping then they will be mutually exclusive and hence

P(A OR B) = P(A) + P(B)

In deducting areas we are saying that the value falls in a particular area excluding a certain part, simply the reverse idea of the addition law.

### Important considerations

The most important characteristics to bear in mind when undertaking this are

■ The area under the curve between any two points corresponds to the probability of observing an item between those two points.

■ The total area under the curve = 1 (i.e. the sum of all the probabilities of all possibilities is 1).

■ The area above the mean = the area below = 0.5 (i.e. the probability of a value falling above the mean = probability of falling below = 0.5).

■ The normal distribution tables give the area beyond the selected point when moving away from the mean (i.e. the probability of being that far from the mean or more).

This all sounds a little complicated when expressed in words and may best be illustrated with a series of examples.

## Example

The mean daily UK temperature has been measured as 12.5° and the standard deviation measured as 7.5°.

What is the probability of

- A freeze on any one day.
- A below average temperature on any one day that does not result in a freeze.
- A temperature above 20° on any one day.
- A temperature between 0° and 20° on any one day.
- A temperature between 20° and 25° on any one day.
- A temperature between 0° and 20° on two consecutive days.
- A temperature between 0° and 20° on any seven days in ten.

## Solution

### Probability of a freeze

Drawing up the normal distribution curve and plotting the relevant points (a freeze corresponding to the temperature falling to $\leq 0°$) reveals the following.

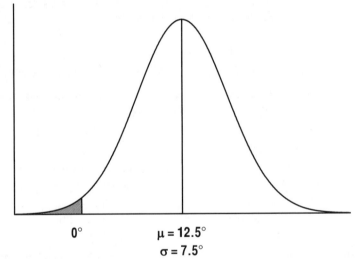

$$0° \qquad \mu = 12.5°$$
$$\sigma = 7.5°$$

The area of this curve that we are interested in is the shaded area below 0°, the probability of which we can directly calculate if we can ascertain its Z value by using

$$Z = \frac{X - \mu}{\sigma}$$

which gives

$$Z = \frac{0 - 12.5}{7.5} = -1.67$$

There are two factors relevant in this Z value, the

- *Sign* (i.e. + or −), a positive sign indicates that the relevant point lies above the mean, a negative sign indicates that it lies below.

- *Value*, this is the factor looked up in the normal distribution tables to give the probability of being *beyond* the selected point. In using the normal distribution tables the sign can be ignored.

Looking up a Z value of 1.67 in the normal distribution tables gives

$$P(\leq 0°) = 0.04746$$

## Probability of below average temperature not resulting in a freeze

This requires the consideration of a temperature between 0° and 12.5° which, using the above diagram, corresponds to the area below the mean which is *not* shaded.

Now we know that the total area below the mean is 0.5000 and hence

$$P(0° \text{ to } 12.5°) = 0.50000 - P(\leq 0°)$$

$$= 0.50000 - 0.04746 = 0.45254$$

In terms of probability theory this corresponds to

$$P(0° \text{ to } 12.5°) = P(\leq 12.5° \text{ NOT} \leq 0°)$$

$$= P(\leq 12.5°) - P(\leq 0°)$$

$$= 0.50000 - 0.04746 = 0.45254$$

## Probability of temperature ≥ 20°

Quickly drawing up the normal distribution curve reveals the following.

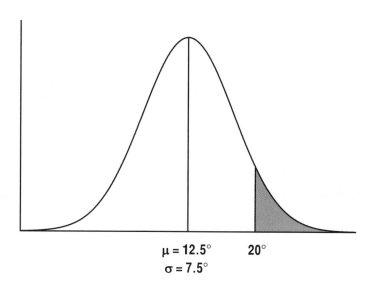

$$\mu = 12.5° \qquad 20°$$
$$\sigma = 7.5°$$

The area of the curve that we are interested in is the shaded area lying above 20°. Calculating the Z value for 20° and looking this up in tables will, therefore, give the desired result.

$$Z = \frac{x - \mu}{\sigma} = \frac{20 - 12.5}{7.5} = 1.00$$

Looking this Z value of 1.00 up in the tables gives

P ($\geq$ 20°) = 0.15866

### Probability of temperature falling between 0° and 20°

Once more the best approach is to draw up the curve and plot the relevant points.

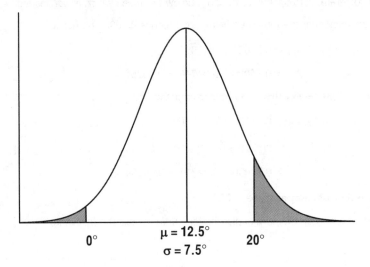

$\mu = 12.5°$

0°

$\sigma = 7.5°$

20°

What we can see is that we are interested in the unshaded region between 0° and 20° There are two possible approaches that we could take.

- P(0° to 20°) = P(0° to 12.5°) + P(12.5° to 20°), i.e. adding together the part we do want.

- P(0° to 20°) = 1 – P($\leq$ 0°) – P($\geq$ 20°), i.e. deducting the bits we do not war from the full area.

*P(0° to 20°) = P(0° to 12.5°) + P( 12.5° to 20°)*

We have already established that

P(0° to 12.5°) = 0.50000 – P($\leq$ 0°)

= 0.50000 – 0.04746 = 0.45254

Similarly

$$P(12.5° \text{ to } 20°) = 0.50000 - P(\geq 20°)$$
$$= 0.50000 - 0.15866 = 0.34134$$

Hence

$$P(0° \text{ to } 20°) \quad = P(0° \text{ to } 12.5°) + P(12.5° \text{ to } 20°)$$
$$= 0.45254 + 0.34134$$
$$= 0.79388$$

$$P(0° \text{ to } 20°) \quad = 1 - P(\leq 0°) - P(\geq 20°)$$

$$P(0° \text{ to } 20°) \quad = 1 - P(\leq 0°) - P(\geq 20°)$$
$$= 1 - 0.04746 - 0.15866$$
$$= 0.79388$$

**Probability of temperature falling between 20° and 25°**

This problem can be graphically illustrated as follows.

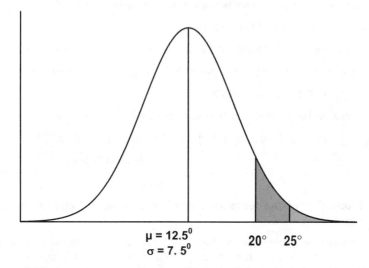

$$\mu = 12.5^0$$
$$\sigma = 7.5^0$$

$$20° \quad 25°$$

The area of this curve that we are interested in is the lighter shaded one beyond 20° but not beyond 25°. We can therefore establish the probability as

$$P(20° \text{ to } 25°) \quad = P(\geq 20°) - P(\geq 25°)$$

We have already established that $P(\geq 20°) = 0.15866$.

Using

$$Z = \frac{x - \mu}{\sigma} = \frac{25 - 12.5}{7.5} = 1.67$$

Looking this Z value of 1.67 up in the tables gives

$$P (\geq 25°) = 0.04746$$

Hence

$$P(20° \text{ to } 25°) = P(\geq 20°) - P(\geq 25°)$$
$$= 0.15866 - 0.04746$$
$$= 0.11120$$

These last two examples illustrate the importance of drawing up the curve before undertaking any calculations. Both examples required the calculation of the probability of a temperature between certain points, however, the approaches were different as in the first case the two points were on opposite sides of the mean and in the second case they are on the same side. Always quickly plot the curve, determine which range you are interested in and then how to get to it by adding or subtracting various parts.

### Probability of the temperature falling between 0° and 20° on two consecutive days

To solve this problem we will need to make an assumption, specifically that the temperature on any one day is independent of the previous days. If this is the case then we can utilise the multiplication law discussed above i.e.

$$P(A \text{ AND } B) = P(A) \times P(B)$$

since what we are looking for is a temperature in that range on one day AND the next.

Now we know that the probability of falling in this range on any one day is

$$P(0° \text{ to } 20°) = 0.79388$$

Hence the probability of such a temperature on two consecutive days is

$$P(0° \text{ to } 20° \text{ AND } 0° \text{ to } 20°) = P(0° \text{ to } 20°) \times P(0° \text{ to } 20°)$$
$$= 0.79388 \times 0.79388$$
$$= 0.63025$$

### Probability of the temperature falling between 0° and 20° on seven days in ten

To solve this problem we must again assume that daily temperatures are independent in which case we can take advantage of the binomial distribution to help us with the calculation as follows.

Now we know, from using the normal distribution above, that the probability of falling in this range on any one day is

$$P(0° \text{ to } 20°) = 0.79388 = p$$

Using the binomial expression

$$P(r) = \frac{n!}{r!(n-r)!} \times p^r \times (1 - p)^{n-r}$$

to calculate the probability temperatures falling within that range for seven days in ten gives

$$P(7) \quad = \frac{10!}{7!-3!} \times 0.79388^7 \times 0.20612^3$$

$$= 120 \times 0.1987394 \times 0.0087571$$

$$= 0.20885$$

## 2.3.3 Calculating values given a probability

An alternative type of question may be to determine the range of values within which a certain proportion of the population lies. There are two broad variations on this theme.

- *Two-tailed test*, where we look for how far we need to go either side of the mean and exclude the extremes on both sides (in the two tails).

- *One-tailed test*, where we look for a value either above which or below which this certain proportion lies, i.e. we exclude the extremes on one side only (in one tail).

## Example

Using our temperatures ideas above, calculate

- The range of temperatures, as a band either side of the mean, that will be suffered/enjoyed 90% of the time.

- The value above which the temperature will rise 7% of the time.

## Solution

**90% temperature band**

This exercise represents a two-tailed test since what we wish to consider is the central 90% of values, hence exclude the extreme highs and lows. More particularly, the ranges we will wish to exclude will be the top 5% and bottom 5% (i.e. exclude 10% in total) leaving the central 90%. This can be illustrated graphically as follows.

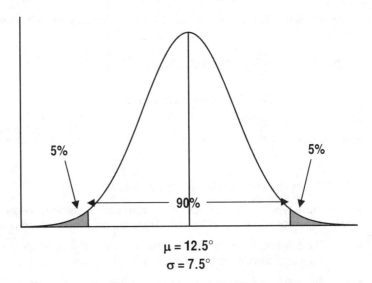

$$\mu = 12.5°$$
$$\sigma = 7.5°$$

We can now use the above approach 'backwards' to ascertain the values of x and y, however, since the distribution is symmetrical we need only calculate how far either one is from the mean as the other is the same distance.

Let us consider y. This is the point above which only 5% of the values fall. Looking up 0.05 (5%) in the body of the normal distribution tables gives us a Z value of 1.645 (averaging between 1.64 and 1.65). Hence

- y lies 1.645 standard deviations or 12.3375° (1.645 × 7.5°) above the mean at a temperature of 24.8375°.

- x lies 1.645 standard deviations or 12.3375° (1.645 × 7.5°) below the mean at a temperature of 0.1625°.

Hence we can state that 90% of the time the temperature will fall within the range 0.1625° to 24.8375°.

### Top 7% of temperatures

This exercise represents a one-tailed test since what we wish to consider is the top 7% of values. We are not concerned with the extreme lows in temperature in this example and are only considering the extreme highs. This can be illustrated graphically as follows.

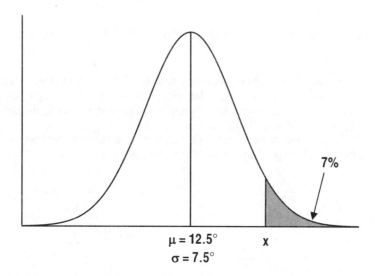

$\mu = 12.5°$
$\sigma = 7.5°$

We can again use our original approach 'backwards' to ascertain the value of x.

This is the point above which only 7% of the values fall.

Looking up 0.07 (7%) in the body of the normal distribution tables gives us a Z value of 1.475 (roughly midway between 1.47 and 1.48). Hence x lies 1.475 standard deviations or 11.0625° (1.475 × 7.5°) above the mean at a temperature of 23.5625°.

Hence we can state that 7% of the time the temperature will fall above 23.5625°.

## Exercise 4

The daily share price of a large retailer is normally distributed with a mean of 60 pence and a standard deviation of 10 pence. What is the probability that on three days out of four the share price lies between 65 pence and 70 pence?

## Exercise 5

The quarterly forecasting error for the annual Retail Price Index by a leading City economist is normally distributed with a mean of zero and a variance of 1.2%. What is the probability that on two consecutive occasions the economist overestimates inflation by over 1% (assuming the forecast errors are independently distributed through time)?

## Exercise 6

An economist believes that the annual return on a country's 'long' government bond is distributed independently from returns on the stock market. Both are normally distributed - the bond has an average return historically of 7% p.a. with a standard deviation of 4% and the stock market has a historical mean return of 11% p.a. with a standard deviation of 6%. Given the economist's beliefs, what is the probability that in any one year both markets will show negative returns?

### 2.3.4 Approximation to the binomial distribution

## Introduction

The binomial distribution is for use with discrete data whereas the normal distribution is for use with continuous data. However, where there are a large number of discrete items in a binomial distribution it becomes almost continuous and the normal distribution may be used as an approximation to it.

To illustrate this point we have plotted below the binomial distribution for a variety of different sample sizes (n = 4 to 1,024) where p = 0.2.

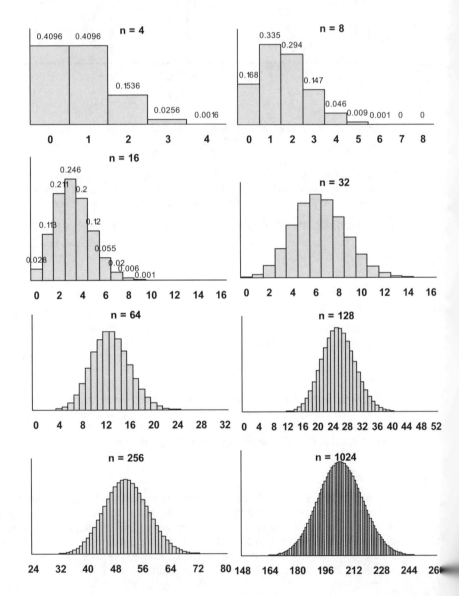

We have not plotted all the values on all the graphs as many of them are 0 (e.g. when n = 32 we have only plotted up to 16). What we can see is that by the time n has reached 32 the outline of the distribution bears a striking resemblance to that of a normal distribution and that resemblance becomes stronger as n is increased.

It should be noted that this relationship does not seem to hold so well for values of p below 0.1 or above 0.9.

The conclusion is that for large quantities (n $\geq$ 30), and values of p between 0.1 and 0.9 the normal distribution may be used as a reasonable approximation to the binominal distribution.

## Use of this relationship

If we wish to establish the probability of observing a range of values, then in order to use the binomial distribution we would need to evaluate the probability of each value individually and then add these probabilities together. If we were dealing with thousands of items this would clearly become a very time-consuming exercise.

Using the normal distribution enables us to calculate the probability of falling in a given range of values fairly simply so long as we have the mean and standard deviation of the distribution. It can be shown (see appendix) that for a binomial distribution the

- Mean = np
- Standard deviation = $\sqrt{np(1-p)}$

There is one more factor we need to appreciate in order to be able to use this approximation, that is how to evaluate the end points of the range we are assessing when using our normal distribution tables and our z values. The diagram below illustrates the idea.

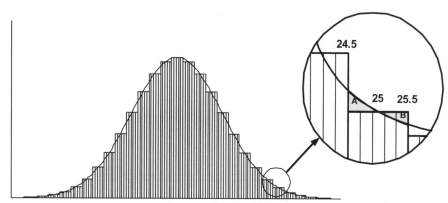

What we can see from this is that the approximating normal distribution cuts through the mid points of the binomial histogram bars. We can see that the normal distribution curve includes some areas (the shaded area A above) and excludes other (the shaded area B above) though these tend to cancel out.

If we therefore wished to establish the probability of observing 25 successes in this binomial distribution we wish to establish the area of the histogram bar at the 25 point. Since, in this example, each bar represents one item we must, in converting the discrete data into continuous data, consider that this bar runs from 0.5 below to 0.5 above the selected value, i.e. from 24.5 up to 25.5. Thus in moving from discrete to continuous data we will be assuming that

- Item 0 runs from −0.5 to +0.5.
- Item 1 runs from +0.5 to +1.5.
- Item 2 runs from +1.5 to +2.5.
- Item 3 runs from +2.5 to +3.5, etc.

Each bar can now be considered to represent a range of values on our continuous normal distribution and hence we can evaluate that or any combination of histogram bars.

## Example

The probability of breaking a leg on a skiing holiday is 0.2. In 256 holidays, what is the probability that the number of broken legs falls between 40 and 60?

## Solution

Mean = np = 256 × 0.2 = 51.2

Standard deviation = $\sqrt{np(1-p)}$ = $\sqrt{256 \times 0.2 \times 0.8}$ = $\sqrt{40.96}$ = 6.4

We wish to include items 40 to 60, i.e. from 39.5 (the start of band 40) to 60.5 (the end of band 60).

Plotting the relevant points gives

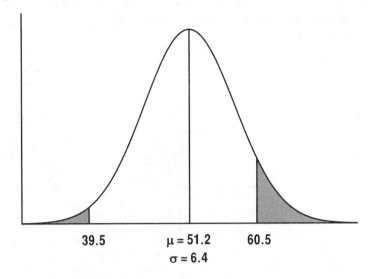

What we can see is that we are interested in the unshaded region between 39.5 and 60.5 which can be calculated as

$$P(39.5 \text{ to } 60.5) = 1 - P(\leq 39.5) - P(\geq 60.5)$$

*P(≤ 39.5)*

Using

$$Z = \frac{x - \mu}{\sigma} = \frac{39.5 - 51.2}{6.4} = 1.83$$

Looking this Z value of 1.83 up in the tables gives

P ($\leq$ 39.5) = 0.03362

*P($\geq$ 60.5)*

Using

$$Z = \frac{x - \mu}{\sigma} = \frac{60.5 - 51.2}{6.4} = 1.45$$

Looking this Z value of 1.45 up in the tables gives

P ($\geq$ 60.5) = 0.07353

*P(39.5 to 60.5)*

P(39.5 to 60.5)  = 1 – P($\leq$ 39.5) – P($\geq$ 60.5)

= 1 – 0.03362 – 0.07353

= 0.89285

If we used the binomial to establish this probability we would have arrived at a figure of 0.89399, the normal giving a reasonably good approximation (difference of only 0.001275) despite the fact that this is a relatively skewed distribution.

## Conclusion

The normal distribution may be used as an approximation to the binomial for the calculation of the probability of observing a range of values for distributions where

- n is large ($\geq$ 30).
- $0.1 \leq p \leq 0.9$.

The greater the number, n, and the more symmetrical the distribution (the closer p is to 0.5), the better the approximation.

## 2.4 Combining independent normal distributions

The sum of or difference between two normal distributions will itself be a normal distribution. The defining characteristics of those distributions (sum and difference) will be

| | Mean | Variance |
|---|---|---|
| Sum (Adding) | $\mu_{Sum} = \mu_1 + \mu_2$ | $\sigma_{Sum}^2 = \sigma_1^2 + \sigma_2^2$ |
| Difference (Subtracting) | $\mu_{Diff} = \mu_1 - \mu_2$ | $\sigma_{Diff}^2 = \sigma_1^2 + \sigma_2^2$ |

The latter of these, the variance of the difference, is *not* a typographical error, the variance of the difference is the *sum* of the variances of the two distributions.

We will use a simple example to illustrate this point without doing any calculations of variances or standard deviations by remembering that these are measures of spread.

### Example

A sample of married couples reveals the following information about their heights in centimetres.

| | Mean | Tallest | Shortest | Spread |
|---|---|---|---|---|
| Husband | 180 | 200 | 160 | 40 |
| Wife | 160 | 175 | 145 | 30 |

What is the mean, tallest and shortest

- Combination (addition)?
- Difference (subtraction)?

### Solution

**Addition**

The tallest and shortest combinations will occur if the tallest man and woman are married to each other as are the shortest. If this is the case then

Mean = 180 + 160 = 340
Tallest = 200 + 175 = 375
Shortest = 160 + 145 = 305
Spread = 375 − 305 = 70 (= 40 + 30)

**Subtraction**

The greatest and smallest differences in height will occur if the tallest man is married to the shortest woman and vice versa. If this is the case then

Mean = 180 − 160 = 20
Tallest = 200 − 145 = 55
Shortest = 160 − 175 = −15
Spread = 55 − (−15) = 70 (again = 40 + 30)

## Conclusion

When we combine distributions by either addition or subtraction, the mean of the combination will be either the sum or the difference of the means, respectively, whereas the spread (or the variance) will always be the summation regardless of whether we are adding or subtracting distributions.

# 3 LOG-NORMAL DISTRIBUTION

## 3.1 Introduction

In the standard normal distribution the horizontal scale is linear. This means that the probability of lying a given number of units above the mean is the same as that of lying the same number of units below the mean. If for example the mean were 100, the probability of lying above 120 would be equal to the probability of lying below 80.

In a log-normal distribution the distribution appears symmetrical when the horizontal axis plots the logarithm of the values. The consequence of this is that it is as probable to see a value double as it is to see the value halve, or to see a price quadruple as it is to see a price reduced to one-quarter of its original value.

For example, if share price movements are log-normally distributed and the current share price is £1, then the probability of the share price falling to 50p (halving in value) is equal to the probability of it rising to £2 (doubling in value), and the probability of the share price falling to 25p (one-quarter of the original price) is equivalent to that of the share price rising to £4 (four times the original price).

This certainly seems more reasonable than a standard normal distribution, since if a company has a share price of £1 then it is as likely to go into liquidation (share price falls to £0) as it is to see the share price rise to £2. This idea appears completely unrealistic and the idea of the log-normally distributed price movement intuitively feels much more sensible.

There is, however, little evidence to support this theory. In fact given human nature and the herding instinct (following the leader) witnessed in the markets, it is quite frequently the case that if a share starts to move a little bit it moves a long way as everybody frantically buys or sells it. This is certainly not what is predicted by a log-normal distribution. Perhaps in a perfect capital market where people did their own securities evaluation rather than following others this would not be the case and a log-normal distribution would be a realistic idea.

## 3.2 Characteristics

A lognormal distribution has the following features.

- It is bounded by zero to the left (contrast this with the normal distribution that has no lower bound.)

- It is skewed to the right, i.e positively skewed (contrast this with the normal distribution, which is symmetrical).

- The lognormal distribution can be fully defined by two parameters.

  - The mean of its associated normal distribution.
  - The variance/standard deviation of its associated normal distribution.

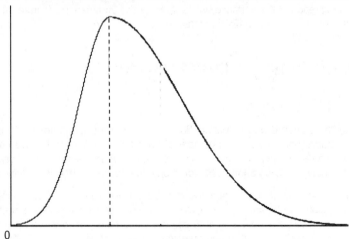

## 3.3 The mean and variance of the lognormal distribution

It was noted above that the lognormal distribution can be fully defined by two parameters.

- The mean of its associated normal distribution.
- The variance/standard deviation of its associated normal distribution.

The mean and variance of the lognormal distribution itself can be related to the mean and variance of its associated normal distribution, as follows.

**Mean** = $\mu_L = e^{(\mu + 0.5\sigma^2)}$

and

Variance = $\sigma_L^2 = e^{(2\mu + \sigma^2)} \times (e^{\sigma^2} - 1)$

where

$\mu$ = the mean of the Normal distribution

$\mu_L$ = the mean of the lognormal distribution

$\sigma$ = the standard deviation of the Normal distribution

$\sigma_L$ = the standard deviation of the lognormal distribution

# 4 KURTOSIS

## 4.1 Definitions

Kurtosis is where the distribution is not normal because it is either more or less peaked than a Normal distribution.

Kurtosis is not to be confused with skewness, which is where a distribution is not normal because of asymmetry.

A Normal distribution is referred to as being **mesokurtic**. Alternatively, a distribution may be **leptokurtic** or **platykurtic**.

## 4.2 Leptokurtosis

A leptokurtic distribution is more slender than the normal distribution. It can be compared to a normal distribution as follows.

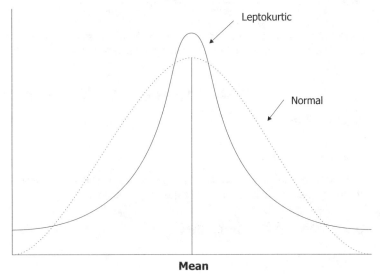

**Mean**

The implication of leptokurtosis is that there is a higher probability of **extreme** movements in either direction than the normal distribution would suggest (due to the fat tails at either end of the distribution).

For the normal distribution, virtually all items lie within three standard deviations of the mean. This distance would be **wider** for a leptokurtic distribution.

## 4.3 Platykurtosis

A platykurtic distribution is less peaked than a normal distribution, the opposite of leptokurtosis. The implication of platykurtosis is that there is a higher probability of observing values close to the mean and a lower probability of observing extreme measurements.

## 4.4 Measuring kurtosis

You will remember that dispersion was measured by taking the square of the deviations around the mean, i.e. calculating the variance or standard deviation. Skewness was based on the cubed deviations around the mean. Kurtosis is based on raising the deviations to the **power of four**.

Kurtosis is usually measured as excess kurtosis. This is the amount by which the kurtosis of a distribution is different from that of a normal distribution.

A normal distribution has kurtosis of 3, with excess kurtosis of zero.

A leptokurtic distribution will have positive excess kurtosis, while a platykurtic distribution will have negative excess kurtosis.

The calculation of excess kutosis for a sample is as follows.

$$\text{Excess kurtosis} = \frac{n(n+1)}{(n-1)(n-2)(n-3)} \times \frac{\sum (x-\bar{x})^4}{s^4} - \frac{3(n-1)^2}{(n-2)(n-3)}$$

Generally speaking, a value for excess kurtosis in excess of 1 for a large sample would be viewed as significantly different from a normal distribution.

# 5 PROBABILITY AND PROBABILITY DISTRIBUTION SUMMARY

## 5.1 Introduction

Probability distributions provide a means of establishing the likelihood of an event occurring in a sample given details of the full population.

## 5.2 Probability distributions

### Binomial distribution

Useful for discrete data where there are a large number of independent trials with just two possible outcomes (a success or a failure). The probability of r successes in n trials is given by

$$P(r) = \frac{n!}{r!(n-r)!} \times p^r \times (1-p)^{n-r}$$

and the mean and standard deviation of this distribution are

Mean = np

Standard deviation = $\sqrt{np(1-p)}$

## Normal distribution

Useful for continuous data. Enables us to calculate the probability of an item falling within a given range by using

$$Z \text{ value} - Z = \frac{x - \mu}{\sigma}$$

Normal distribution tables give the probability of a value lying beyond the point with the given Z value.

*Approximation to the binomial*

Can be used to speed the calculation of observing a value within a range if

- n is large ($\geq 30$);

- $0.1 \leq p \leq 0.9$.

When it is, the defining characteristics of the distribution are

Mean $= np$

Standard deviation $= \sqrt{np(1-p)}$

| | *Mean* | *Variance* |
|---|---|---|
| Sum (Adding) | $\mu_{Sum} = \mu_1 + \mu_2$ | $\sigma_{Sum}^2 = \sigma_1^2 + \sigma_2^2$ |
| Difference (Subtracting) | $\mu_{Dif} = \mu_1 - \mu_2$ | $\sigma_{Dif}^2 = \sigma_1^2 + \sigma_2^2$ |

# 6 SOLUTIONS TO EXERCISES

1. P (7 days or less) = 1 − P(8 OR 9 OR 10) = 1 − [P(8)+P(9)+P(10)]

Using the binomial with p = $^2/3$

$$P(10) = \frac{10!}{10!0!} \left(\frac{2}{3}\right)^{10} \left(\frac{1}{3}\right)^{0} \qquad 0.0173$$

$$P(9) = \frac{10!}{9!1!} \left(\frac{2}{3}\right)^{9} \left(\frac{1}{3}\right)^{1} \qquad 0.0867$$

$$P(8) = \frac{10!}{8!2!} \left(\frac{2}{3}\right)^{8} \left(\frac{1}{3}\right)^{2} \qquad \underline{0.1951}$$

P(8 OR 9 OR 10) $\qquad \underline{0.2991}$

P (7 or less) = 1 − 0.2991 = 0.7009

2. P(Falls at least 4 days) = P(4 OR 5 days) = P(4) + P(5)

Using the binomial with p = probability a fall = $^1/3$

$$P(5) = \frac{5!}{5!0!} \left(\frac{1}{3}\right)^{5} \left(\frac{2}{3}\right)^{0} \qquad 0.0041$$

$$P(4) = \frac{5!}{4!1!} \left(\frac{1}{3}\right)^{4} \left(\frac{2}{3}\right)^{1} \qquad \underline{0.0412}$$

P(Falls at least 4 days) $\qquad \underline{0.0453}$

3. P(Falls < 2 days) = P(0 OR 1 days) = P(0) + P(1)

Using the binomial with p = P(DM falls against £) = $^1/3$

$$P(0) = \frac{5!}{0!5!} \left(\frac{1}{3}\right)^{0} \left(\frac{2}{3}\right)^{5} \qquad 0.1317$$

$$P(1) = \frac{5!}{1!4!} \left(\frac{1}{3}\right)^{1} \left(\frac{2}{3}\right)^{4} \qquad \underline{0.3292}$$

P(Falls < 2 days) $\qquad \underline{0.4609}$

4.  *P(> 70)*

    Z =    = 1 giving P (> 70) = 0.1587

    *P(> 65)*

    $Z = \dfrac{65 - 60}{10}$ = 0.5 giving P (> 65) = 0.3085

    *P (65 – 70)* = P (>65) – P (> 70) = 0.3085 – 0.1587 = 0.1498

    P (3 days in four) = $\dfrac{4!}{3!1!}$ × $0.1498^3$ × $(1 – 0.1498)^1$ = 0.0114 or 1.14%

5.  Variance = $\sigma^2$ = 1.2, hence σ = 1.0954.

    Probability of a single 1% overestimate can be found using

    $Z = \dfrac{X - \mu}{\sigma} = \dfrac{1 - 0}{1.0954}$ = 0.9129        hence  P(>1% overestimate) = 0.1814

    Probability of this overestimate on two consecutive occasions is 0.1814 × 0.1814 = 0.0329 or 3.29%.

6.  *Long bond*

    $z = \dfrac{x - \mu}{\sigma} = \dfrac{0 - 7}{4} = -1.75$ hence P(< 0) = 0.0401

    *Stock market*

    $z = \dfrac{x - \mu}{\sigma} = \dfrac{0 - 11}{6} = -1.83\,Z$  hence P(< 0) = 0.0336

    P(Both < 0)    = P(Bond < 0 AND Stock < 0) = P(Bond <0) × P(Stock <0)

    = 0.0401 × 0.0336 = 0.0013

# APPENDIX 1 – NORMAL DISTRIBUTION TABLES

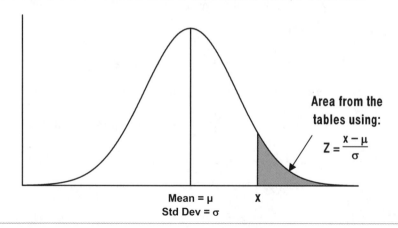

Area from the tables using:

$$Z = \frac{x - \mu}{\sigma}$$

Mean = μ        X
Std Dev = σ

| Z | 0.00 | 0.01 | 0.02 | 0.03 | 0.04 | 0.05 | 0.06 | 0.07 | 0.08 | 0.09 |
|------|------|------|------|------|------|------|------|------|------|------|
| **0.00** | 0.50000 | 0.49601 | 0.49202 | 0.48803 | 0.48405 | 0.48006 | 0.47608 | 0.47210 | 0.46812 | 0.46414 |
| **0.10** | 0.46017 | 0.45620 | 0.45224 | 0.44828 | 0.44433 | 0.44038 | 0.43644 | 0.43251 | 0.42858 | 0.42465 |
| **0.20** | 0.42074 | 0.41683 | 0.41294 | 0.40905 | 0.40517 | 0.40129 | 0.39743 | 0.39358 | 0.38974 | 0.38591 |
| **0.30** | 0.38209 | 0.37828 | 0.37448 | 0.37070 | 0.36693 | 0.36317 | 0.35942 | 0.35569 | 0.35197 | 0.34827 |
| **0.40** | 0.34458 | 0.34090 | 0.33724 | 0.33360 | 0.32997 | 0.32636 | 0.32276 | 0.31918 | 0.31561 | 0.31207 |
| **0.50** | 0.30854 | 0.30503 | 0.30153 | 0.29806 | 0.29460 | 0.29116 | 0.28774 | 0.28434 | 0.28096 | 0.27760 |
| **0.60** | 0.27425 | 0.27093 | 0.26763 | 0.26435 | 0.26109 | 0.25785 | 0.25463 | 0.25143 | 0.24825 | 0.24510 |
| **0.70** | 0.24196 | 0.23885 | 0.23576 | 0.23270 | 0.22965 | 0.22663 | 0.22363 | 0.22065 | 0.21770 | 0.21476 |
| **0.80** | 0.21186 | 0.20897 | 0.20611 | 0.20327 | 0.20045 | 0.19766 | 0.19489 | 0.19215 | 0.18943 | 0.18673 |
| **0.90** | 0.18406 | 0.18141 | 0.17879 | 0.17619 | 0.17361 | 0.17106 | 0.16853 | 0.16602 | 0.16354 | 0.16109 |
| **1.00** | 0.15866 | 0.15625 | 0.15386 | 0.15151 | 0.14917 | 0.14686 | 0.14457 | 0.14231 | 0.14007 | 0.13786 |
| **1.10** | 0.13567 | 0.13350 | 0.13136 | 0.12924 | 0.12714 | 0.12507 | 0.12302 | 0.12100 | 0.11900 | 0.11702 |
| **1.20** | 0.11507 | 0.11314 | 0.11123 | 0.10935 | 0.10749 | 0.10565 | 0.10383 | 0.10204 | 0.10027 | 0.09853 |
| **1.30** | 0.09680 | 0.09510 | 0.09342 | 0.09176 | 0.09012 | 0.08851 | 0.08692 | 0.08534 | 0.08379 | 0.08226 |
| **1.40** | 0.08076 | 0.07927 | 0.07780 | 0.07636 | 0.07493 | 0.07353 | 0.07215 | 0.07078 | 0.06944 | 0.06811 |
| **1.50** | 0.06681 | 0.06552 | 0.06426 | 0.06301 | 0.06178 | 0.06057 | 0.05938 | 0.05821 | 0.05705 | 0.05592 |
| **1.60** | 0.05480 | 0.05370 | 0.05262 | 0.05155 | 0.05050 | 0.04947 | 0.04846 | 0.04746 | 0.04648 | 0.04551 |
| **1.70** | 0.04457 | 0.04363 | 0.04272 | 0.04182 | 0.04093 | 0.04006 | 0.03920 | 0.03836 | 0.03754 | 0.03673 |
| **1.80** | 0.03593 | 0.03515 | 0.03438 | 0.03362 | 0.03288 | 0.03216 | 0.03144 | 0.03074 | 0.03005 | 0.02938 |
| **1.90** | 0.02872 | 0.02807 | 0.02743 | 0.02680 | 0.02619 | 0.02559 | 0.02500 | 0.02442 | 0.02385 | 0.02330 |
| **2.00** | 0.02275 | 0.02222 | 0.02169 | 0.02118 | 0.02068 | 0.02018 | 0.01970 | 0.01923 | 0.01876 | 0.01831 |
| **2.10** | 0.01786 | 0.01743 | 0.01700 | 0.01659 | 0.01618 | 0.01578 | 0.01539 | 0.01500 | 0.01463 | 0.01426 |
| **2.20** | 0.01390 | 0.01355 | 0.01321 | 0.01287 | 0.01255 | 0.01222 | 0.01191 | 0.01160 | 0.01130 | 0.01101 |
| **2.30** | 0.01072 | 0.01044 | 0.01017 | 0.00990 | 0.00964 | 0.00939 | 0.00914 | 0.00889 | 0.00866 | 0.00842 |
| **2.40** | 0.00820 | 0.00798 | 0.00776 | 0.00755 | 0.00734 | 0.00714 | 0.00695 | 0.00676 | 0.00657 | 0.00639 |
| **2.50** | 0.00621 | 0.00604 | 0.00587 | 0.00570 | 0.00554 | 0.00539 | 0.00523 | 0.00508 | 0.00494 | 0.00480 |

| Z | 0.00 | 0.01 | 0.02 | 0.03 | 0.04 | 0.05 | 0.06 | 0.07 | 0.08 | 0.09 |
|---|------|------|------|------|------|------|------|------|------|------|
| **2.60** | 0.00466 | 0.00453 | 0.00440 | 0.00427 | 0.00415 | 0.00402 | 0.00391 | 0.00379 | 0.00368 | 0.00357 |
| **2.70** | 0.00347 | 0.00336 | 0.00326 | 0.00317 | 0.00307 | 0.00298 | 0.00289 | 0.00280 | 0.00272 | 0.00264 |
| **2.80** | 0.00256 | 0.00248 | 0.00240 | 0.00233 | 0.00226 | 0.00219 | 0.00212 | 0.00205 | 0.00199 | 0.00193 |
| **2.90** | 0.00187 | 0.00181 | 0.00175 | 0.00169 | 0.00164 | 0.00159 | 0.00154 | 0.00149 | 0.00144 | 0.00139 |
| **3.00** | 0.00135 | 0.00131 | 0.00126 | 0.00122 | 0.00118 | 0.00114 | 0.00111 | 0.00107 | 0.00104 | 0.00100 |
| **3.10** | 0.00097 | 0.00094 | 0.00090 | 0.00087 | 0.00084 | 0.00082 | 0.00079 | 0.00076 | 0.00074 | 0.00071 |
| **3.20** | 0.00069 | 0.00066 | 0.00064 | 0.00062 | 0.00060 | 0.00058 | 0.00056 | 0.00054 | 0.00052 | 0.00050 |
| **3.30** | 0.00048 | 0.00047 | 0.00045 | 0.00043 | 0.00042 | 0.00040 | 0.00039 | 0.00038 | 0.00036 | 0.00035 |
| **3.40** | 0.00034 | 0.00032 | 0.00031 | 0.00030 | 0.00029 | 0.00028 | 0.00027 | 0.00026 | 0.00025 | 0.00024 |
| **3.50** | 0.00023 | 0.00022 | 0.00022 | 0.00021 | 0.00020 | 0.00019 | 0.00019 | 0.00018 | 0.00017 | 0.00017 |
| **3.60** | 0.00016 | 0.00015 | 0.00015 | 0.00014 | 0.00014 | 0.00013 | 0.00013 | 0.00012 | 0.00012 | 0.00011 |
| **3.70** | 0.00011 | 0.00010 | 0.00010 | 0.00010 | 0.00009 | 0.00009 | 0.00008 | 0.00008 | 0.00008 | 0.00008 |
| **3.80** | 0.00007 | 0.00007 | 0.00007 | 0.00006 | 0.00006 | 0.00006 | 0.00006 | 0.00005 | 0.00005 | 0.00005 |
| **3.90** | 0.00005 | 0.00005 | 0.00004 | 0.00004 | 0.00004 | 0.00004 | 0.00004 | 0.00004 | 0.00003 | 0.00003 |
| **4.00** | 0.00003 | 0.00003 | 0.00003 | 0.00003 | 0.00003 | 0.00003 | 0.00002 | 0.00002 | 0.00002 | 0.00002 |

# APPENDIX 2 - BINOMIAL MEAN AND STANDARD DEVIATION

## Illustration

The following example illustrates that the relationships given above for the binomial mean and standard deviation provide the correct result, specifically

- Mean = np
- Standard deviation = $\sqrt{np(1-p)}$

This is not intended as a full blown mathematical proof, which is beyond the scope of the syllabus, simply as an illustration.

## Example

The probability of breaking a leg on a skiing holiday is 0.2. What are the probabilities for all the possible number of times of breaking a leg on eight holidays?

## Solution

### First principles

| $x$ | Probability | | $p$ | $px$ | $p(x-\bar{x})^2$ |
|---|---|---|---|---|---|
| 0 | $P(0) = \dfrac{8!}{0!-8!} \times 0.2^0 \times 0.8^8 =$ | | 0.16777216 | 0.00000000 | 0.42949673 |
| 1 | $P(1) = \dfrac{8!}{1!-7!} \times 0.2^1 \times 0.8^7 =$ | | 0.33554432 | 0.33554432 | 0.12079596 |
| 2 | $P(2) = \dfrac{8!}{2!-6!} \times 0.2^2 \times 0.8^6 =$ | | 0.29360128 | 0.58720256 | 0.04697620 |
| 3 | $P(3) = \dfrac{8!}{3!-5!} \times 0.2^3 \times 0.8^5 =$ | | 0.14680064 | 0.44040192 | 0.28772925 |
| 4 | $P(4) = \dfrac{8!}{4!-4!} \times 0.2^4 \times 0.8^4 =$ | | 0.04587520 | 0.18350080 | 0.26424115 |
| 5 | $P(5) = \dfrac{8!}{5!-3!} \times 0.2^5 \times 0.8^3 =$ | | 0.00917504 | 0.04587520 | 0.10606346 |
| 6 | $P(6) = \dfrac{8!}{6!-2!} \times 0.2^6 \times 0.8^2 =$ | | 0.00114688 | 0.00688128 | 0.02220360 |
| 7 | $P(7) = \dfrac{8!}{7!-1!} \times 0.2^7 \times 0.8^1 =$ | | 0.00008192 | 0.00057344 | 0.00238879 |
| 8 | $P(8) = \dfrac{8!}{8!-0!} \times 0.2^8 \times 0.8^0 =$ | | 0.00000256 | 0.00002048 | 0.00010486 |
| | | | 1.00000000 | 1.60000000 | 1.28000000 |
| | | | | $\bar{x}$ | $\sigma^2$ |

BPP
LEARNING MEDIA

i.e.

- Mean = 1.60000000
- Standard Deviation = $\sqrt{1.28000000}$ = 1.13137085

**Formulae**

- Mean = np = 8 × 0.2 = 1.6
- Standard deviation = $\sqrt{np(1-p)}$ = $\sqrt{8 \times 0.2 \times 0.8}$ = $\sqrt{1.2800}$ = 1.13137085

## Conclusion

Since the formulae give the same results as our first principles approach and the selected population was reasonably random (skewed), this would appear to support the formulae.

# 7

# Sampling theory

## Contents

## Introduction

Probability theory is applicable when we know some information about a full population and we are trying to deduce some information regarding a sample taken from the population.

Sampling theory is effectively the reverse of this. It is applicable when we know some information about a sample (e.g. we have conducted a survey) and we are trying deduce some information about the full population.

There are four different aspects of sampling theory that we need to consider.

- Large samples (sample sizes $\geq$ 30).
- Small samples (sample sizes < 30).
- Proportions in large samples.
- Differences between samples.

# 1 LARGE SAMPLES

## 1.1 Introduction

Here we are considering the selection of *large samples*, i.e. samples of size $\geq$ 30, from very large population. At first we shall consider the population to be infinite and then consider what adjustments may be necessary to cope with a finite population.

Our aim is to determine some attributes of the population from those observed in sample. In particular, we will be trying to determine the population mean and standard deviation from those observed in the sample.

The notation we will use throughout this section when referring to either the population or the sample is

|                    | *Population* | *Sample* |
|--------------------|--------------|----------|
| Mean               | $\mu$        | $\bar{x}$ |
| Standard Deviation | $\sigma$     | $s$      |
| Size               | $N$          | $n$      |

## 1.2 Central limit theorem

### 1.2.1 Introduction

The basis for sampling theory is provided by the central limit theorem. We will not attempt to prove this theorem mathematically, although we illustrate the idea conceptually.

### 1.2.2 Distribution of sample mean (DOSM)

If we were to select all possible samples of size n from a population, determine the means of each of those samples and plot those means and associated frequencies as another distribution, we would have plotted the distribution of sample means (DOSM). The properties of this distribution of sample means is given by the central limit theorem.

## 1.2.3 The Theorem

### Normally distributed population

For a normally distributed population with a mean $\mu$, and standard deviation of $\sigma$, the distribution of sample means is also normally distributed with

- Mean = $\mu$

- Standard deviation = $\dfrac{\sigma}{\sqrt{n}}$

The standard deviation of this distribution is referred to as the *Standard Error of Sample Means*.

### Not normally distributed population

For any large population with a mean $\mu$ and a standard deviation $\sigma$ which is *not* normally distributed, the distribution of sample means will be approximately normally distributed and again its characteristics will be

- Mean = $\mu$

- Standard deviation = $\dfrac{\sigma}{\sqrt{n}}$

### Justification

If we were to take every possible sample of size 1 from the population, calculate its mean, (the value of the item, clearly) and plot these means as a distribution (the distribution of sample means), then this new distribution will obviously be an exact match to the population since there is a one for one match for items in each distribution. The mean and standard deviation of this distribution will match those of the population as the above equations would suggest.

If we increased the sample size to just 2 and repeated the exercise of extracting every possible sample, calculating its mean and plotting these sample means as a new distribution, we would find that the mean of the new distribution is again equal to the mean of the population but the standard deviation of the distribution would be much lower. The following example, based on a small sample from an infinite population clearly illustrates this point.

### Example

**Population**

We have an infinite population with items having a value of either 1 or 2, there being equal numbers of each, i.e. the population has the following characteristics.

| $x$ | $p$ | $px$ | $(x - \bar{x})$ | $f(x - \bar{x})^2$ |
|-----|-----|------|-----------------|---------------------|
| 1 | 0.5 | 0.5 | −0.5 | 0.125 |
| 2 | 0.5 | 1.0 | 0.5 | 0.125 |
| | $\sum 1.0$ | $\sum p_i x_i = 1.5$ | $\sum p(x - \bar{x})^2 =$ | 0.250 |

Hence for this population

$$\mu = \sum p_i x_i = 1.50$$

$$\sigma_n = \sqrt{\sum p(x - \bar{x})^2} = \sqrt{0.25} = 0.50$$

## Samples size of two

If we now selected all possible samples of size two, there are three possibilities.

- Two 1's and no 2's - giving a sample mean of 1.0.
- One 1 and one 2 - giving a sample mean of 1.5.
- No 1's and two 2's - giving a sample mean of 2.0.

If we plot these means as a new distribution, the DOSM, we would have (using the binomial to establish the probabilities):

| $x$ | $p$ | $px$ | $(x - \bar{x})$ | $p(x - \bar{x})^2$ |
|---|---|---|---|---|
| 1 | 0.25 | 0.25 | −0.5 | 0.0625 |
| 1.5 | 0.50 | 0.75 | 0.0 | 0.0000 |
| 2 | 0.25 | 0.50 | 0.5 | 0.0625 |
| | 1.00 | 1.50 | $\sum p(x - \bar{x})^2$ | = 0.1250 |

Hence

$$\bar{x} = \sum p_i x_i = 1.50$$

$$\sigma_n = \sqrt{\sum p(x - \bar{x})^2} = \sqrt{0.1250} = 0.35355$$

What we can see this time is that the DOSM has the same mean but a much lower standard deviation. Indeed the standard deviation of this distribution (0.35355) equates to $\dfrac{\sigma}{\sqrt{n}} = \dfrac{0.50}{\sqrt{2}} = 0.35355$ based on the population standard deviation of 0.50.

---

This example, albeit based on a very small sample, illustrates what we can expect to find when plotting our distribution of sample means, specifically that there will be a heavy weighting of samples with means close to the population mean and very few samples with extremely low valued or high valued means. This will occur because there are many samples that could have means close to the population mean, e.g.

- Samples composed of items close to the population means.
- Samples composed of items evenly spread throughout the population.
- Samples composed of extremely low and extremely high valued items; etc.

However, there are very few samples that will demonstrate an extreme mean since these samples would need to be composed entirely of extreme value items from the population.

This idea supports the relationships we have noted above since the heavy concentration of sample means around the population mean should ensure that

- The mean of the DOSM is equal to the population mean.

- The standard error (standard deviation of the DOSM) is lower than the population standard deviation and the higher the sample size, the lower this standard error. Indeed the relationship is that the standard error (SE) for a large sample from a large population is given by

$$SE = \frac{\sigma}{\sqrt{n}}$$

This relationship between the distribution of the population and the distribution of the sample means for various different sample sizes could be illustrated diagrammatically as follows.

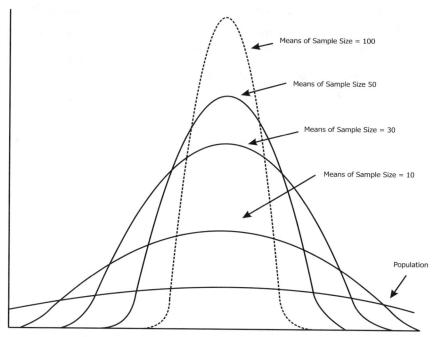

Means of Sample Size = 100

Means of Sample Size 50

Means of Sample Size = 30

Means of Sample Size = 10

Population

## 1.2.4 Usefulness

## Introduction

The usefulness of this result is that we can now use details of the sample to establish details of the population with certain levels of confidence. In particular we can establish

- A point estimate of the population mean being our best guess based on current information from the sample.

- Confidence intervals, i.e. a range within which the population mean lies with a given level of certainty.

## Point estimate of mean

As we noted above a point estimate is an initial estimate of the value of the population mean based on the value of the sample mean. The calculation is fairly simple, specifically

- Mean $\mu = \bar{x}$

That is, a point estimate assumes that a sample is perfectly representative of the population and hence its mean and standard deviation are also representative.

## Confidence intervals

Of course it is unlikely that any sample will be perfectly representative of the population and therefore it is unlikely that the point estimate will be exactly correct. What we are trying to establish with confidence intervals is the range within which that population mean must lie given certain confidence requirements or tolerable error limits.

The approach to establishing the confidence intervals is based on the fact that the distribution of sample means either is, or approximately is, normally distributed with a mean equal to the population mean and a standard error (standard deviation) being a function of the population standard deviation and sample size.

If we plotted on the distribution of sample means the mean of the particular sample that we have selected we may get the following.

### Distribution of Sample Means

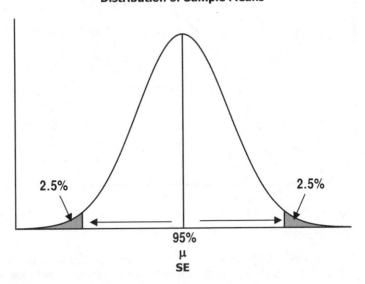

Based on our knowledge of the normal distribution and the use of the normal distribution tables, we know that, when conducting a two-tailed test as we are here 95% of the distribution lies within 1.96 standard deviations (standard errors) from the mean.

Hence, based on the use of Z values, 95% of the time we will have

$$\frac{\bar{x} - \mu}{SE} \leq 1.96 \quad \text{(the Z value from normal distribution tables leaving 2½% in the tails)}$$

Rearranging this gives

$$\bar{x} - \mu \leq 1.96 \times SE$$

What this means is that 95% of the time $\bar{x}$ falls within $1.96 \times SE$ from $\mu$, from which it follows that $\mu$ falls within $1.96 \times SE$ from $\bar{x}$. Hence our 95% confidence interval for the value of $\mu$ is

$$\mu = \bar{x} \pm 1.96 \times SE$$

More generally this could be stated as

$$\mu = \bar{x} \pm Z \times SE$$

Where Z is the Z value associated with the given confidence level required.

There is one problem with this, however, which is that

$$SE = \frac{\sigma}{\sqrt{n}}$$

Clearly, if we are uncertain about the mean value of the population, we will be uncertain about its standard deviation, $\sigma$. What we need to use as an alternative is our point estimate of $\sigma$, i.e. s, the standard deviation of the sample.

*NB.* In calculating s, we must use the sample standard deviation calculation. The purpose of this, you will recall, is to cater for the fact that the sample standard deviation is likely to be less than the population standard deviation since the sample is unlikely to exhibit the extremes inherent in the full population. Hence we must calculate s using the formula

$$s = \sqrt{\frac{\Sigma f (x - \bar{x})^2}{n - 1}}$$

## Conclusion

Given this final point we can now establish our confidence intervals based on our sample measurements as

$$\mu = \bar{x} \pm Z \times SE$$

where

$$SE = \frac{s}{\sqrt{n}} \left( = \frac{\sigma}{\sqrt{n}} \text{ if } \sigma \text{ is known} \right)$$

$$s = \sqrt{\frac{\Sigma f (x - \bar{x})^2}{n - 1}}$$

Z is the Z value associated with the given confidence level required.

## Example

A sample of 100 students' GCSE Maths exam results is taken with the aim of determining statistics regarding all the students. The sample is observed to have a mean of 55% and a sample standard deviation of 5%. Calculate

- The point estimate of the true average mark.

- The 99% confidence interval.

- The sample size required to estimate the true mean to within 1% at the 99% confidence level (assuming that the standard deviation of the sample will be unaltered by increasing the sample size).

## Solution

### Point estimate

Mean $\mu = \bar{x} = 55\%$

### 99% Confidence interval

For 99% confidence we may only exclude 1% of the population, i.e. 0.5% at each extreme. From the normal distribution tables the Z value associated with a probability of 0.005 (0.5%) is 2.575.

Now

$$SE = \frac{s}{\sqrt{n}} = \frac{5}{\sqrt{100}} = 0.5$$

and

$$\mu = \bar{x} \pm Z \times SE$$
$$= 55 \pm 2.575 \times 0.5$$
$$= 55 \pm 1.288$$

i.e. we can be 99% certain that the true average mark lies in the range

$53.712 \leq$ True average $\leq 56.288$

### Sample size to reduce interval to ±1% at the 99% confidence level

For our confidence interval to be ±1% we need

$$Z \times SE = Z \times \frac{s}{\sqrt{n}} = 1$$

At the 99% confidence level, Z = 2.575, hence

$$2.575 \times \frac{5}{\sqrt{n}} = 1$$

BPP
LEARNING MEDIA

giving

$$\frac{12.875}{\sqrt{n}} = 1$$

$$\sqrt{n} = 12.875$$

$$n = 165.76, \text{ i.e. a sample size of } 166$$

## Exercise 1

A sample of 100 daily share price movements demonstrates a mean of 1% and a standard deviation of 0.1%. Estimate

(a)     The population mean.

(b)     95%, 98% and 99% confidence intervals.

(c)     The sample size required to reduce the margin of error at 95% to 0.015%.

# 2     SMALL SAMPLES

## 2.1 Introduction

Once again our aim is to determine the population mean and standard deviation from those observed in a sample. This time, however, we are considering samples of size less than 30.

The small sample size has the following effects with respect to the central limit theorem.

### Normally distributed population

If the population is normally distributed, the central limit theorem still holds to the extent that the distribution of sample means follows a known distribution with a mean equal to that of the population mean $\mu$. The difference here is that this distribution is not a normal distribution, rather it is a student t-distribution. Otherwise all the ideas are the same as for large samples regarding the calculation of

- Point estimates.
- Confidence intervals.

### Not normally distributed population

If the population is not normally distributed and we have only selected a small sample, then the central limit theorem does not hold, i.e. the DOSM does *not* follow any defined pattern and we can not deduce anything about the population from the sample.

## 2.2 Normally distributed population

### 2.2.1 Introduction

When dealing with large samples ($\geq 30$) we established the following relationships regarding the point estimates and confidence intervals.

**Large sample point estimate of mean**

Mean  $\mu = \bar{x}$

**Large sample confidence intervals**

$$\mu = \bar{x} \pm Z \times SE$$

where

$$SE = \frac{s}{\sqrt{n}} \left( = \frac{\sigma}{\sqrt{n}} \text{ if } \sigma \text{ is known} \right)$$

$$s = \sqrt{\frac{\Sigma f(x - \bar{x})^2}{n-1}}$$

Z is the Z value associated with the given confidence level required.

For small samples the only variation we need to make to any of these formulae is to replace the Z value obtained from normal distribution tables by a t value obtained from the student t-distribution tables giving the following.

**Small sample point estimate of mean**

Mean  $\mu = \bar{x}$

**Small sample confidence intervals**

$$\mu = \bar{x} \pm t \times SE \ (\mu = \bar{x} \pm Z \times SE \text{ if } \sigma \text{ is known } *)$$

where

$$SE \ = \frac{s}{\sqrt{n}} \left( = \frac{\sigma}{\sqrt{n}} \text{ if } \sigma \text{ is known} \right)$$

$$s = \sqrt{\frac{\Sigma f(x - \bar{x})^2}{n-1}}$$

t is the t value associated with the given confidence level required.

All that is required now is to understand the student t-distribution and how to read the tables.

  ***NB***  Even with a small sample, if the population standard deviation is known we use the normal distribution giving $\mu = \bar{x} \pm Z \times SE$.

## Exercise 2

25 investment analysts are interviewed by a City recruitment firm trying to get a clear picture of industry salaries for a particular research sector. If the population distribution is normal with a mean salary of £40,000 and a standard deviation of £6,000, what is the probability that the sample mean salary is less than £38,000?

# 2.3 Student t-distribution

When we have taken a reasonably large sample, the sample standard deviation will provide a reasonable approximation to the population standard deviation.

Where we have only selected a small sample, the spread of values observed in that sample is likely to be significantly lower than the spread of items in the true population and therefore even the sample standard deviation calculated from the sample data is likely to underestimate the standard deviation of the full population.

Large samples are likely to pick up some of those extremes but, as we reduce the sample size, those extremes are less and less likely to be selected. As a result, the variability observed in the small sample will understate the true variability of the full population.

The student t-distribution is a variation from the normal distribution which reflects this characteristic of a broader spread of values. Student t-distribution tables are included as an appendix at the end of this section and the shape of the distribution is illustrated below.

We should note, however, that it is really a misnomer to talk about *a* student t-distribution as, in fact, there are many different distributions. We have already noted that the smaller the sample size, the larger the population spread is likely to be compared to that observed in the sample. This student t-distribution takes account of the sample size in determining the spread of the population.

For the normal distribution there are just two relevant factors.

- Z value.
- Probability (the area beyond a point).

Given the Z value you could determine the related probability or given a probability you could determine the related Z value.

The student t distribution is defined by three factors.

- The t value.
- Probabilities (the area beyond a point).
- The degrees of freedom.

This third item, the degrees of freedom, is related to the size of the sample that is being used and the number of variables considered. We will use

- $n - 1$ for sample variations about a mean, e.g. we need two points to measure one variation, i.e. the number of variations is $n - 1$.

- $n - 2$ for sample variations about a line, e.g. we need two points to define a line and a third point to provide one variation from that line hence the number of variation, degrees of freedom, is $n - 2$.

The general term for the degrees of freedom (DF) is

DF = n − v

where v is the number of variables.

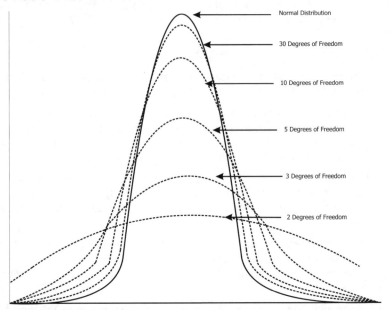

As this diagram shows, the lower the sample size (the lower the degrees of freedom), the less certain we are about the population and hence the broader the potential spread of that population (the wider the confidence intervals) based on our sample.

Conversely, the larger the sample size (and degrees of freedom), the more certain we are about the population and hence the narrower the potential population spread until at the limit when our sample size becomes infinite the student t-distribution coincides with the normal distribution.

## 2.3.1 Using the t-distribution tables

If we look for a second to the t-distribution tables in the appendix we will see that at first sight they look very similar to the normal distribution tables but they are, in fact, laid out in a completely different way. In the normal distribution tables, the Z value heads up the rows and columns and the probabilities can then be read from the body of the table.

In the student t-distribution the probabilities head up the columns, the degrees of freedom head up the rows and the t values can then be read from the bodies of the table.

This difference of layout is required as a result of the three input factors rather than two, however, its use is identical to that of the normal distribution tables as regards sampling theory as we illustrate with the following example.

## Example

A sample of 20 students' GCSE Maths exam results is taken with the aim of determining statistics regarding all the students. The sample is observed to have a mean of 55% and a sample standard deviation of 5%.

Calculate

- The point estimate of the true average mark.

- The 99% confidence interval.

- The sample size required to estimate the true mean to within 1% at the 99% confidence level (assuming that the standard deviation of the sample will be unaltered by increasing the sample size).

## Solution

**Point estimate**

$$\text{Mean } \mu = \bar{x} = 55\%$$

**99% Confidence Interval**

For 99% confidence we may only exclude 1% of the population, i.e. 0.5% at each extreme. From the student t-distribution tables the t value associated with a probability of 0.005 (0.5%) where the degrees of freedom ($v$) is $n - 1 = 19$, is 2.86094.

Now

$$SE = \frac{s}{\sqrt{n}} = \frac{5}{\sqrt{20}} = 1.118$$

and

$$\mu = \bar{x} \pm t \times SE$$
$$= 55 \pm 2.86094 \times 1.118$$
$$= 55 \pm 3.199$$

i.e. we can be 99% certain that the true average mark lies in the range

$$51.801 \leq \text{True average} \leq 58.199$$

As we can see, this represents a broader range than we found when the sample size was 100 which gave

$$53.712 \leq \text{True average} \leq 56.288$$

Given the smaller sample size we should expect greater uncertainty and hence this wider confidence interval.

### Sample size to reduce interval to ±1% at the 99% confidence level

For our confidence interval to be ±1% we need

$$t \times SE = t \times \frac{s}{\sqrt{n}} = 1$$

Strictly speaking, we cannot solve this relationship except through trial and error as both t and $\sqrt{n}$ vary with n (indeed s is also likely to vary). The only practical approach is to use the initial values of s and t and solve for n. This will not be perfectly accurate as t falls when n rises, however, it will ensure that a sufficiently large sample will be taken since we ignore this fall.

At the 99% confidence level we had t = 2.86094 for a sample size of 19 resulting in a potential sample error of ± 3.199. To reduce this to ±1.000 we need

$$2.86094 \times \frac{5}{\sqrt{n}} = 1$$

giving

$$\frac{14.3047}{\sqrt{n}} = 1$$

$$\sqrt{n} = 14.3047$$

$$n = 204.6, \text{ i.e. a sample size of 205}$$

This is much larger than the 166 we previously estimated in our large sample example as a result of keeping the t value based on $v = n - 1 = 19$. Since we have determined that we require a large sample (205 or 166), the large sample result would be better.

## Exercise 3

A sample of 20 daily share price movements demonstrates a mean of 1% and a standard deviation of 0.1%. Estimate

(a)     The population mean.

(b)     95%, 98% and 99% confidence intervals.

(c)     The sample size required to reduce the margin of error at 95% to 0.02%.

# 3     PROPORTIONS IN LARGE SAMPLES

## 3.1 Introduction

In using the sampling theory of proportions, we are again trying to determine the characteristics of the full population from details established in a sample.

The sampling theory of proportions is useful where we have a large sample ($n \geq 30$) from a population that has binomial properties, i.e. two distinct segments with different attributes, e.g.

- Population - males/females.
- Men - bald/not.
- Exam results - pass/fail.

In such a population a certain proportion of that population will have one characteristic and the remainder will demonstrate the other. Our aim is that given that relevant proportion from a sample, we are trying to conclude about the proportion in the full population with some degree of certainty.

The notation we will use throughout this section when referring to either the population or the sample is

|            | Population | Sample |
|------------|:----------:|:------:|
| Proportion | $\pi$      | p      |
| Size       | N          | n      |

It is unnecessary to talk about a population standard deviation here as we do not have a smooth distribution with items showing some variation from a mean, rather we have two completely distinct groups (male, female) with no variation in between.

## 3.2 Central limit theorem

### 3.2.1 Introduction

If we pick a sample, it is highly unlikely that the proportion of, say, males in that sample will exactly match the proportion of males in the full population.

If we take all possible samples of a given size n, calculate the proportions within each of these samples and plot these proportions as a distribution (the distribution of sample proportions), the central limit theorem states that these sample proportions will be normally distributed with

- Mean $= \pi$

- Standard error $= \sqrt{\dfrac{\pi(100-\pi)}{n}}$ where $\pi$ is stated as a *percentage;*

  $= \sqrt{\dfrac{\pi(1-\pi)}{n}}$ where $\pi$ is stated as a *decimal.*

*NB.* You will need to be careful as to whether you use percentages or decimals in your calculations and throughout this section we have used percentages as this is the most likely form in which proportional data will be presented.

### 3.2.2 Usefulness

### Introduction

The usefulness of this is that once again we are able to establish point estimates of the population proportions and confidence intervals given certain confidence levels. The approach to any calculations would be identical to that for large samples above since, once more, the sample proportions would follow a normal distribution.

## Point estimate of proportion

Mean $\quad \pi = p$

## Confidence intervals

$$\pi = p \pm Z \times SE$$

where

$$SE = \sqrt{\frac{p(100-p)}{n}} \quad \text{where p is stated as a } \textit{percentage}$$

p being substituted in place of $\pi$ in this relationship since it is a good estimate when we have a large sample (n $\geq$ 30).

## Example

A sample of 120 staff members is surveyed to determine whether staff prefer defined working hours or flexitime.  77.5% of those in the sample said that they would prefer flexitime, calculate

- The point estimate of the likely proportions in the full staff.

- The 99% confidence interval.

- The sample size required to estimate the true proportion to within 5% at the 95% confidence level.

## Solution

**Point estimate**

Mean $\quad \pi = p = 77.5\%$

**99% confidence interval**

For 99% confidence we may only exclude 1% of the population, i.e. 0.5% at each extreme.  From the normal distribution tables the Z value associated with a probability of 0.005 (0.5%) is 2.575.

Now

$$SE = \sqrt{\frac{p(100-p)}{n}} = \sqrt{\frac{77.5(100-77.5)}{120}} = 3.812$$

and

$$\pi = p \pm Z \times SE$$
$$= 77.5 \pm 2.575 \times 3.812$$
$$= 77.5 \pm 9.82$$

i.e. we can be 99% certain that the true average mark lies in the range

$67.68 \leq$ True proportion $\leq 87.32$

## Sample size to reduce interval to ±5% at the 95% confidence level

The problem that we will have here is that the sample proportions are likely to vary as we alter the sample size. As a result, we have two alternatives.

- Take the initial sample proportion p as representative.

- Use p = 50% if we are unsure about p or do not know it as this will always result in the largest required sample.

## Using initial sample proportion of 77.5%

For our confidence interval to be ±5% we need

$$Z \times SE = Z \times \sqrt{\frac{p(100-p)}{n}} = 5$$

At the 95% confidence level, Z = 1.96, hence

$$1.96 \times \sqrt{\frac{p(100-p)}{n}} = 5$$

giving

$$\sqrt{\frac{77.5(100-77.5)}{n}} = 2.551$$

therefore

$$\frac{1,743.75}{n} = 6.508$$

$$\frac{1,743.75}{6.508} = n$$

$$n = 267.9, \text{ i.e. } 268.$$

## Using sample proportion of 50%

Again we need

$$1.96 \times \sqrt{\frac{p(100-p)}{n}} = 5$$

giving

$$\sqrt{\frac{50(100-50)}{n}} = 2.551$$

therefore

$$\frac{2,500}{n} = 6.508$$

$$\frac{2,500}{6.508} = n$$

n = 384.1, i.e. 385.

# 4 DIFFERENCES BETWEEN INDEPENDENT LARGE SAMPLES

## 4.1 Introduction

If a population can be broken down into two or more categories (e.g. male and female) then we may wish to determine the differences (e.g. height, weight, etc.) between these two categories.

The analysis relies on the rules for calculating the differences between the normal distributions, specifically

- Mean of Difference $\mu_{Diff} = \mu_1 - \mu_2$
- Standard Deviation of Difference $\sigma_{Diff} = \sqrt{\sigma_1^2 + \sigma_2^2}$

## 4.2 Differences between large sample means

### 4.2.1 Central limit theorem

If we have two populations with

- Means $\mu_1, \mu_2$
- Standard deviations $\sigma_1, \sigma_2$

then we could draw samples of size $n_1$ and $n_2$, calculate their means and the difference between them.

If we repeated this for all possible samples of size and calculate all the possible differences between the means, then the distribution of these differences (the distribution of differences between means) would be normal with

Mean $\mu_{Diff} = \mu_1 - \mu_2$

Standard Error $SE_{Diff} = \sqrt{SE_1^2 + SE_2^2}$

based on the rules for the difference between normal distributions.

Now considering the standard error of each distribution

$$SE^1 = \frac{\sigma^1}{\sqrt{n^1}} = \frac{s^1}{\sqrt{n^1}}$$

$$SE^2 = \frac{\sigma^2}{\sqrt{n^2}} = \frac{s^2}{\sqrt{n^2}}$$

giving

$$SE_{Diff} = \sqrt{SE_1^2 + SE_2^2} = \sqrt{\frac{s_1^2}{n_1} + \frac{s_2^2}{n_2}}$$

And hence

Mean $\mu_{Diff} = \mu_1 - \mu_2$

Standard Error $SE_{Diff} = \sqrt{\frac{s_1^2}{n_1} + \frac{s_2^2}{n_2}}$

## 4.2.2 Usefulness

### Introduction

Once again we can use these relationships to try to establish a point estimate of the difference between the means and confidence intervals enabling us to state with a given degree of certainty the range within which that difference between the means will lie.

The formulae we use are very much just an extension of the formulae that we have used earlier.

### Point estimate of mean

Mean $\mu_{Diff} = \bar{x}_1 - \bar{x}_2$

### Confidence intervals

$$\mu_{Diff} = \bar{x}_1 - \bar{x}_2 \pm Z \times SE$$

where

$$SE = \sqrt{\frac{s_1^2}{n_1} + \frac{s_2^2}{n_2}} \left( = \sqrt{\frac{\sigma_1^2}{n_1} + \frac{\sigma_2^2}{n_2}} \text{ if } \sigma_1 \text{ and } \sigma_2 \text{ are known} \right)$$

$$s = \sqrt{\frac{\Sigma f(x - \bar{x})^2}{n-1}} \text{ for both } s_1 \text{ and } s_2.$$

Z is the Z value associated with the given confidence level required.

## Example

A sample of 100 men and 120 women is drawn, their heights measured and the following data determined.

|  | Men | Women |
|---|---|---|
| Mean | 180cm | 160cm |
| Standard Deviation | 7cm | 6cm |
| Sample Size | 100 | 120 |

Establish for the population

- A point estimate of the difference between heights.
- 95% confidence interval for the difference.

## Solution

### Point estimate

Mean   $\mu\text{Diff}= \mu_1 - \mu_2 = 180 - 160 = 20\text{cm}$

### Confidence interval at 95%

$$SE = \sqrt{\frac{S_1^2}{n_1} + \frac{S_2^2}{n_2}} = \sqrt{\frac{7^2}{100} + \frac{6^2}{120}} = \sqrt{0.85} = 0.92$$

Hence at the 95% confidence level (Z value 1.96)

$$\mu_{\text{Diff}} = \overline{X}_1 - \overline{X}_2 \pm Z \times SE$$

$$= 180 - 160 \pm 1.96 \times 0.92$$

$$= 20 \pm 1.8$$

i.e. we can be 95% certain that the true difference in height lies in the range

$18.2\text{cm} \leq \text{True difference} \leq 21.8$

## 4.3 Differences between proportions

### 4.3.1 Introduction

Exactly the same relationships apply for differences between proportions, i.e.

Mean $\pi_{\text{Diff}} = \pi_1 - \pi_2$

Standard Error $SE_{\text{Diff}} = \sqrt{SE_1^2 + SE_2^2}$

based on the rules for the difference between normal distributions.

This time considering the standard error of each distribution we have

$$SE_1 = \sqrt{\frac{\pi_1(100 - \pi_1)}{n_1}} = \sqrt{\frac{p_1(100 - p_1)}{n_1}}$$

$$SE_2 = \sqrt{\frac{\pi_2(100 - \pi_2)}{n_2}} = \sqrt{\frac{p_2(100p_2)}{n_2}}$$

giving

$$SE_{Diff} = \sqrt{SE_1^2 + SE_2^2} = \sqrt{\frac{p_1(100 - p_1)}{n_1} + \frac{p_2(100 - p_2)}{n_2}}$$

And hence

Mean $\pi_{Diff} = p_1 - p_2$

Standard Error $SE_{Diff} = \sqrt{\frac{p_1(100 - p_1)}{n_1} + \frac{p_2(100 - p_2)}{n_2}}$

### 4.3.2 Usefulness

**Point estimate of mean**

Mean $\quad \pi_{Diff} = p_1 - p_2$

## Confidence intervals

$$\pi_{Diff} = p_1 - p_2 \pm Z \times SE$$

where

$$SE = \sqrt{\frac{p_1(100 - p_1)}{n_1} + \frac{p_2(100 - p_2)}{n_2}}$$

Z is the Z value associated with the given confidence level required.

## Example

A sample of 160 men and 120 women are surveyed regarding their drinking habits and the following data determined.

|  | Men | Women |
|---|---|---|
|  | % | % |
| Proportion of Drinkers | 80 | 65 |
| Sample Size | 160 | 120 |

Establish for the population

- A point estimate of the difference between the proportion of drinkers.
- 95% confidence interval for the difference.

## Solution

**Point estimate**

Mean $\pi_{Diff} = \pi_1 - \pi_2 = 80 - 65 = 15\%$

**Confidence interval at 95%**

$$SE = \sqrt{\frac{p_1(100 - p_1)}{n_1} + \frac{p_2(100 - p_2)}{n_2}}$$

$$= \sqrt{\frac{80(100 - 80)}{160} + \frac{65(100 - 65)}{120}}$$

$$= \sqrt{10 + 18.96}$$

$$= \sqrt{28.96}$$

$$= 5.38$$

Hence at the 95% confidence level (Z value 1.96)

$$\pi_{Diff} = p_1 - p_2 \pm Z \times SE$$

$$= 80 - 65 \pm 1.96 \times 5.38$$

$$= 15 \pm 10.55$$

i.e. we can be 95% certain that the true average mark lies in the range

$$4.55\% \leq \text{True difference} \leq 25.55\%$$

# 4.4 Differences between small sample means

## 4.4.1 Introduction

Once again we get very similar results, but remember we must use the t-distribution. The extra factor that this requires us to consider is the degrees of freedom in the samples. The degrees of freedom for each sample will be

$$v_1 = n_1 - 1$$

$$v_2 = n_2 - 1$$

and when we combine these two to calculate the differences

$$v_{Diff} = (n_1 - 1) + (n_2 - 1) = n_1 + n_2 - 2$$

The sample sizes will also, however, influence the standard error since they influence the sample standard deviations. The calculation of the standard error becomes quite complex but an outline follows.

Earlier we established the relationship

$$SE_{Diff} = \sqrt{SE_1^2 + SE_2^2} = \sqrt{\frac{s_1^2}{n_1} + \frac{s_2^2}{n_2}}$$

If we could establish a pooled standard deviation, $s_p$, which provides a substitute for both $s_1$ and $s_2$ then we could write this as

$$SE_{Diff} = \sqrt{\frac{s_1^2}{n_1} + \frac{s_2^2}{n_2}} = \sqrt{\frac{s_p^2}{n_1} + \frac{s_p^2}{n_2}} = sp\sqrt{\frac{1}{n_1} + \frac{1}{n_2}}$$

This pooled standard deviation may be established as

$$s_p = \sqrt{\frac{(n_1 - 1)s_1^2 + (n_2 - 1)s_2^2}{n_1 + n_2 - 2}}$$

## 4.4.2 Usefulness

### Point estimate of mean

Mean $\mu_{Diff} = \bar{x}_1 - \bar{x}_2$

### Confidence intervals

$$\mu_1 - \mu_2 = \bar{x}_1 - \bar{x}_2 \pm t \times SE$$

$$\mu_1 - \mu_2 = \bar{x}_1 - \bar{x}_2 \pm t \times S_p\sqrt{\frac{1}{n_1} + \frac{1}{n_2}}$$

where

$$S_p = \sqrt{\frac{(n_1 - 1)s_1^2 + (n_2 - 1)s_2^2}{n_1 + n_2 - 2}}$$

$$s = \sqrt{\frac{\sum f(x-\bar{x})^2}{n-1}}\ \text{ for both } s_1 \text{ and } s_2.$$

$$v_{Diff} = n_1 + n_2 - 2$$

t is the t value associated with the given confidence level required and the given degrees of freedom.

# 5 OTHER FACTORS

## 5.1 Confidence intervals for the median

If we have a highly skewed population, the arithmetic mean may not be the most appropriate measure of the central point of a distribution. As an alternative we may choose to use the median, i.e. the central item in an ordered listing. The median item can be established using the relationship

$$n_m = \frac{n+1}{2}$$

Since the median is determined by ranking all the items in order and then locating the central one, the distribution we will be dealing with must be discrete and hence confidence intervals could be determined exactly by using the binomial distribution.

If, however, our sample is reasonably large making the use of the binomial unwieldy, we may prefer to use the normal distribution as an approximation to the binomial distribution in order to calculate the confidence intervals.

### Point estimate

The item to consider in determining the point estimate of the population median is

$$\text{Item number} = n_m = \frac{n+1}{2}$$

the median being the value of this item.

### Confidence intervals

Once again we need to determine the number of the item to evaluate which we can do using

$$\text{Upper limit item number} = \frac{n}{2} + Z \times \frac{\sqrt{n}}{2} \quad \text{rounded up to the}$$

nearest whole number

$$\text{Lower limit item number} = \frac{n}{2} - Z \times \frac{\sqrt{n}}{2} + 1 \quad \text{rounded down to the}$$

nearest whole number

These appear a little unsymmetrical since the lower item has one added to it whereas the upper one does not. This is a function of the direction of the rounding. Adding one then rounding down will give the same result as simply rounding up.

# 5.2 Finite population correction factor

## 5.2.1 Introduction

Throughout this section so far we have made no great mention of the population size, assuming it to be infinite, or at least very large in comparison to the sample size.

As the proportion of the population included in the sample increases, the size of any potential sampling errors reduce as we have already seen. Taking this to an absolute extreme, if our sample consists of 100% of the population then there can be no error due to sampling.

The relationship that we established earlier in relation to the confidence interval for large samples is

$$\mu = \bar{x} \pm Z \times \frac{s}{\sqrt{n}}$$

This would seem to imply that even if we sample 100% of the population we would still have a sampling error of

$$\text{Sampling Error} = \pm Z \times \frac{s}{\sqrt{n}}$$

This clearly cannot be the case - if we have sampled the full population then we will have no sampling error as we stated above.

To take this factor into account in any of our confidence interval calculations, we need to adjust the sampling error by multiplying it by the finite population correction factor which is given by

$$\text{Finite population correction factor} = \sqrt{\left(1 - \frac{n}{N}\right)}$$

While n is small in relation to N this has no effect on our calculations. However, as our sample gets larger in proportion to the full population, this term will tend to reduce the sampling error and our confidence interval becomes

$$\mu = \bar{x} \pm Z \sqrt{\left(1 - \frac{n}{N}\right)} \times \frac{s}{\sqrt{n}}$$

In the limit when the sample is the full population (i.e. n = N) this term becomes zero and hence when we sample the full population we cannot face any sampling error.

# 6 SUMMARY

|  | Population | Sample |
|---|---|---|
| Mean | $\mu$ | $\bar{x}$ |
| Standard Deviation | $\sigma$ | $s$ |
| Proportion | $\pi$ | $p$ |
| Size | $N$ | $n$ |

## 6.1 Large sample

Mean $\qquad \mu = \bar{x}$

Standard Error $\qquad SE = \dfrac{s}{\sqrt{n}} \left( = \dfrac{\sigma}{\sqrt{n}} \text{ if } \sigma \text{ is known} \right)$

Confidence Interval $\qquad \mu = \bar{x} \pm Z \times SE$

## 6.2 Small sample

Mean $\qquad \mu = \bar{x}$

Standard Error $\qquad SE = \dfrac{s}{\sqrt{n}} \left( = \dfrac{\sigma}{\sqrt{n}} \text{ if } \sigma \text{ is known} \right)$

Confidence Interval $\qquad \mu = \bar{x} \pm t \times SE$

Degrees of Freedom $\qquad v = n - 1$ for a point

$\qquad\qquad\qquad\qquad\quad n - 2$ for a line

## 6.3 Proportions in a large or small sample

Proportion $\qquad \pi = p$

Standard Error $\qquad SE = \sqrt{\dfrac{p(100 - p)}{n}}$

Confidence Interval $\qquad \pi = p \pm Z \times SE$

## 6.4 Differences between means in large sample

Mean $\qquad \mu_{Diff} = \bar{x}_1 - \bar{x}_2$

Standard Error $\qquad SE = \sqrt{\dfrac{s_1^2}{n_1} + \dfrac{s_2^2}{n_2}} \left( = \sqrt{\dfrac{\sigma_1^2}{n_1} + \dfrac{\sigma_2^2}{n_2}} \text{ if } \sigma_1 \text{ and } \sigma_2 \text{ are known} \right)$

Confidence Interval $\qquad \mu_1 - \mu_2 = \bar{x}_1 - \bar{x}_2 \pm Z \times SE$

## 6.5 Differences between proportions in large sample

Proportion $\quad\quad\quad \pi_{Diff} = p_1 - p_2$

Standard Error $\quad SE_{Diff} = \sqrt{\dfrac{p_1(100-p_1)}{n_1} + \dfrac{p_2(100-p_2)}{n_2}}$

Confidence Interval $\quad \pi_1 - \pi_2 = p_1 - p_2 \pm Z \times SE$

## 6.6 Differences between means in small sample

Mean $\quad\quad\quad \mu_{Diff} = \overline{x}_1 - \overline{x}_2$

Standard Error $\quad s_p = \sqrt{\dfrac{(n_1-1)s_1^2 + (n_2-1)s_2^2}{n_1 + n_2 - 2}}$

Confidence Interval $\quad \mu_1 - \mu_2 = x_1 - x_2 \pm t \times s_p\sqrt{\dfrac{1}{n_1} + \dfrac{1}{n_2}}$

Degrees of Freedom $\quad v_{Diff} = n_1 + n_2 - 2$

## 6.7 Confidence intervals for the median

Upper limit item number $= \dfrac{n}{2} + Z \times \dfrac{\sqrt{n}}{2}$ rounded up to the nearest whole number

Lower limit item number $= \dfrac{n}{2} - Z \times \dfrac{\sqrt{n}}{2} + 1$ rounded down to the nearest whole number

## 6.8 Finite population correction factor

Finite population correction factor $= \sqrt{\left(1 - \dfrac{n}{N}\right)}$

Confidence Interval $\quad \mu = \overline{x} \pm \dfrac{s}{\sqrt{n}} Z \times \sqrt{\left(1 - \dfrac{n}{N}\right)}$

# 7 SOLUTIONS TO EXERCISES

1.  (a)  Population mean

    $\mu \qquad = \bar{x} = 1$

    (b)  Confidence intervals

    $$SE = \frac{S}{\sqrt{n}} = \frac{0.1}{\sqrt{100}} = 0.01$$

    $\mu = \bar{x} \pm Z \times SE$

    $= 1 \pm Z \times 0.01$

    | Confidence Level | Confidence Interval |
    |---|---|
    | 95% | $1 \pm 1.96 \times 0.01 = 1 \pm 0.0196$ or $0.98040 - 1.01960$ |
    | 98% | $1 \pm 2.325 \times 0.01 = 1 \pm 0.02325$ or $0.97675 - 1.02325$ |
    | 99% | $1 \pm 2.575 \times 0.01 = 1 \pm 0.02575$ or $0.97425 - 1.02575$ |

    (c)  Margin for error

    $$\text{Margin for error} = Z \times SE = \times \frac{S}{\sqrt{n}}$$

    $$0.015 = 1.96 \times \frac{0.1}{\sqrt{n}}$$

    $$\sqrt{n} = \frac{1.96 \times 0.1}{0.015} = 13.067$$

    $n = 171$

2.  Given the standard deviation for the population ($\sigma$) of £6,000, the standard deviation of a sample (standard error) of size 25 drawn from this population is given by

    $$SE = \frac{\sigma}{\sqrt{n}} = \frac{6,000}{\sqrt{25}} = £1,200$$

    The Z value for a sample mean of £38,000 is

    $$Z = \frac{\bar{x} - \mu}{SE} = \frac{38,000 - 40,000}{1,200} = 1.67 \quad \text{hence P(Mean} < £38,000)$$

    $= 0.0475$

3.   (a)   Population mean

$$\mu \quad = \bar{x} = 1$$

(b)   Confidence intervals

$$SE = \frac{s}{\sqrt{n}} = \frac{0.1}{\sqrt{20}} = 0.02236$$

$$\mu \quad = \bar{x} \pm t \times SE$$

$$= 1 \pm t \times 0.02236$$

| Confidence Level | Confidence Interval |
|---|---|
| 95% | $1 \pm 2.093 \times 0.02236 = 1 \pm 0.0468$ or $0.9532 - 1.0468$ |
| 98% | $1 \pm 2.539 \times 0.02236 = 1 \pm 0.0568$ or $0.9432 - 1.0568$ |
| 99% | $1 \pm 2.861 \times 0.02236 = 1 \pm 0.0640$ or $0.9360 - 1.0640$ |

(c)   Margin for error

$$\text{Margin for error} = t \times SE = t \times \frac{s}{\sqrt{n}}$$

$$0.02 = 2.093 \times \frac{0.1}{\sqrt{n}}$$

$$\sqrt{n} = \frac{2.093 \times 0.1}{0.02} = 10.465$$

$$n = 110$$

# APPENDIX 1 - STUDENT T-DISTRIBUTION

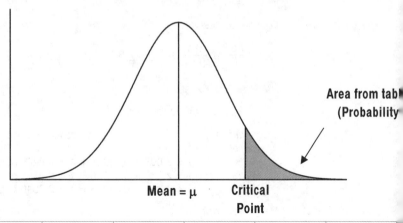

Mean = μ · Critical Point

Area from tab▊
(Probability

| Degrees of Freedom (v) | Probability | | | | |
|---|---|---|---|---|---|
| | 0.1 | 0.05 | 0.025 | 0.01 | 0.005 |
| 1 | 3.07768 | 6.31375 | 12.70615 | 31.82096 | 63.65590 |
| 2 | 1.88562 | 2.91999 | 4.30266 | 6.96455 | 9.92499 |
| 3 | 1.63775 | 2.35336 | 3.18245 | 4.54071 | 5.84085 |
| 4 | 1.53321 | 2.13185 | 2.77645 | 3.74694 | 4.60408 |
| 5 | 1.47588 | 2.01505 | 2.57058 | 3.36493 | 4.03212 |
| 6 | 1.43976 | 1.94318 | 2.44691 | 3.14267 | 3.70743 |
| 7 | 1.41492 | 1.89458 | 2.36462 | 2.99795 | 3.49948 |
| 8 | 1.39682 | 1.85955 | 2.30601 | 2.89647 | 3.35538 |
| 9 | 1.38303 | 1.83311 | 2.26216 | 2.82143 | 3.24984 |
| 10 | 1.37218 | 1.81246 | 2.22814 | 2.76377 | 3.16926 |
| 11 | 1.36343 | 1.79588 | 2.20099 | 2.71808 | 3.10582 |
| 12 | 1.35622 | 1.78229 | 2.17881 | 2.68099 | 3.05454 |
| 13 | 1.35017 | 1.77093 | 2.16037 | 2.65030 | 3.01228 |
| 14 | 1.34503 | 1.76131 | 2.14479 | 2.62449 | 2.97685 |
| 15 | 1.34061 | 1.75305 | 2.13145 | 2.60248 | 2.94673 |
| 16 | 1.33676 | 1.74588 | 2.11990 | 2.58349 | 2.92079 |
| 17 | 1.33338 | 1.73961 | 2.10982 | 2.56694 | 2.89823 |
| 18 | 1.33039 | 1.73406 | 2.10092 | 2.55238 | 2.87844 |
| 19 | 1.32773 | 1.72913 | 2.09302 | 2.53948 | 2.86094 |
| 20 | 1.32534 | 1.72472 | 2.08596 | 2.52798 | 2.84534 |
| 21 | 1.32319 | 1.72074 | 2.07961 | 2.51765 | 2.83137 |
| 22 | 1.32124 | 1.71714 | 2.07388 | 2.50832 | 2.81876 |
| 23 | 1.31946 | 1.71387 | 2.06865 | 2.49987 | 2.80734 |

| Degrees of Freedom ($\nu$) | | | Probability | | |
|---|---|---|---|---|---|
| | 0.1 | 0.05 | 0.025 | 0.01 | 0.005 |
| 24 | 1.31784 | 1.71088 | 2.06390 | 2.49216 | 2.79695 |
| 25 | 1.31635 | 1.70814 | 2.05954 | 2.48510 | 2.78744 |
| 26 | 1.31497 | 1.70562 | 2.05553 | 2.47863 | 2.77872 |
| 27 | 1.31370 | 1.70329 | 2.05183 | 2.47266 | 2.77068 |
| 28 | 1.31253 | 1.70113 | 2.04841 | 2.46714 | 2.76326 |
| 29 | 1.31143 | 1.69913 | 2.04523 | 2.46202 | 2.75639 |
| 30 | 1.31042 | 1.69726 | 2.04227 | 2.45726 | 2.74998 |
| 35 | 1.30621 | 1.68957 | 2.03011 | 2.43772 | 2.72381 |
| 40 | 1.30308 | 1.68385 | 2.02107 | 2.42326 | 2.70446 |
| 45 | 1.30065 | 1.67943 | 2.01410 | 2.41212 | 2.68959 |
| 50 | 1.29871 | 1.67591 | 2.00856 | 2.40327 | 2.67779 |
| 60 | 1.29582 | 1.67065 | 2.00030 | 2.39012 | 2.66027 |
| 70 | 1.29376 | 1.66692 | 1.99444 | 2.38080 | 2.64790 |
| 80 | 1.29222 | 1.66413 | 1.99007 | 2.37387 | 2.63870 |
| 90 | 1.29103 | 1.66196 | 1.98667 | 2.36850 | 2.63157 |
| 100 | 1.29008 | 1.66023 | 1.98397 | 2.36421 | 2.62589 |
| $\infty$ | 1.28156 | 1.64484 | 1.95996 | 2.32635 | 2.57583 |

# 8 Hypothesis testing

## Contents

**217**

## Introduction

Probability theory is useful when we know the attributes of the full population and we are trying to deduce the attributes of a sample.

Sampling theory is useful when we know the attributes of a sample and we are trying to determine the attributes of the full population.

Hypothesis or significance testing, the two terms being interchangeable, is used when we think we know about the characteristics of the population and we are testing a sample to see if it supports this hypothesis.

Hypothesis testing hinges on sampling theory ideas, i.e. being able to establish confidence intervals within which we can be sure that the majority of the population falls.

The basic idea behind the approach to hypothesis testing is to determine the confidence intervals within which we expect sample means to fall, based on the confidence level with which we wish to work (or error level that we are willing to accept) and the size of the selected sample used to test the hypothesis.

In determining our confidence intervals we will need to bear in mind

- The size of the sample (and possibly the size of the population) as this will determine whether we are using the normal distribution characteristics or the student t-distribution characteristics.

- Whether we are working with means, proportions, or differences between either of these as these factors impact on the calculation of the standard error and hence the calculation of the confidence intervals.

- The type of test we are considering, specifically

   - **A two-tailed test** - where we are trying to test whether the population differs from what we believe being either greater than or less than.

   - **A one-tailed test** - where we are trying to test whether the true population is either greater than or less than what we believe, we are concentrating on just one side of the distribution.

# 1 APPROACH TO HYPOTHESIS TESTING

## 1.1 Introduction

The general approach to hypothesis testing is identical regardless of the specifics of the scenario. If you are happy with the ideas of confidence intervals and can appreciate the basic idea you will be able to apply it to any situation.

We illustrate the approach for four different scenarios

- Large samples.
- Small samples.
- Proportions.
- Differences, which we illustrate with a difference between two large sample means.

Although considered last, do not overlook the differences example since it has many practical uses, e.g. in assessing whether the apparent difference in performance between two fund managers is significant.

## 1.2 Reconsidering confidence intervals

Discussing this initially in terms of testing the means of a large sample (although the same ideas are applicable to all types of samples), the confidence interval will be given by

$$\mu = \bar{x} \pm Z \times SE \text{ (or } \pi = p \pm Z \times SE \text{ for sample proportions)}$$

This can be rearranged as follows.

$$\mu = \bar{x} \pm Z \times SE$$

$$\bar{x} - \mu = \pm Z \times SE$$

$$\frac{\bar{x} - \mu}{SE} = \pm Z$$

the sign of Z depending on whether $\bar{x}$ lies above or below $\mu$.

## Large samples

Normally the sign is ignored in describing the relationship which is generally stated as

$$Z = \frac{\bar{x} - \mu}{SE} \left( \text{or } Z = \frac{p - \pi}{SE} \text{ for sample proportions} \right)$$

## Small samples

If we were using small samples the only difference would be that we would be utilising t values rather than Z values, giving

$$t = \frac{\bar{x} - \mu}{SE} \left( \text{or } t = \frac{p - \pi}{SE} \text{ for sample proportions} \right)$$

## Result

Thus it is possible to state the confidence limits (the limits to the confidence interval) in terms of Z or t factors for large or small sample sizes respectively rather than values.

## 1.3 General approach

The general approach is then to

- Determine the acceptable confidence limits (the critical value) in terms of Z or t values based on the acceptable error levels and whether the test is one-tailed or two-tailed.

- Calculate the Z or t value corresponding to the observed sample mean using the above equations.

- Compare this sample Z or t value to the predetermined critical value in order to make a conclusion.

We would expect sample means to fall within our confidence interval and therefore would expect the observed Z or t value to have less than the predetermined critical value. If that is the case, then the sample appears to support our belief about the population mean, if it is not the case then it would appear that our initial hypothesis is incorrect.

This idea is most easily illustrated with a series of examples. The first example will break down each of these steps into smaller stages and introduce other bits of terminology, the later examples just illustrate the ideas.

## 1.4 Large samples

### 1.4.1 Introduction

With large samples we will be utilising the normal distribution.

### 1.4.2 Two-tailed test

We undertake a two-tailed test when we are not willing to accept any variability in either direction. What we are doing in a two-tailed test is rejecting both extremely high values and extremely low ones.

### Example

A firm claims that its trainees work on average 80 hours overtime per annum. A sample of 60 is selected to determine whether this figure is true or not. The sample results were

$$\bar{x} = 85$$

$$s = 18$$

Test the employer's assertion that the overtime does not differ significantly from 80 hours at the

- 95% confidence/5% significance level.
- 98% confidence/2% significance level.
- 99% confidence/1% significance level.

### Solution - 5% significance level

#### Null hypothesis

The first thing we must do in any hypothesis test is to state the null hypothesis, denoted by $H_0$. This is what we believe to be true about the population and are wishing to test. In this example our null hypothesis is that the number of overtime hours per annum is 80. This could be noted as

$$H_0: \mu = 80$$

## Alternative hypothesis

The next step is to state the alternative hypothesis. The alternative hypothesis states what will be the case if the null hypothesis is not true.

It is important to be very careful in determining the hypothesis as it is this which determines whether we are undertaking a one or two-tailed test.

In our example the alternative hypothesis will simply be that the mean does not equal 80 hours per annum. The question asks us to determine whether the value *differs significantly*, this could either be greater than or less than and hence we are undertaking a *two-tailed test*. We could note the alternative hypothesis as follows.

$H_1$: $\mu \neq 80$ $\Rightarrow$ *a two-tailed test*

## Significance or error level

The next step is to determine our significance or error level, that is the chance that we are willing to take of being wrong. Most tests tend to be conducted at the 5% significance level, although we may use a 1% significance level in highly critical situations.

For this example our significance level is

Significance level = 5%

## Rejection area

We have selected a large sample ($\geq$ 30) and hence we will be using the normal distribution. Quickly plotting the curve of what we believe the distribution to be reveals the following.

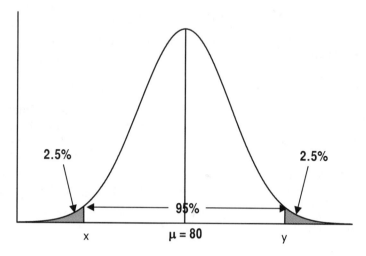

In this diagram, x and y represent the lower and upper limits of our confidence interval, respectively.

In conducting a two-tailed test at the 5% significance level, we wish to ensure that 95% of the population is covered and only the most extreme 5% (2½% at each of the upper and lower extremes) has been excluded.

### Critical values

Looking up 2.5% in the body of the normal distribution tables reveals a Z value associated with this of

$$Z_{0.025} = 1.960$$

Thus if the Z value of the observed sample mean is less than 1.96, we will accept the null hypothesis as this value falls within our confidence interval. If the Z value for the sample exceeds 1.96 than we must reject the null hypothesis, the conclusion being that the number of hours overtime worked per annum is significantly different from 80.

### Sample Z value

Now

$$SE = \frac{s}{\sqrt{n}} = \frac{18}{\sqrt{60}} = 2.324$$

Hence

$$Z = \frac{x - \mu}{SE} = \frac{8580}{2.324} = 2.151$$

### Conclusion

What this shows is that the sample mean lies 2.151 standard errors from the assumed population mean. This clearly lies in the rejection area above our confidence interval.

In conclusion

Sample Z Value (2.151) > Critical Value (1.96) $\Rightarrow$ *Reject the Null Hypothesis*

Thus the number of overtime hours is significantly different from 80 at the 5% significance level.

## Solution - 2% significance level

You may have wondered why we changed the critical values to consider them in terms of Z or t values rather than consider the confidence interval in units (hours). The reason is to enable us to undertake the test easily at different significance levels without undertaking any further work other than looking up values in tables.

The only factor that varies in any of the above when we consider a different significance level is the last step in determining the critical values by looking up in the tables.

With a significance level of 2% we will be rejecting the most extreme 1% in either tail (remember it is still a two-tailed test). Hence we have

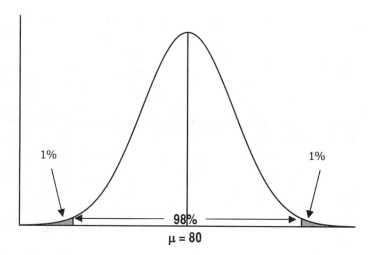

$\mu = 80$

**Critical values**

From the normal distribution tables the critical value, i.e. the Z value corresponding to a probability of 0.01 is 2.325.

Hence at a 2% significance level

Sample Z Value (2.151) < Critical Value (2.325) $\Rightarrow$ *Accept the Null Hypothesis*

Thus if we are only willing to accept a 2% possibility of error, we would conclude that the number of overtime hours is *not* significantly different from 80.

## Solution - 1% significance level

What we can see from the above is that as we reduce the significance level (the chance we are willing to take of coming to the wrong conclusion), we automatically increase the confidence interval. As a result, hypotheses that were previously rejected as they fell outside the confidence interval (had Z values above the critical value) may now be accepted as they fall within this expanded confidence interval as above.

Reducing the significance level further will only tend to expand the confidence interval to cover an even broader range. Hence, anything that is accepted at a significance level must automatically be accepted at any lower significance levels.

As a result, we need do no work whatsoever in relation to solving this particular problem. Since the null hypothesis was accepted at the 2% significance level, it must be accepted at the 1% significance level.

## Solution summary

Since the only factor that has varied between these three questions is the critical value based on the significance level, these three questions could have been dealt with in one go and the results summarised as follows.

| Significance Level | Critical Value | | Sample Z Value | Conclusion re Null Hypothesis |
|---|---|---|---|---|
| 5% | 1.960 | < | 2.151 | Reject |
| 2% | 2.325 | > | 2.151 | Accept |
| 1% | 2.575 | > | 2.151 | Accept |

The sample evidence supports the claim that the average overtime differs from 80 hours at the 5% level. It does not support this at either the 2% or 1% levels where the null hypothesis is accepted.

## 1.4.3 One-tailed test

A one-tailed test is conducted when we are trying to determine whether the population mean is either

- Significantly *greater than* the null hypothesis figure.
- Significantly *less than* the null hypothesis figure.

In either case we are only concerned with figures above or below the null hypothesis mean, $\mu_0$, respectively.

## Example

How would our analysis alter if the firm asserts that the true level is *not more* than 80 and we wished to determine whether this is true or whether the number of overtime hours in the above question was significantly *more* than 80?

## Solution

The difference here is that we are undertaking a one-tailed test. We are trying to determine whether the true hours overtime significantly *exceeds* 80. We will be unconcerned with the possibility that it may take any value below 80. This factor ( one-tailed test) would be brought out in determining the alternative hypothesis.

Following through as before

**Null hypothesis**

$$H_0: \mu \le 80$$

**Alternative hypothesis**

$$H_1: \mu > 80 \implies \text{a one-tailed test}$$

**Significance or error level**

Significance level = 5%, 2%, 1%

*Rejection area*

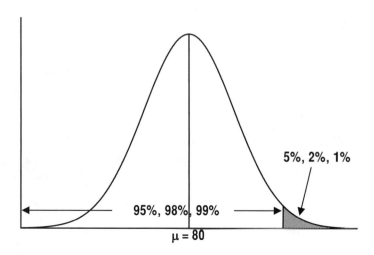

**Critical values**

$$Z_{0.050} = 1.645$$

$$Z_{0.020} = 2.055$$

$$Z_{0.010} = 2.325$$

**Sample Z value**

As we calculated before

$$SE = \frac{s}{\sqrt{n}} = \frac{18}{\sqrt{60}} = 2.324$$

Hence

$$Z = \frac{x - \mu}{SE} = \frac{85 - 80}{2.324} = 2.151$$

**Conclusion**

| Significance Level | Critical Value | | Sample Z Value | Conclusion re Null Hypothesis |
|---|---|---|---|---|
| 5% | 1.645 | < | 2.151 | Reject |
| 2% | 2.055 | < | 2.151 | Reject |
| 1% | 2.325 | > | 2.151 | Accept |

The sample evidence supports the claim that the average overtime exceeds 80 hours at both the 5% and 2% levels. It does not support this at the 1% level where the null hypothesis is accepted.

## 1.5 Small samples

### 1.5.1 Introduction

With small samples we will need to utilise the student t-distribution.

### 1.5.2 Two-tailed test

### Example

A firm claims that its trainees work on average 80 hours overtime per annum. A sample of 20 is selected to determine whether or not this figure is true. The sample results were

$$\bar{x} = 85$$

$$s = 10.5$$

Test the employer's assertion that the hours overtime does not differ significantly from 80 hours at the

- 95% confidence/5% significance level.
- 98% confidence/2% significance level.
- 99% confidence/1% significance level.

### Solution - all significance levels

**Null hypothesis**

$$H_0: \mu = 80$$

**Alternative hypothesis**

$$H_1: \mu \neq 80 \Rightarrow \textit{a two-tailed test}$$

**Significance or error level**

Significance levels = 5%, 2%, 1%

BPP
LEARNING MEDIA

*Rejection Area*

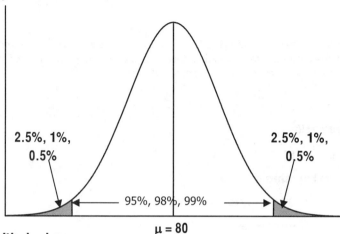

**2.5%, 1%, 0.5%**

**2.5%, 1%, 0,5%**

95%, 98%, 99%

$\mu = 80$

**Critical values**

With a sample size of 20 we have 19 degrees of freedom, i.e. $\nu = 19$, giving

$$t_{0.025} = 2.093$$

$$t_{0.010} = 2.539$$

$$t_{0.005} = 2.861$$

**Sample t value**

Now

$$SE = \frac{s}{\sqrt{n}} = \frac{10.5}{\sqrt{20}} = 2.348$$

Hence

$$t = \frac{\bar{x} - \mu}{SE} = \frac{85 - 80}{2.348} = 2.130$$

**Conclusion**

| Significance Level | Critical Value | | Sample t Value | Conclusion re Null Hypothesis |
|---|---|---|---|---|
| 5% | 2.093 | < | 2.130 | Reject |
| 2% | 2.539 | > | 2.130 | Accept |
| 1% | 2.861 | > | 2.130 | Accept |

The sample evidence supports the claim that the average overtime differs from 80 hours at the 5% level. It does not support this at either the 2% or 1% levels where the null hypothesis is accepted.

### 1.5.3 One-tailed test

## Example

How would our analysis alter if the firm asserts that the true level is *not more* than 80 and we wished to determine whether this is true or whether the number of overtime hours in the above question was significantly *more* than 80?

## Solution

**Null hypothesis**

$H_0$: $\mu \leq 80$

**Alternative hypothesis**

$H_1$: $\mu > 80$ $\Rightarrow$ *a One-Tailed Test*

**Significance or error level**

Significance level = 5%, 2%, 1%

*Rejection area*

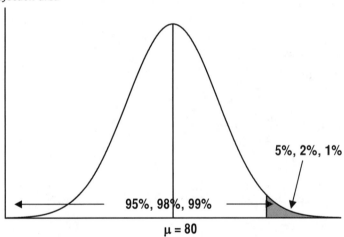

**5%, 2%, 1%**

**95%, 98%, 99%**

$\mu = 80$

**Critical values**

Again, with a sample size of 20 we have 19 degrees of freedom, ie. $v = 19$, giving

$t_{0.050}$ = 1.729

$t_{0.020}$ = 2.205 (**NB**. The 2% level is not in the tables)

$t_{0.010}$ = 2.539

## Sample t value

As we calculated before

$$SE = \frac{s}{\sqrt{n}} = \frac{10.5}{\sqrt{20}} = 2.348$$

Hence

$$t = \frac{\bar{x} - \mu}{SE} = \frac{85 - 80}{2.348} = 2.130$$

## Conclusion

| Significance Level | Critical Value | | Sample t Value | Conclusion re Null Hypothesis |
|---|---|---|---|---|
| 5% | 1.729 | < | 2.130 | Reject |
| 2% | 2.205 | > | 2.130 | Accept |
| 1% | 2.539 | > | 2.130 | Accept |

The sample evidence supports the claim that the average overtime exceeds 80 hours at the 5% level. It does not support this at either the 2% or 1% levels where the null hypothesis is accepted.

## Exercise 1

A sample of 61 'smaller companies' showed an average total return of 5.5% for the month of January, with a sample standard deviation of returns of 3%. Calculate the t-statistic to test the hypothesis that the true average smaller companies' return for January was 5%. At what significance level is the null hypothesis rejected for a one-tailed test and a two-tailed test?

## Exercise 2

From a sample of 30 developing countries, the average annual inflation rate for the 2000s was 27%, with a sample standard deviation of 18.67%. Test the hypothesis that the true mean is not significantly different from 20%.

## Exercise 3

We have a sample of 25 investment funds' compounded returns over the last five years. The average compounded return is 42%, and the sample standard deviation of returns is 6%. Test the hypothesis that the true average investment fund return is 44% and determine the significance level at which this hypothesis is accepted.

## 1.6 Proportions

### 1.6.1 Introduction

With large sample proportions we will need to utilise the normal distribution again.

### 1.6.2 Two-tailed test

### Example

A firm claims that its product has a 40% market share. 500 consumers are surveyed to determine the validity of that claim and the proportion of those buying the product in the sample was 35%.

Test the firm's assertion that the market share does not differ significantly from 40% at the

- 95% confidence/5% significance level.
- 98% confidence/2% significance level.
- 99% confidence/1% significance level.

### Solution - all significance levels

**Null hypothesis**

$H_0$: $\pi = 40\%$

**Alternative hypothesis**

$H_1$: $\pi \neq 40\% \Rightarrow$ *a two-tailed test*

**Significance or error level**

Significance levels = 5%, 2%, 1%

*Rejection area*

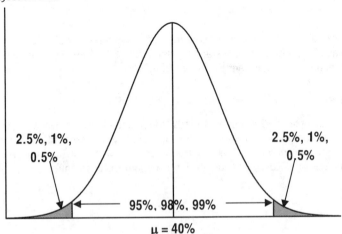

2.5%, 1%, 0.5%        2.5%, 1%, 0,5%

95%, 98%, 99%

$\mu = 40\%$

BPP
LEARNING MEDIA

**Critical values**

$$Z_{0.025} = 1.960$$

$$Z_{0.010} = 2.325$$

$$Z_{0.005} = 2.575$$

**Sample Z value**

Now

$$SE = \sqrt{\frac{\pi(100 - \pi)}{n}}$$

Note we use $\pi$, the assumed population proportion in place of p here, since, if the null hypothesis is correct, this will be the most accurate measure, hence:

$$SE = \sqrt{\frac{\pi(100 - \pi)}{n}} = \sqrt{\frac{40(100 - 40)}{500}} = 2.191$$

Hence

$$Z = \frac{\bar{x} - \mu}{SE} = \frac{35 - 40}{2.191} = -2.282$$

**Conclusion**

| Significance Level | Critical Value | | Sample Z Value | Conclusion re Null Hypothesis |
|:---:|:---:|:---:|:---:|:---:|
| 5% | 1.960 | < | 2.282 | Reject |
| 2% | 2.325 | > | 2.282 | Accept |
| 1% | 2.575 | > | 2.282 | Accept |

**NB.** We ignore the sign and just consider the absolute value of the Z value.

The sample evidence does not support the claim that the market share is 40% at the 5% level. It does support this assertion at both the 2% and 1% levels where the null hypothesis is accepted.

## 1.6.3 One-tailed test

### Example

How would our analysis alter if the firm asserts that the true market share is *at least* 40% and we wished to determine whether this is true or whether the market share in the above question was significantly *less* than 40%?

## Solution

### Null hypothesis

$$H_0: \mu \geq 40\%$$

### Alternative hypothesis

$$H_1: \mu < 40 \Rightarrow \textit{a one-tailed test}$$

### Significance or error level

Significance level = 5%, 2%, 1%

*Rejection area*

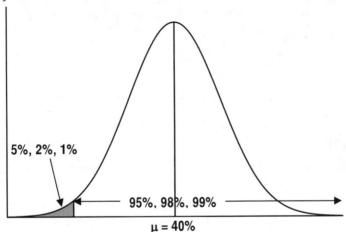

### Critical values

This gives

$Z_{0.050} = 1.645$

$Z_{0.020} = 2.055$

$Z_{0.010} = 2.325$

### Sample Z value

As we calculated before

$$SE = \sqrt{\frac{\pi(100 - \pi)}{n}} = \sqrt{\frac{40(100 - 40)}{500}} = 2.191$$

Hence

$$Z = \frac{\bar{x} - \mu}{SE} = \frac{35 - 40}{2.191} = -2.282$$

## Conclusion

| Significance Level | Critical Value | | Sample Z Value | Conclusion re Null Hypothesis |
|---|---|---|---|---|
| 5% | 1.645 | < | 2.282 | Reject |
| 2% | 2.055 | < | 2.282 | Reject |
| 1% | 2.325 | > | 2.282 | Accept |

**NB.** Again we ignore the sign and just consider the absolute value of the Z value.

The sample evidence does not support the claim that the market share is at least 40% at the 5% and 2% levels. It does support this claim at the 1% level where the null hypothesis is accepted.

# 1.7 Differences

## 1.7.1 Introduction

We will illustrate the approach to significance testing of differences with large samples and hence will need to utilise the normal distribution function again.

## 1.7.2 Two-tailed test

## Example

Two fund managers are being compared, both of which manage large and extremely diversified portfolios. A sample of 100 securities is drawn from one and 144 drawn from the other and the following data calculated regarding their returns.

| | Manager 1 | Manager 2 |
|---|---|---|
| Mean | 22.5 | 21.0 |
| Standard deviation | 6.0 | 5.0 |
| Sample size | 100 | 144 |

Test the assertion that their performance does not differ significantly at the

- 95% confidence/5% significance level.
- 98% confidence/2% significance level.
- 99% confidence/1% significance level.

## Solution - all significance levels

### Null hypothesis

$$H_0: \mu_1 = \mu_2 \quad \Rightarrow \quad \mu_{Dif} = \mu_1 - \mu_2 = 0$$

### Alternative hypothesis

$$H_1: \mu_1 \neq \mu_2 \quad \Rightarrow \quad \mu_{Dif} = \mu_1 - \mu_2 \neq 0 \quad \Rightarrow \text{ a Two-Tailed Test}$$

### Significance or error level

Significance Levels = 5%, 2%, 1%

*Rejection Area*

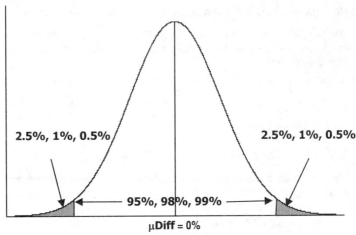

2.5%, 1%, 0.5%            2.5%, 1%, 0.5%

95%, 98%, 99%

$\mu$Diff = 0%

### Critical values

$Z_{0.025} = 1.960$
$Z_{0.010} = 2.325$
$Z_{0.005} = 2.575$

### Sample Z value

Now

$$SE = \sqrt{\frac{s_1^2}{n_1} + \frac{s_2^2}{n_2}} = \sqrt{\frac{6^2}{100} + \frac{5^2}{144}} = 0.7305$$

and

Confidence interval     $\mu_1 - \mu_2 = \bar{x}_1 - \bar{x}_2 \pm Z \times SE$

or

Confidence interval     $\mu_{Diff} = \bar{x}_{Diff} \pm Z \times SE$

Now according to the null hypothesis

$\mu_{Diff} = 0$

Hence

$$Z = \frac{\bar{x}_{Diff} - \mu_{Diff}}{SE} = \frac{(22.5 - 21.0) - 0}{0.7305} = 2.053$$

## Conclusion

| Significance Level | Critical Value | | Sample Z Value | Conclusion re Null Hypothesis |
|---|---|---|---|---|
| 5% | 1.960 | < | 2.053 | Reject |
| 2% | 2.325 | > | 2.053 | Accept |
| 1% | 2.575 | > | 2.053 | Accept |

The sample evidence does not support the claim that there is no significant performance difference at the 5% level, i.e. we would conclude that there *is* a difference. It does support the claim that there is no significant performance difference at both the 2% and 1% levels where the null hypothesis is accepted.

### 1.7.3 One-tailed test

### Example

How would our analysis alter if we wished to test the assertion that manager 2's performance was superior to manager 1's?

### Solution

**Null hypothesis**

$$H_0: \mu_1 < \mu_2 \quad \Rightarrow \quad \mu_{Diff} = \mu_1 - \mu_2 < 0$$

**Alternative hypothesis**

$$H_1: \mu_1 \geq \mu_2 \quad \Rightarrow \quad \mu_{Diff} = \mu_1 - \mu_2 \geq 0 \quad \Rightarrow \text{ a one-tailed test}$$

**Significance or error level**

Significance level = 5%, 2%, 1%

*Rejection Area*

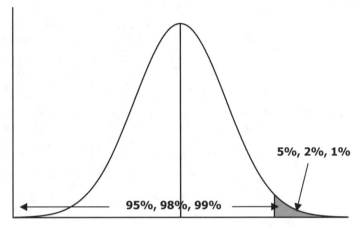

**Critical values**

$\mu_{Diff} = 0$

$Z_{0.050} = 1.645$
$Z_{0.020} = 2.055$
$Z_{0.010} = 2.325$

**Sample Z value**

As we calculated before

$$SE = \sqrt{\frac{S_1^2}{n_1} + \frac{S_2^2}{n_2}} = \sqrt{\frac{6^2}{100} + \frac{5^2}{144}} = 0.7305$$

and

Confidence interval $\mu_{Dif} = \bar{X}_{Dif} \pm Z \times SE$

Now according to the null hypothesis, the upper limit for the mean is

$\mu_{Diff} = 0$

Hence

$$Z = \frac{\bar{X}_{Diff} - \mu_{Diff}}{SE} = \frac{(22.5 - 21.0) - 0}{0.7305} = 2.053$$

**Conclusion**

| Significance Level | Critical Value | | Sample Z Value | Conclusion re Null Hypothesis |
|---|---|---|---|---|
| 5% | 1.645 | < | 2.053 | Reject |
| 2% | 2.055 | > | 2.053 | Accept |
| 1% | 2.325 | > | 2.053 | Accept |

The sample evidence does not support the claim that the performance is superior at the 5% level. It does support this claim at both the 2% and 1% levels where the null hypothesis is accepted.

### 1.7.4 Conclusion

You will undoubtedly have noticed the consistency of the approach throughout, that is

- We calculate the critical values based on the confidence intervals for the appropriate type of test.
- We calculate the Z or t value for the observed sample mean and compare it to this critical value.

As we noted at the outset, the ideas hinge on an appreciation of sampling theory and in particular the idea of confidence intervals for various types of samples.

## 2 ERRORS

### 2.1 Introduction

Since we have not tested the full population we can never be 100% certain that the conclusion we have drawn is correct. There is always the possibility that we will draw the wrong conclusion as a result of selecting an unusual sample.

There are two circumstances under which an error could arise which could be represented as follows.

|  | *Accept Null Hypothesis* | *Reject Null Hypothesis* |
|---|---|---|
| Null hypothesis is correct | Correct Decision Made | Type I Error |
| Null hypothesis is incorrect | Type II Error | Correct Decision Made |

## 2.2 Type I error

### 2.2.1 Introduction

As we noted above a type I error occurs when we reject the null hypothesis even though that hypothesis is correct. This will arise when the sample mean lies in the rejection area above the critical value. This can be illustrated as follows.

**Type I Error**

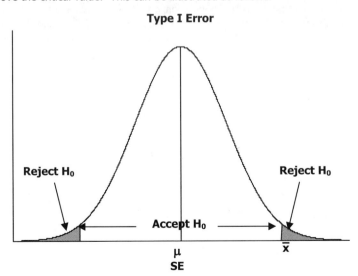

The effect of making a type I error could be that unnecessary remedial work is undertaken since we believe that something is wrong but it is not.

### 2.2.2 Probability of suffering a type I error

The probability of suffering a type I error will be the probability of observing a sample mean in the rejection area. This is clearly a direct function of our confidence or significance level. A 95% confidence level, which corresponds to a 5% significance level, has a rejection area of 5%. Hence there is a 5% chance of suffering a type I error.

In conclusion we could state the probability of suffering a type I error is equal to the significance level.

Note we have illustrated this type I error in the context of a two-tailed test; type I errors can still occur in a one-tailed test, the difference being that the rejection area resides completely at one side.

## 2.3 Type II error

### 2.3.1 Introduction

A type II error occurs when we accept the null hypothesis when it is incorrect.

If the null hypothesis is incorrect then the true population distribution differs in some way from what we are proposing in the null hypothesis, in particular, the mean must differ.

The consequence of suffering a type II error is that we may continue to consider that something is acceptable when it is not, e.g. we may continue to use inaccurate scales.

### 2.3.2 Probability of suffering a type II error

To evaluate the probability of suffering a type II error we need to have details of a possible alternative to the population distribution. What we do then is calculate the probability that a sample mean from this population falls within the confidence interval in which we will be accepting the original null hypothesis. This could be represented diagrammatically as follows.

**Type II Error**

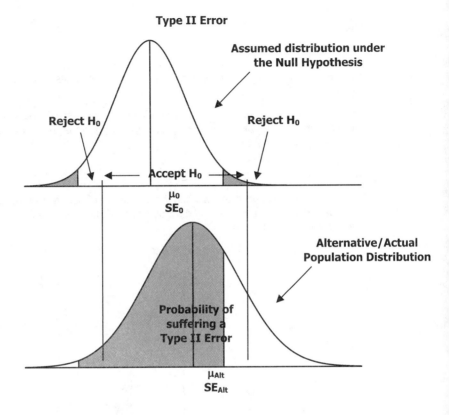

To calculate the probability of suffering a type II error we therefore need to

- Ascertain the confidence limits giving the range over which we will be accepting the null hypothesis from our original distribution.

- Calculate the probability of lying between the same two points based on the second alternative/actual distribution.

## Example

In our first hypothesis test where we were trying to determine whether overtime levels were significantly different from 80 hours, we found that the critical value at a 2% significance level was $Z_{0.01} = 2.325$ and the null hypothesis was accepted at this level. The standard error was 2.324, based on our sample whose mean and standard deviation were 85 and 18, respectively. Using this gives 98% confidence limits of

Confidence Limits $= \mu \pm Z \times SE$

$$= 80 \pm 2.325 \times 2.324$$

$$= 80 \pm 5.403$$

Therefore

$$74.597 \leq \mu \leq 85.403$$

Since the sample mean fell within these confidence limits, we accepted the null hypothesis.

What if we are now told that the overtime levels average at 83 hours with a standard deviation of 20? What is the probability of having suffered a type II error when conducting our original test?

## Solution

To determine this we need to ascertain the probability of observing a sample mean from this alternative distribution between 74.597 and 85.403 (reminder - sample size 60). This can be done as follows.

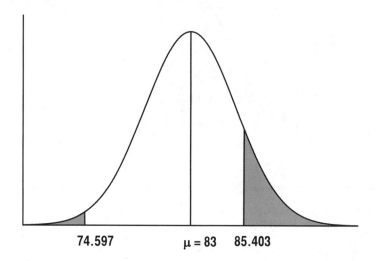

74.597          $\mu = 83$    85.403

We are interested in the unshaded region which can be found as

$$P(74.597 \text{ to } 85.403) = 1 - P(\leq 74.597) - P(\geq 85.403)$$

We will be using the usual relationships, except that since we now know the population standard deviation we will be calculating the standard error as

$$SE = \frac{\sigma}{\sqrt{n}} = \frac{20}{\sqrt{60}} = 2.582$$

$P(\leq 74.597)$

$$Z = \frac{\bar{x} - \mu}{SE} = \frac{74.597 - 83}{2.582} = -3.25$$

giving from tables

$P(\leq 74.597) = 0.00058$

*P(≥ 85.403)*

$$Z = \frac{x - \mu}{SE} = \frac{85.403 - 83}{2.582} = 0.93$$

giving from tables

$P(\geq 85.403) = 0.17619$

*P(74.597 to 85.403)*

$$\begin{aligned} P(74.597 \text{ to } 85.403) &= 1 - P(\leq 74.597) - P(\geq 85.403) \\ &= 1 - 0.00058 - 0.17619 \\ &= 0.82323 \end{aligned}$$

## Conclusion

The probability if suffering a type II error is 0.82323 or 82.323%.

## 2.4 Relationship between type I and type II errors

What we can see from the above in relation to type I and type II errors is that a lower significance level results in

- A smaller rejection area, resulting in a smaller probability of suffering a type I error.

- A larger confidence interval for accepting the null hypothesis, resulting in a larger probability of suffering type II errors.

We can see therefore that there is an inverse relationship between the probability of incurring a type I error and probability of incurring a type II error. As we adjust the sample size to reduce, say, the probability of incurring a type I error, a natural consequence of this is that we will increase the probability of incurring a type II error.

When conducting sample tests it is never possible to eliminate the potential for error completely. What we can see is that there are two possible ways in which we could be making an error and any efforts to minimise one of these types will only result in the maximisation of the other.

# 3 SUMMARY

## 3.1 Tails

- Two-tailed test = where we are trying to determine whether a population differs from what we believe (i.e. is either greater or smaller)

- One tailed test = where we are trying to determine one of
    - whether a population mean is greater than an assumed value
    - whether a population mean is less than an assumed value

## 3.2 Approach

- Determine the critical values for rejecting the hypothesis in terms of Z or t values (ie Z or t value used to determine the confidence intervals at the associated confidence/significance level)

- Calculate the Z or t value based on the sample observations using

$$Z = \frac{x - \mu}{SE}$$

$$t = \frac{\bar{x} - \mu}{SE}$$

Where

$$SE = \frac{s}{\sqrt{n}}$$

## 3.3 Type I error and type II error

- Type I error = where we incorrectly reject a valid Null hypothesis. Probability of Type I error = significance level

- Type II error = where we incorrectly do not reject an invalid Null hypothesis. Probability of a type II error can only be determined if we know the true population distribution.

# 4 SOLUTIONS TO EXERCISES

1.  $SE = \dfrac{s}{\sqrt{n}} = \dfrac{3}{\sqrt{61}} = 0.38411$

    $t = \dfrac{\bar{x} - \mu}{SE} = \dfrac{5.5 - 5.0}{0.38411} = 1.3017$

    and hence with 60 (n − 1) degrees of freedom

| Significance Level One-Tailed | Two-Tailed | Critical Values (v = 60) | | Sample t Value | Conclusion re. Null Hypothesis |
|---|---|---|---|---|---|
| 10% | 20% | 1.296 | < | 1.3017 | Reject |
| 5% | 10% | 1.670 | > | 1.3017 | Accept |
| 2.5% | 5% | 2.000 | > | 1.3017 | Accept |

Hence

- For a one-tailed test the null hypothesis is rejected at 10% and above.

- For a two-tailed test the null hypothesis is rejected at 20% and above.

2.  $H_0$: true mean = 20%

    $H_1$: true mean ≠ 20%  ⇒  two tailed test

    $SE = \dfrac{s}{\sqrt{n}} = \dfrac{18.67}{\sqrt{30}} = 3.4087$

    $t\dfrac{\bar{x} - \mu}{SE} = \dfrac{27 - 20}{3.4087} = 2.054$

    and hence with 29 (n − 1) degrees of freedom.

| Two-Tailed Sig. Level | Critical Values (v = 29) | | Sample t Value | Conclusion re. Null Hypothesis |
|---|---|---|---|---|
| 20% | 1.311 | < | 2.054 | Reject |
| 10% | 1.699 | < | 2.054 | Reject |
| 5% | 2.045 | < | 2.054 | Reject |
| 2% | 2.462 | > | 2.054 | Accept |
| 1% | 2.756 | > | 2.054 | Accept |

Therefore the null hypothesis is rejected at significance levels of 5% or above.

3. $H_0$: true mean = 44%

$H_1$: true mean $\neq$ 44% $\Rightarrow$ two-tailed test

$$SE = \frac{s}{\sqrt{n}} = \frac{6}{\sqrt{25}} = 1.20$$

$$t\frac{\bar{x} - \mu}{SE} = \frac{42 - 44}{1.20} = 1.667$$

and hence with 24 (n – 1) degrees of freedom.

| Two-Tailed Sig. Level | Critical Values (v = 24) | | Sample t Value | Conclusion re Null Hypothes. |
|---|---|---|---|---|
| 20% | 1.318 | < | 1.667 | Reject |
| 10% | 1.711 | < | 1.667 | Accept |
| 5% | 2.064 | < | 1.667 | Accept |
| 2% | 2.492 | > | 1.667 | Accept |
| 1% | 2.797 | > | 1.667 | Accept |

Therefore the null hypothesis is accepted at significance levels of 10% or below.

# 9

# Regression and correlation

## Contents

# 1 PURPOSE

## 1.1 Introduction

In many business situations we are trying to establish whether a relationship exists between factors, and what exactly that relationship is. For example, if we consider the profits that a company may generate, a company's profit is clearly a function of its sales revenues and its costs. The higher the sales the higher the profits, the higher the cost the lower the profits.

Many other relationships also exist in business, investment and economics. For example in investments it is generally believed that a higher risk will result in a higher return from a security. Alternatively we may believe that the required return on an investment is influenced by several factors.

Where such relationships exist, it would be very useful to be able to quantify them. If we were able to do this, we would be placed in a much better position to make rational decisions.

Thinking to our business example above, we know that higher sales will result in higher profits. A question we may wish to ask is would it be worthwhile hiring a new salesman in order to generate those extra sales and hence extra profits? The answer would have to be that if the extra profits generated would more than cover the salesman's salary then would be worthwhile. The question is how much extra profit could be earned from the sales that the new salesman could generate? This is just one example but it illustrates the point that being able to establish how factors are related could be of vital importance.

Regression and correlation analysis provide the means of achieving this aim. If, for example, we plotted the profits achieved each month against the sales that have been generated we may find the following.

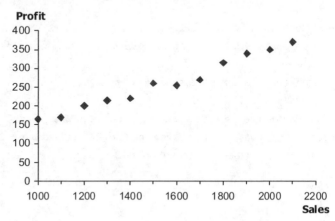

The data on which this is based are

| | Jan £'000 | Feb £'000 | Mar £'000 | Apr £'000 | May £'000 | Jun £'000 | Jul £'000 | Aug £'000 | Sep £'000 | Oct £'000 | Nov £'000 | Dec £'000 |
|---|---|---|---|---|---|---|---|---|---|---|---|---|
| Sales | 1,000 | 1,300 | 1,700 | 2,000 | 2,100 | 1,800 | 1,900 | 1,600 | 1,500 | 1,400 | 1,200 | 1,100 |
| Profit | 165 | 215 | 270 | 350 | 370 | 315 | 340 | 255 | 260 | 220 | 200 | 170 |

There clearly appears to be some kind of relationship here along the lines that we would expect, i.e. higher sales result in higher profits. What we want to be able to do is establish the relationship between profits and sales such that if we could project a sales figure we could establish the associated profit.

One way we could try to achieve this would be to take a ruler, place it over this graph and try to visibly draw the line that achieves the best fit to the points noted. In the example above this may well produce a reasonable result since all the plotted points appear to fall in a fairly straight line. This technique would certainly give a rough and ready indicator but could not be considered precise.

Regression and correlation calculations add a degree of precision to this idea. In outline, these two calculations establish the following.

- **Regression** - the mathematical equation of the line of best fit, giving a much more accurate result than the visibly drawn line.

- **Correlation** - an indication of the accuracy or strength of the relationship, i.e. whether this line is a good or poor fit.

## 1.2 Uses

### 1.2.1 Introduction

The uses of regression and correlation analysis are to aid the quantification of relationships and provide an indication of their validity/accuracy.

We have already given an indication of how this relationship could be used if it could be ascertained through regression analysis. How valid or useful the result is, however, may well depend on exactly how we intend to use it. That is do we wish to use it for

- **Interpolation**, where we try to estimate values within ranges already experienced (e.g. the profits that will arise from sales within the already observed range).

- **Extrapolation**, where we try to predict values beyond those previously experienced (e.g. the profits that will arise beyond (either above or below) the observed range of sales).

### 1.2.2 Interpolation

Using the result of our regression analysis for the purposes of interpolation, e.g. estimating profit levels arising from sales within the noted range, should provide reasonable results since there will be some fairly close data to support the conclusions we arrive at.

## 1.2.3 Extrapolation

Using the results of regression analysis to extrapolate beyond the end of the noted data ranges, i.e. to estimate profits arising from sales levels above £2.2m or below £1.0m could be dangerous since we do not have the data to support the results we will be estimating. It is quite possible that a relationship that appears linear over a short range of values turns out to be non-linear when we move beyond those values making any extrapolated results worthless or even dangerous.

We can, however, use the data to establish an expected value, and use the variability of the data to try to establish confidence limits within which we can be sure, with a given degree of confidence, that the observed value will lie.

# 1.3 Limitations

## 1.3.1 Introduction

We have commented above on one major limitation, that is the dangers involved in extrapolating results. Regression and correlation analysis does, however, have some other limitations which we discuss below.

## 1.3.2 Linear relationships

Regression and correlation analysis can be used with reference to linear relationships only. The calculations are designed to produce the equation of the straight line that best fits the noted points and an indication of the accuracy of that fit.

Though many of the relationships we may wish to establish may be linear, there will be many which are not.

There are, however, ways of overcoming this limitation *if the general form of the relationship is known or can be established* as we discussed below. This may in practice be a very big if!

### 1.3.3 Spurious relationships

In our analysis we are trying to establish the relationship between two variables. It is quite possible, however, that two variables appear to be related but are not, in truth, directly related at all. Consider for example the following graph.

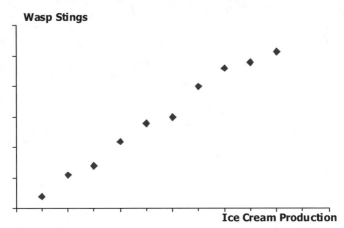

**Wasp Stings**

**Ice Cream Production**

Do ice cream production levels really determine the number of wasp stings that are suffered in the summer, or vice-versa? It seems unlikely that it does, and, if it did, ice cream production would certainly have been banned.

What we are observing here is a spurious relationship. A more likely reason is that both the frequency of wasp stings and the level of ice cream production are related to a common factor, say the number of sunny days. The greater the number of sunny days, the greater time people will spend outdoors. The more time spent outside on a sunny day is likely to result in two things.

- More ice cream being eaten per person, hence higher ice cream production.

- Greater periods of exposure to any hazards of nature, in particular wasp stings, resulting in greater levels of wasp stings being suffered.

We must be very careful in our regression analysis in determining that a relationship actually exists between the two sets of variables. We noted above that the purpose of regression analysis is to establish the equation for *the relationship*.

## 2    REGRESSION ANALYSIS

### 2.1 Linear relationships

#### 2.1.1 Introduction

If we plot a straight line on a graph where y is the vertical axis and x is the horizontal axis, then the equation of a straight line would take the form

$$y = a + bx$$

where

a = Intercept, i.e. the height at which the line cuts the y axis.

b = Slope, i.e. the change in the value of y per unit change in the value of x.

Graphically this would appear as follows.

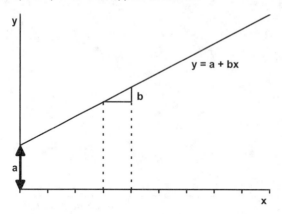

### 2.1.2 The variables and the relationship

If we plot our variables on such a graph, regression analysis gives us the value of the factors a and b which determine the relationship. To do this, however, we must first determine which variable should be plotted along the x axis and which along the y axis which depends on the form of the relationship.

If a relationship exists between two variables, then the value of one will drive/determine the value of the other, i.e. we have cause and effect.

### Independent variable - x axis

The variable whose value does the driving, the cause, is known as the *independent variable* (x). This variable should always be plotted along the x axis and represents the variable whose value we will be wishing to feed into the relationship to find its effect.

### Dependent variable - y axis

The *dependent variable* (y) is a variable whose value is driven by the independent variable (x), i.e. the effect. The value of the dependent variable (y) is, as its name suggests, dependent upon the value of the independent variable (x).

It is the value of the dependent variable (y) that we will be wishing to interpolate or extrapolate from given expectations regarding the independent variable (x).

### 2.1.3 Regression coefficients

The output from regression analysis is the two regression coefficients a and b which determine the relationship between the two variables. These two coefficients can be determined by one of two means.

- Simultaneous equation approach - solving simultaneously what are referred to as the 'normal equations' for the least-squares line, which are (see appendix for derivation):

$$\Sigma y = na + b\Sigma x$$

$$\Sigma xy = a\Sigma x + b\Sigma x^2$$

- Formulae approach – applying the following formulae:

$$b = \frac{n\Sigma xy - \Sigma x \Sigma y}{n\Sigma x^2 - (\Sigma x)^2}$$

$$a = \bar{y} - b\bar{x}$$

giving the equation of the relationship as

$$y = a + bx$$

Although it is not obvious what these equations are doing, they are calculating the line which results in the minimum sum of squared deviation of the observed points from that line, i.e. calculating the line for which the points show a minimum divergence. This could be illustrated graphically as follows.

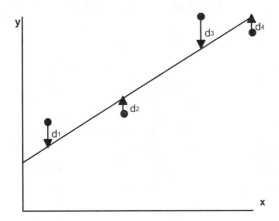

i.e. what these formulae are providing are the values of a and b for which

$$\sum_{1}^{n} d_i^2 = d_1^2 + d_2^2 + d_3^2 + \cdots + d_n^2$$

is minimised and hence the line provides the closest possible fit to all the points. Note, items lying above the line would have a positive value for d, those below a negative value. $d^2$ is used to remove the positive or negative sign and just consider the value of the deviations.

## 2.1.4 Error term

A regression equation is often expressed in the following form.

$y = a + bx + e$

In this, e is an error or disturbance term. If the regression line represents the best linear unbiased estimate of the relationship between x and y, the error term will have a random variable with a mean of zero. It reflects the fact that we cannot guarantee that the value of y will actually be as predicted by the regression equation. On a random basis, the actual values will lie both above and below the predicted values.

## Example

We will use, for this example, the data regarding the relationship between sales and profits noted in our introduction above.

## Solution

### Dependent and independent variables

In this scenario the profit is clearly dependent upon the sales generated. The company, through the activities of its sales force, can directly influence the level of sales but they cannot directly influence the level of profits - the profit is a consequence of the sales. We will therefore take sales as the independent variable (x) and profits as the dependent variable (y).

### Calculating the coefficients

| $x$ | $x_2$ | $y$ | $xy$ |
|---|---|---|---|
| 1,000 | 1,000,000 | 160 | 160,000 |
| 1,300 | 1,690,000 | 215 | 279,500 |
| 1,700 | 2,890,000 | 270 | 459,000 |
| 2,000 | 4,000,000 | 350 | 700,000 |
| 2,100 | 4,410,000 | 370 | 777,000 |
| 1,800 | 3,240,000 | 315 | 567,000 |
| 1,900 | 3,610,000 | 340 | 646,000 |
| 1,600 | 2,560,000 | 255 | 408,000 |
| 1,500 | 2,250,000 | 260 | 390,000 |
| 1,400 | 1,960,000 | 220 | 308,000 |
| 1,200 | 1,440,000 | 200 | 240,000 |
| 1,700 | 2,890,000 | 170 | 289,000 |
| 19,200 | 31,940,000 | 3,125 | 5,223,500 |

### Simultaneous equation approach

The first normal equation gives:

$\Sigma y = na + b\Sigma x$

$3,125 = 12a + 19,200b$

or

$12a = 3,125 - 19,200b$

$a = 260.41666 - 1,600b$

The second normal equation gives:

$$\sum xy = a\sum x + b\sum x^2$$

$$5{,}223{,}500 = 19{,}200a + 31{,}940{,}000b$$

or

$$19{,}200a = 5{,}223{,}500 - 31{,}940{,}000b$$

$$a = 272.05729 - 1{,}663.54167b$$

Solving simultaneously gives:

$$260.41666 - 1{,}600b = 272.05729 - 1{,}663.54167b$$

$$11.64063 = 63.54167b$$

$$b = 0.18320$$

Substituting this is the first normal equation gives:

$$a = 260.41666 - 1{,}600 \times 0.18320 = -32.7034$$

Undertaking the same calculation applying the formulae gives

**Formulae approach**

$$b \quad = \frac{n\sum xy - \sum x\sum y}{n\sum x^2 - \left(\sum x\right)^2}$$

$$= \frac{12 \times 5{,}223{,}500 - 19{,}200 \times 3{,}125}{12 \times 31{,}940{,}000 - \left(19{,}200\right)^2}$$

$$= \frac{2{,}682{,}000}{14{,}640{,}000} = 0.81320$$

$$a \quad = \bar{y} - b\bar{x}$$

$$= \frac{3{,}125}{12} - 0.18320 \times \frac{19{,}200}{12}$$

$$= 260.417 - 293.115$$

$$= -32.70$$

**Giving the same result**

**Regression line**

Irrespective of the approach used to calculate the regression coefficients, we have derived the equation of the relationship as

$$y = -32.70 + 0.18320x$$

i.e.

$$\text{Profit} = -32.70 + 0.18320 \times \text{Sales}$$

In this context we can interpret this result as

- The company has fixed costs of £32,700 - the level of profit (loss) when the sale are zero.

- The company generates a profit margin of 18.320% (0.18320) as every extra £ of sales generates an extra £0.18320 of profits.

## 2.2 Non-linear relationships

### 2.2.1 Introduction

Many business and economic relationships do follow the linear trend illustrated in th example above. Many others, however, demonstrate a much more complicate relationship. If, for example, we wish to plot a graph of terminal value against time for investment undergoing compound growth, then a plot of this graph would sho accelerating (exponential) growth.

As a second example, if we plotted the value of a bond against interest rates, then c graph would demonstrate a non-linear decay in value as an increase in interest rat results in a fall in bond prices.

The above regression analysis is suitable for establishing the details of any *lin* relationships but cannot be immediately applied to these non-linear ones.

Since there are many such non-linear relationships that we may be interested in, this i severe limitation of our regression analysis and we need to find some way of overcom it.

### Approach

The method for dealing with such non-linear relationships is to rescale one or both or axes. We illustrate this below for a number of common growth and decay functions wh fall into one of three broad categories.

- Exponential growth or decay.
- Polynomial growth or decay.
- Logarithmic growth or decay.

If we are to apply these ideas, then there are two things which we need to know.

- Under what circumstances would each of the approaches be applicable?
- How do we actually apply the idea?

We will first discuss the circumstances and then go on to illustrate the application wit example.

### 2.2.2 Exponential growth/decay

Linear growth or decay means that a one unit change in the value of x will cause same absolute change in the value of y regardless of what value y currently takes.

Exponential growth or decay occurs where a unit change in the value of x causes a constant proportion or percentage change in the value of y. As a result, the absolute change in the value of y will differ as y differs and a graph plotting y against x will show a curve. This is illustrated in the left hand diagrams below for both exponential growth and exponential decay.

If, however, we plot the logarithm of y (log y) against x these relationships become linear as you can see in the right hand diagrams below. Where y changes by a constant proportionate amount, log y changes by a constant absolute value and hence the graph produces a straight line.

This, indeed, is the general idea we should always keep in our minds for rescaling graphs. Where variables change by constant absolute values we simply plot those values (x and y). If either or both of the variables change in constant proportion then we should plot the log of that variable along the appropriate axis to produce a linear relationship.

## Exponential growth

An example of a relationship that would demonstrate exponential growth is the value of an investment which generates compound interest against time.

If the investment generated simple interest then the relationship would be linear since the same amount of interest would be generated each year (the interest being based on the capital value only). Where an investment generates compound interest, the value grows exponentially as the interest each year increases (being based on the initial capital plus all previous accumulated interest).

Obviously if we were trying to work out the value of such an investment we would not need to use the ideas of regression analysis since the relationship is fairly firmly established by discounted cash flow ideas. However, the relationship may be appropriate for other types of investment opportunity, the return from which are much less certain but may be assumed to follow the same general pattern.

$y = e^x$

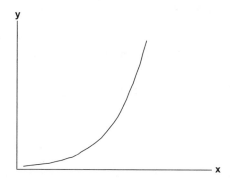
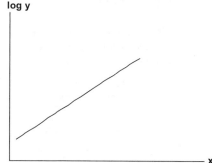

## Exponential decay

An example of a relationship that would demonstrate an exponentially decaying function would be the market value of a zero coupon bond plotted against time. The longer the time to maturity the lower the market value (present value). This can be seen from examining the equation we have used as a heading for the graphs. If we replaced e in that equation by 1 + r and replaced x by n, then y would be giving us the present value of £1 due to be received in n years' time, i.e. the market value of that £1.

$$y = \frac{1}{e^x}$$

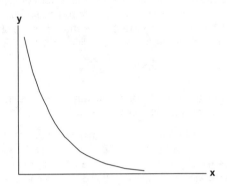
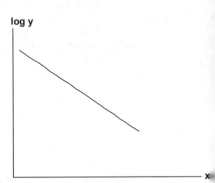

## 2.2.3 Polynomial growth/decay

A polynomial is a relationship of the form

$$y = a + b_1x + b_2x^2 + b_3x^3 + \dots + b_nx^n$$

i.e. where y is a function of powers of x.

Polynomial growth occurs when we are raising x to positive powers, polynomial decay occurs where we are raising x to negative powers (i.e. $x^{-n} = \frac{1}{x^n}$).

These sort of relationships are frequently seen in the context of present value and terminal value calculations where y is either the present or terminal value and x is the interest rate (or 1 + r).

To deal with this sort of relationship we need to plot log y against log x. This will result in a straight line relationship as illustrated below.

## Accelerating polynomial growth

This is the relationship that would exist between the terminal value of an investment and the rate of return expected to maturity. For example, if we need to estimate the terminal value of a pension fund which could be subject to different possible rates of return over the future years to maturity then the relationship would demonstrate this general form.

In an economic context total cost curves and marginal cost curves (supply curves) may also follow this form of relationship.

$y = x^n$

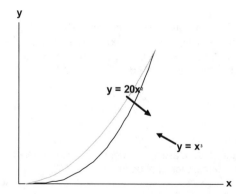

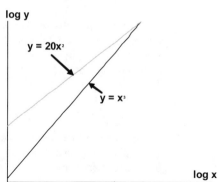

## Decelerating polynomial growth

Accelerating polynomial growth occurs when x is raised to a power greater than 1. Decelerating polynomial growth where x is raised to some power between 0 and 1,

i.e. $x^{1/n} = \sqrt[n]{x}$ .

Mathematically the yield curve for UK gilts should show a relationship of this form were it not for additional supply and demand feature impacting on its shape.

Once more plotting log y against log x provides a linear relationship as the diagram below shows.

$y = x^{1/2}$

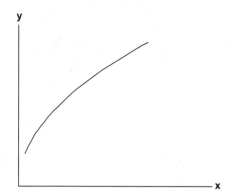

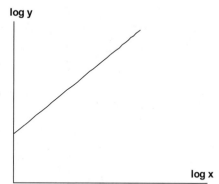

## Polynomial decay

If we were to plot the market value of a bond against interest rates, that graph would demonstrate polynomial decay. For example, if we replaced x in the equation heading up the graphs below by 1 + r then we would be calculating the present value of £1 as a function of interest rates. The relationship we would now have would be

$$y = \frac{1}{(1+r)^n}$$

Another function that is likely to demonstrate this sort of relationship is the price elasticity of demand. When we calculate the price elasticity of demand we are working out the percentage change in price over the percentage change in quantity, i.e.

$$\text{Elasticity} = \frac{\text{Percentage change in price}}{\text{Percentage change in quantity}}$$

If we were to plot price against quantity for a product it is likely to demonstrate this sort of relationship (i.e. a falling demand curve). If we then solve for the regression coefficients having plotted log y against log x we would find that regression coefficient corresponds to the elasticity of demand.

Thinking about what we mentioned earlier in relation to proportionate or percentage changes, this idea follows immediately. In establishing elasticity we are needing compare proportionate changes in one variable (price) against proportionate changes the other variable (quantity). We noted above that where proportionate changes need be related, these can be reduced to a linear form by plotting the log of those variables. As a result, plotting log price against log quantity (log y against log x) will provide a linear relationship.

$y = x^{-n}$

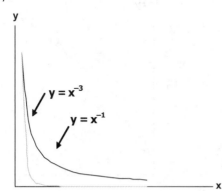
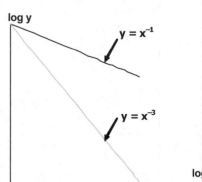

## 2.2.4 Logarithmic growth/decay

Logarithmic growth or decay corresponds to circumstances where an absolute value change in y results from a proportionate change in the value of x.

In an economic context it is quite probable that a graph of consumption against income follows this form.

In this relationship if we plot y against log x we will get a straight line to which we can apply our regression analysis ideas. If we were to do this in relation to our consumption against income idea above, then the regression coefficient b would correspond to the marginal propensity to consume, the slope of this line representing the extra pounds spent on consumption per extra pound of income.

### Logarithmic growth

$y = \log_{10} x$

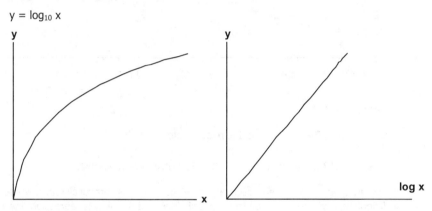

## 2.2.5 Judging the relationship

If we have some data and we are trying to establish the relationship that exists then we first need to establish its general form, i.e. is it linear or non-linear and if it is non-linear is it exponential or polynomial or logarithmic? How can this be achieved?

Perhaps the best approach to the first of these problems (determining whether the relationship is linear or non-linear) is to plot a scatter graph of the observed points and visually determine whether or not the relationship is linear.

If the relationship turns out to be non-linear it is not possible, simply by viewing the graph, to determine which of the above three categories it falls into (exponential, polynomial, logarithmic) as the graph below shows.

Of the two lines on the graph below, one is an exponential relationship and the other is a polynomial but which is which? You will see that they are remarkably similar over this range of values of x.

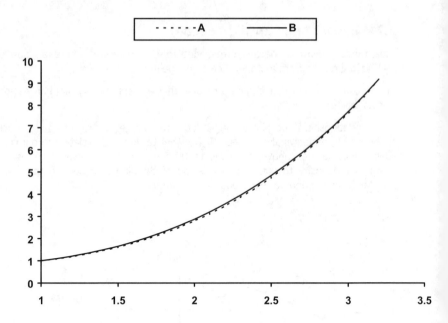

For your information

A plots y = 0.3679e$^x$ an exponential relationship

B plots y = 1.18175[0.2(x + 0.1)$^3$ + 0.58] a polynomial relationship

Hence judging a non-linear relationship visually is not practically achievable. Give
sufficient time we could try all three possibilities and see which regression line gives t
best fit (as indicated by the correlation coefficient discussed below).

As an alternative if we have prior knowledge as to the general form of the relationship
can clearly establish which scaling to use.

## 2.2.6 Illustration

In applying this idea of rescaling one or both of the axes, we will have to be very care
as to the values that we feed into the linear regression relationship (or the correlati
calculation - see below), and about how we interpret the results that we get from t
relationship.

## Example

To illustrate the idea we will plot the relationship Y = X$^3$, a polynomial relationship.
appropriate scaling to use will, therefore, be log Y against log X.

## Solution

The approach is to use the scaled figures in the regression calculations. What we will do is let

$y = \log Y$

$x = \log X$

and perform our regression analysis as usual since a graph of y against x will be linear (being log Y against log X).

Doing this gives

| X | $Y = X^3$ | $x = log_{10}X$ | $x^2$ | $y = log_{10}Y$ | xy |
|----|----------|-----------------|----------|-----------------|----------|
| 1 | 1 | 0.00000 | 0.00000 | 0.00000 | 0.00000 |
| 2 | 8 | 0.30103 | 0.09062 | 0.90309 | 0.27186 |
| 3 | 27 | 0.47712 | 0.22764 | 1.43136 | 0.68293 |
| 4 | 64 | 0.60206 | 0.36248 | 1.80618 | 1.08743 |
| 5 | 125 | 0.69897 | 0.48856 | 2.09691 | 1.46568 |
| 6 | 216 | 0.77815 | 0.60552 | 2.33445 | 1.81656 |
| 7 | 343 | 0.84510 | 0.71419 | 2.53529 | 2.14257 |
| 8 | 512 | 0.90309 | 0.81557 | 2.70927 | 2.44671 |
| 9 | 729 | 0.95424 | 0.91058 | 2.86273 | 2.73174 |
| 10 | 1,000 | 1.00000 | 1.00000 | 3.00000 | 3.00000 |
| | | 6.55976 | 5.21516 | 19.67929 | 15.64548 |

### Simultaneous equation approach

The first normal equation gives:

$\Sigma y = na + b\Sigma x$

$19.67929 = 10a + 6.55976b$

$a = 1.967929 - 0.655976b$

The second normal equation gives:

$\Sigma xy = a\Sigma x + b\Sigma x^2$

$15.64548 = 6.55976a + 5.21516b$

$a = 2.385069 - 0.795023b$

Solving simultaneously gives:

$1.967929 - 0.655976b = 2.385069 - 0.795023b$

$0.139047b = 0.417140$

$b = 3.0000$

Substituting this into the first normal equation gives:

$a = 1.967929 - 0.655976 \times 3 = 0$

Undertaking the same calculation applying the formulae gives

$$b \quad = \frac{n\sum xy - \sum x \sum y}{n\sum x^2 - (\sum x)^2}$$

$$= \frac{10 \times 15.64548 - 6.55976 \times 19.67929}{10 \times 5.21516 - (6.55976)^2}$$

$$= \frac{27.36331}{9.12110} = 3.0000$$

$$a \quad = \bar{y} - b\bar{x}$$

$$= \frac{19.67929}{10} - 3 \times \frac{6.55976}{10}$$

$$= 1.96793 - 1.96793$$

$$= 0$$

## Regression line

Once again, irrespective of the approach used to calculate the regression coefficients, w
have derived the equation of the relationship as

$$y = 0 + 3x$$

or

$$\log_{10}Y = 0 + 3\log_{10}X$$

which can be proved by trying some values as follows.

| X | $log_{10}X$ | $log_{10}Y$ $(= 0 + 3 \log_{10}X)$ | Y $(= antilog\ (log_{10}Y))$ | $X^3$ |
|---|---|---|---|---|
| 2 | 0.30103 | 0.90309 | 8 | 8 |
| 15 | 1.17609 | 3.52827 | 3,375 | 3,375 |
| 456 | 2.65896 | 7.97689 | 94,818,816 | 94,818,816 |

The figures in the fourth column have been calculated as the anti-log of the figures in
third column and can be seen to be equal to the figures in the fifth column, which is
value we know we should have for Y. The conclusion we can draw is that our regress
equation does give us a valid measurement of the relationship.

## Conclusion

Whichever axes have been rescaled, we must remember to convert the relevant val
into log values for both the calculation of the regression coefficients using the norr
relationships and in using the resultant regression line.

## Exercise 1

To test the hypothesis that economic growth (**Y**) is related to broad money growth (**M**), an analyst collects data for 2008 for eight countries.

| Country | Australia | Belgium | Canada | France | Germany | Holland | Italy | Japan |
|---|---|---|---|---|---|---|---|---|
| Y | 2.4 | 1.6 | 1.3 | 0.8 | −0.2 | 0.9 | 0.8 | 0.9 |
| M | 8.7 | 7.0 | 7.1 | 5.7 | 8.1 | 6.3 | 5.4 | −0.3 |

What are the coefficients **a** and **b** in the regression

$$Y = a + bM?$$

## Exercise 2

The productivity growth in a developing economy, g, is related linearly to a time trend, **T**, and constant, **a**

$$g = a + bT$$

The growth in productivity (% p.a.) over the last eight years is given as below.

| 2008 | 2007 | 2006 | 2005 | 2004 | 2003 | 2002 | 2001 |
|---|---|---|---|---|---|---|---|
| −16 | −22 | 10 | 15 | 6 | 5 | 6 | −8 |

Calculate the regression coefficients **a** and **b** if the linear time trend takes the value 1 in 2008, 2 in 2007, etc. and note the regression line.

# 2.3 Multiple regression

## 2.3.1 Introduction

So far we have only considered examples where the value of the dependent variable (y) is based upon the value of just one independent variable (x). It is quite possible, however, that the value of the dependent variable is a function of two or more independent variables. For example, the market of a zero coupon bond is a function of time to maturity and interest rates. In an economic context it is possible that inflation may be a function of wage rate increases and monetary growth. We will not debate this point here (i.e. the causes of inflation) but it goes to illustrate that there could be many relationships that are a function of two or more variables.

To make the matter worse it is quite possible that when we are gathering the data, we are uncertain as to which variables are relevant and which are not. To try to establish a relationship may, therefore, involve a trial and error exercise incorporating various different variables and trying to determine which provides the best regression line by consideration of the correlation coefficient (see below).

Where more and more variables are involved the form of the regression relationship will be

$$y = a + b_1x_1 + b_2x_2 + b_3x_3 + \cdots + b_nx_n$$

Here we have n variables and n corresponding b coefficients. The general approach to determining the coefficients is exactly the same as it was above when we only had one variable. That is, we try to minimise the sum of the square of the deviation of the regression space away from the observed values by the use of partial differentiation and simultaneous equations. The number of equations to be solved by simultaneous means is equal to the number of regression coefficients rendering manual solution difficult where there are many variables.

## 2.3.2 Regression coefficients

The output from regression analysis is the regression coefficients a, $b_1$, $b_2$, $b_3$, $\cdots$ ,$b_n$ which determine the relationship between the variables. These coefficients can be determined by solving simultaneously what are referred to as the 'normal equations for the least squares area or space' (the formulae approach becomes impractical at this stage), which for two input variables, are (see appendix for derivation):

$$\Sigma y \quad = na + b_1\Sigma x_1 + b_2\Sigma x_2$$

$$\Sigma x_1 y \; = a\Sigma x_1 + b_1\Sigma x_1^2 + b_2\Sigma x_1 x_2 \; = \; a\Sigma x_1 + b_1\Sigma x_1 x_1 + b_2\Sigma x_1 x_2$$

$$\Sigma x_2 y \; = a\Sigma x_2 + b_1\Sigma x_1 x_2 + b_2\Sigma x_2^2 \; = \; a\Sigma x_2 + b_1\Sigma x_2 x_1 + b_2\Sigma x_2 x_2$$

And more generally for n input variables are (see appendix for derivation):

$$\Sigma y \quad = na + b_1\Sigma x_1 + b_2\Sigma x_2 + b_3\Sigma x_3 + \cdots + b_2\Sigma x_2$$

$$\Sigma x_1 y \; = a\Sigma x_1 + b_1\Sigma x_1 x_1 + b_2\Sigma x_1 x_2 + b_3\Sigma x_1 x_3 + \cdots + b_n\Sigma x_1 x_n$$

$$\Sigma x_2 y \; = a\Sigma x_2 + b_1\Sigma x_2 x_1 + b_2\Sigma x_2 x_2 + b_3\Sigma x_2 x_3 + \cdots + b_n\Sigma x_2 x_n$$

$$\Sigma x_3 y \; = a\Sigma x_3 + b_1\Sigma x_3 x_1 + b_2\Sigma x_3 x_2 + b_3\Sigma x_3 x_3 + \cdots + b_n\Sigma x_3 x_n$$

$$\vdots \qquad \qquad \vdots \qquad \qquad \vdots \qquad \qquad \vdots$$

$$\vdots \qquad \qquad \vdots \qquad \qquad \vdots \qquad \qquad \vdots$$

$$\Sigma x_n y \; = a\Sigma x_n + b_1\Sigma x_n x_1 + b_2\Sigma x_n x_2 + b_3\Sigma x_n x_3 + \cdots + b_n\Sigma x_n x_n$$

## Example

The return from a security (y) is considered to be of the form:

$$y = a + b_1x_1 + b_2x_2$$

i.e. dependent on two variables, $x_1$ and $x_2$. Quarterly statistics for the last two years have been as follows.

| Return % | $x_1$ | $x_2$ |
|---|---|---|
| 11.3 | 3 | 2 |
| 9.8 | 2 | 1 |
| 12.9 | 4 | 3 |
| 9.7 | 2 | 1 |
| 11.6 | 3 | 2 |
| 10.0 | 2 | 2 |
| 14.5 | 5 | 3 |
| 12.6 | 4 | 2 |

Establish the relationship quantifying the return

## Solution

| y | $x_1$ | $x_2$ | $x_1y$ | $x_2y$ | $x_1^2$ | $x_2^2$ | $x_1x_2$ |
|---|---|---|---|---|---|---|---|
| 11.3 | 3 | 2 | 33.9 | 22.6 | 9 | 4 | 6 |
| 9.8 | 2 | 1 | 19.6 | 9.8 | 4 | 1 | 2 |
| 12.9 | 4 | 3 | 51.6 | 38.7 | 16 | 9 | 12 |
| 9.7 | 2 | 1 | 19.4 | 9.7 | 4 | 1 | 2 |
| 11.6 | 3 | 2 | 34.8 | 23.2 | 9 | 4 | 6 |
| 10.0 | 2 | 2 | 20.0 | 20.0 | 4 | 4 | 4 |
| 14.5 | 5 | 3 | 72.5 | 43.5 | 25 | 9 | 15 |
| 12.6 | 4 | 2 | 50.4 | 25.2 | 16 | 4 | 8 |
| 92.4 | 25 | 16 | 302.2 | 192.7 | 87 | 36 | 55 |
| $\Sigma y$ | $\Sigma x_1$ | $\Sigma x_2$ | $\Sigma x_1y$ | $\Sigma x_2y$ | $\Sigma x_1^2$ | $\Sigma x_2^2$ | $\Sigma x_1x_2$ |

The first normal equation gives:

$$\Sigma y = na + b_1\Sigma x_1 + b_2\Sigma x_2$$

$$92.4 = 8a + 25b_1 + 16b_2$$

$$a = 11.55 - 3.125b_1 - 2b_2$$

The second normal equation gives:

$$\Sigma x_1y = a\Sigma x_1 + b_1\Sigma x_1^2 + b_2\Sigma x_1x_2$$

$$302.2 = 25a + 87b_1 + 55b_2$$

The third normal equation gives:

$$\Sigma x_2 y = a\Sigma x_2 + b_1\Sigma x_1 x_2 + b_2\Sigma x_2{}^2$$

$$192.7 = 16a + 55b_1 + 36b_2$$

Substituting the first into the second gives:

$$302.2 = 25(11.55 - 3.125b_1 - 2b_2) + 87b_1 + 55b_2$$

$$302.2 = 288.75 - 78.125b_1 - 50b_2 + 87b_1 + 55b_2$$

$$13.45 = 8.875b_1 + 5b_2$$

$$b_2 = 2.69 - 1.775b_1$$

Substituting this and the first into the third gives:

$$192.7 = 16(11.55 - 3.125b_1 - 2b_2) + 55b_1 + 36(2.75 - 1.775b_1)$$

$$192.7 = 16[11.55 - 3.125b_1 - 2(2.69 - 1.775b_1)] + 55b_1 + 36(2.69 - 1.775b_1)$$

$$192.7 = 184.8 - 50b_1 - 86.08 + 56.8b_1 + 55b_1 + 96.84 - 63.9b_1$$

$$2.1b_1 = 2.86$$

$$b_1 = 1.3619048$$

Substituting $b_1$ back into:

$$b_2 = 2.69 - 1.775b_1$$

gives:

$$b_2 = 2.69 - 1.775 \times 1.3619048$$

$$b_2 = 0.2726190$$

And substituting $b_1$ and $b_2$ back into:

$$a = 11.55 - 3.125b_1 - 2b_2$$

gives:

$$a = 11.55 - 3.125 \times 1.3619048 - 2 \times 0.2726190$$

$$a = 11.55 - 4.2559525 - 0.545238$$

$$a = 6.7488095$$

Hence, the relationship we have to determine the return (y) is:

$$y = 6.7488095 + 1.3619048x_1 + 0.2726190x_2$$

and we may now look to use this to determine expected returns given the two inputs.

### 2.3.3 Continuous and dummy variables

Most variables in regression analysis are continuous in that they can assume an infinite number of values. Sometimes dummy variables may be used in regression analysis which take a value of 0 or 1. These provide a means of distinguishing between two or more mutually exclusive groups (e.g. men and women) or two or more time periods (e.g. seasons of the year) with different features in the regression analysis.

## 2.4 Assumptions underlying regression analysis

### 2.4.1 Introduction

The objective of regression analysis is to give an estimate of y from given input variable values. For this to be the case, a number of assumptions that have been relied upon in the mathematical derivation of the formulae for the coefficients must hold good. If these assumptions do not hold, then the estimate of y will be biased and hence less reliable.

### 2.4.2 A Linear relationship exists

The first assumption is that the relationship between x and y is linear or can be expressed in a linear form. If this is not the case, then there is no point in constructing a relationship based on a straight line and using this to predict values of y.

### 2.4.3 Observed variations (i.e. error terms) are random

The second assumption in deriving the coefficients is that any observed deviations of the actual figures from the regression line (any error terms) are completely random, i.e. they

- *Are independent of the values of **x** and **y*** – i.e. the error terms are uncorrelated with each other or with the values of the x or y variable.

- *Are normally distributed* – i.e. the scattering of the actual values of y around the regression line is normally (randomly) distributed.

- *Have a mean of zero* – i.e. the scattering of the actual value of y is unbiased in either direction from that predicted by the regression line.

- *Have a constant standard deviation for all values of **x** and **y*** – i.e. the spread of actual y values around the predicted y value is the same, regardless of the value of y. This is known as homoskedasticity.

### 2.4.4 Relationship is stable

The final assumption is that the relationship between the various variables has been stable over the observation period. If this is not the case then it will be difficult, if not pointless, to try to establish any relationship. Indeed, the utilisation of regression results for, say, forecasting purposes requires that the relationships will continue to be stable.

## 2.5 Problems inherent in regression analysis

### 2.5.1 Introduction

There are several problems we need to be aware of in the context of regression, which we discuss below. Moving from a relationship which gives the value of one variable as a function of one other variable (linear regression) to a relationship which gives a value of one variable as a function of many other variables (multiple regression) introduces additional problems over and above the complexity of the calculations.

The issues that we need to consider are

- ▪ Multicollinearity.
- • Autocorrelation.
- • Heteroskedasticity.
- • Lack of data.
- • Measurement of data.
- • Time and cost constraints.
- ▪ Under-identification.
- ▪ Specification (partially).

*Key*
- • *Problems of all regression analysis.*
- ▪ *Problems of multiple regression only.*

## 2.5.2 Multicollinearity

In setting up our relationship we have been defining the y value on the left hand side as the dependent variable and the x value along the bottom as the independent variable. We have meant by these definitions that y is dependent on x, although x is independent of y.

When we have several independent variables it is quite possible that, although they may be independent from y, they are in some way related to each other.

Ideally we would like these variables to be completely independent so that the change the value of one has no effect on the others. This would certainly help with the calculations we have to perform.

Frequently, however, two or more of the independent variables may be related in some way. What problems does this introduce to our analysis?

If there is a strong and stable relationship between two or more of the input variables then we may be able to simplify the problem by removing all but one of them.

If, on the other hand, a relationship exists which is not stable and varies considerably then this will compound the problems we have of establishing the regression coefficient. It will be very difficult to determine what factor has caused the observed change in the value of y - is it the change in the value of one input variable, the other or the strength the relationship?

Where such an unstable relationship exists it is quite probable that the relevant regression coefficients will also be unstable, somewhat limiting the usefulness of the result as a regression equation.

## 2.5.3 Autocorrelation

In undertaking regression analysis we are establishing the relationship from which the variance of the observed values is minimised. If we were to measure the value of the error terms (the difference between the observed and the predicted values) then would expect them to be normally and independently distributed with a mean of zero we noted under the assumptions above.

Since we expect this error term to be zero on average we would conclude that our regression line gives the best indicator of any potential value of y from a given value of x. We could go further than this and calculate confidence intervals within which we believe that value of y will lie if we calculate the standard deviation of the distribution of these error terms.

A common problem when dealing with time series is that these error terms may not be independently distributed, rather there may be some correlation between adjacent error terms such as seasonal effects. We may find that every summer the value of y is greater than that predicted by the regression line and every winter the value of y is less. This relationship between the scale of the error in corresponding seasons is known as serial correlation or autocorrelation.

If such seasonal swings (autocorrelation) exist then we should always be predicting summer values above that indicated by the regression line and winter values below but if we are not aware of this autocorrelation we will not be. Under these circumstances regression, simple analysis is not perfectly appropriate unless we try to cater for this seasonality by either:

- Dealing with each season separately and establishing coefficients for each.
- Including a dummy time dependent variable to cater for the seasonal effects.

Clearly an alternative model that builds in this autocorrelation would produce a superior result.

## 2.5.4 Heteroskedasticity

We noted above that we expect the error term to be normally distributed with a mean of zero and a measurable and constant standard of deviation. Given this, we would be able to calculate some confidence intervals for our prediction.

Heteroskedasticity arises when the standard deviation of the error term is not constant but, say, grows as the value of y grows due to changes in the value of x. The result of this is that our predictions will become less and less reliable and hence less useful.

## 2.5.5 Lack of data

In order to establish a reliable relationship we will need to have a reasonable volume of accurately measured data.

Lack of data can arise in one of two situations.

- Where data has only been gathered for a relatively short period, for example, the values of the newly developed financial products or the profits of newly formed companies.

- Unsuitable data, i.e. where data has been gathered over some period of time that is in some way deficient within the context of the analysis, e.g. companies that have been changing recently, either organically or through mergers and acquisitions.

## 2.5.6 Measurement of data

In undertaking regression analysis, it is assumed that the data being relied upon have been correctly measured or evaluated. Many statistics that we may wish to use prove difficult to evaluate precisely, especially economic statistics. Indeed, many government statistics are released, only to be subject to later re-evaluations.

Any inaccuracies in the data used for the analysis will lead to errors in the established coefficients and limit the usefulness of the resulting model.

## 2.5.7 Time and cost constraints

In a business context all work should be undertaken on a cost versus benefit basis, i.e. investigation should be undertaken so long as the perceived benefits that result from an analysis will outweigh the costs incurred in gathering the information and undertaking the analysis.

If we are trying to use economic predictions to determine production and distribution decisions then the time we will have to undertake the work and the costs we are prepared to pay will both be limited, and hence the validity of our conclusions may also be restricted.

## 2.5.8 Under-identification

It is quite possible in a multiple regression situation that we may not be able to determine unique regression coefficients from the data we have available. It may be that the best we can do is say that a particular regression coefficient takes on one of two values but we are uncertain which.

If this is the case, then we have under-identified our regression coefficients (i.e. we have not exactly determined them all). We therefore have two or more regression equations only one of which may actually be correct. Being unable to identify the correct equation will result in us being unable to make any predictions with any confidence.

## 2.5.9 Specification

Specification refers to the problem of determining two things.

- The relevant independent variables.
- The form (linear/non-linear) of the relationship.

We may be reasonably certain about some of the variables and how they relate to the dependent variable but unsure about others. If we construct a model that does not include a relevant variable or assumes a linear relationship where it is in fact non-linear then any predicted results from our model will be inaccurate.

Conversely, if we build a model which includes variables that are not relevant, then any error terms are liable to be higher than they would otherwise be, again reducing the accuracy of the model. In addition, multicollinearity may be introduced if the irrelevant variable is not completely independent of other input variables.

# 3 CORRELATION

## 3.1 Introduction

The purpose of the correlation measure is to measure the strength or accuracy of the relationship between two variables. In the context of regression analysis with only one independent variable, the correlation coefficient will give an indication of how accurately the regression line matches the observed values.

## 3.2 Correlation coefficient and coefficient of determination

### 3.2.1 Idea

The correlation coefficient is a relative measure indicating how two variables move with respect to each other.

A correlation coefficient will have any value between +1 and −1 and the meaning of the correlation coefficient can best be understood by considering the extremes.

### Perfect positive correlation – (correlation coefficient = +1)

If two variables are perfectly positively correlated then they move up and down together and in proportion.

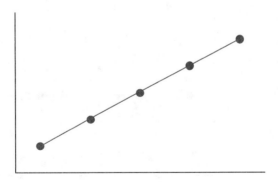

Here it can be seen that the line is upward sloping and all the actual values of y are exactly the same as the predicted values given the regression line.

### Perfect negative correlation – (correlation coefficient = –1)

If two variables are perfectly negatively correlated then they move up and down in exact opposition and in proportion.

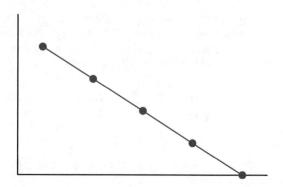

Once again, all the actual values of y are as predicted by the regression line, meaning that the relationship is perfect. However, the slope is downward, indicating a negative relationship.

### Uncorrelated – (correlation coefficient = 0)

If two variables are uncorrelated then they move independently of each other, i.e. if one goes up, the other may go up or down or not move at all.

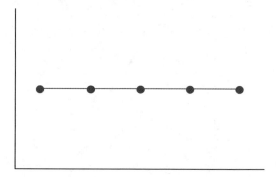

In this case, it can be seen that the value of y is independent from the value of x - it does not change regardless of the value of x. An alternative presentation of zero correlation would be to have points randomly scattered across the whole of the diagram.

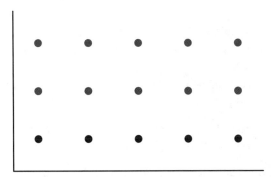

## Imperfect correlation

In between perfect correlation and no correlation, there are relationships between variables of varying strength.

Here it can be seen that there is a positive relationship between the two variables - as the value of x increases, so does the value of y. However, the relationship is not exact and so this is not perfect correlation. The correlation coefficient here may be +0.8, for example.

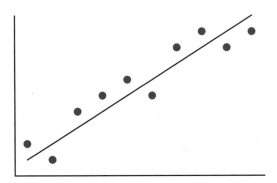

Generally, a correlation coefficient of 0.5 would be viewed as moderate correlation. Values of less than this would be viewed as weak correlation while values above this would be viewed as strong correlation.

## Conclusion

There are two relevant factors in a correlation coefficient, the sign ( + or −) and the value. Their effects are

- Positive correlation implies that variables move up and down together, negative correlation means that they move in opposition.

- The value of the figure, ignoring the sign, gives an indication of the strength of the relationship, the closer to a value of 1 the stronger the relationship.

### 3.2.2 Calculating the correlation coefficient

## Coefficient of determination - $r^2$

The coefficient of determination shows what proportion of the total variation in the value of y can be explained by its association with x as established with the regression line. The total variation is defined here as $\Sigma(y - \bar{y})^2$ i.e. the sum of squared deviation. We could therefore write this as

$$r^2 = \frac{\text{Explained variation of y}}{\text{Total variation of y}} = \frac{\Sigma(y_e - \bar{y})^2}{\Sigma(y - \bar{y})^2}$$

where $y_e$ = predicted value of y from the regression equation.

## Correlation coefficient - r

The correlation coefficient is simply the square root of the coefficient of determination (or the coefficient of determination is the square of the correlation coefficient). Both measures have their uses, as do variances and standard deviations which are equally related.

Based on this definition of the coefficient of determination, the formula for the correlation coefficient can be shown to be (see appendix for derivation).

$$r = \frac{n\Sigma xy - \Sigma x\Sigma y}{\sqrt{[n\Sigma x^2 - (\Sigma x)^2][n\Sigma y^2 - (\Sigma y)^2]}}$$

Although this looks a little complicated, the various terms that need to be inserted can be established using the tabular calculation we used for establishing the regression coefficients and adding one more column.

## Example

Calculate the correlation coefficient for the regression line established in our earlier example involving the determination of a profit figure from a sales figure.

## Solution

**NB.** The first four columns of this table were calculated above, we have only needed add the fifth.

| x (Sales) | $x^2$ | y (Profit) | xy | $y^2$ |
|---|---|---|---|---|
| 1,000 | 1,000,000 | 160 | 160,000 | 25,600 |
| 1,300 | 1,690,000 | 215 | 279,500 | 46,225 |
| 1,700 | 2,890,000 | 270 | 459,000 | 72,900 |
| 2,000 | 4,000,000 | 350 | 700,000 | 122,500 |
| 2,100 | 4,410,000 | 370 | 777,000 | 136,900 |
| 1,800 | 3,240,000 | 315 | 567,000 | 99,225 |
| 1,900 | 3,610,000 | 340 | 646,000 | 115,600 |
| 1,600 | 2,560,000 | 255 | 408,000 | 65,025 |
| 1,500 | 2,250,000 | 260 | 390,000 | 67,600 |
| 1,400 | 1,960,000 | 220 | 308,000 | 48,400 |
| 1,200 | 1,440,000 | 200 | 240,000 | 40,000 |
| 1,700 | 2,890,000 | 170 | 289,000 | 28,900 |
| 19,200 | 31,940,000 | 3,125 | 5,223,500 | 868,875 |

Hence

$$r = \frac{n\Sigma xy - \Sigma x \Sigma y}{\sqrt{[n\Sigma x^2 - (\Sigma x)^2][n\Sigma y^2 - (\Sigma y)^2]}}$$

$$= \frac{12 \times 5,223,500 - 19,200 \times 3,125}{\sqrt{[12 \times 31,940,000 - (19,200)^2][12 \times 868,875 - (3,125)^2]}}$$

$$= \frac{2,682,000}{\sqrt{[14,640,000][660,875]}}$$

$$= \frac{2,682,000}{3,110,500} = 0.86224$$

This answer is probably along the lines that we would have expected. It is positive, which indicates that profits increase as sales increase, and it is relatively close to one, indicating a reasonably strong relationship between the two.

## Exercise 3

An analyst's forecast of earnings per share for a large conglomerate over the last five years, together with the actual outcomes, is given below. What is the correlation coefficient between the forecast and actual values?

| Year | 1 | 2 | 3 | 4 | 5 |
|---|---|---|---|---|---|
| Forecast | 8.0 | 8.4 | 7.5 | 7.8 | 8.7 |
| Actual outcome | 7.2 | 8.5 | 7.3 | 7.9 | 7.5 |

## Exercise 4

Average annual inflation and broad money supply growth rates for the 2000 for seven countries are given below. What is the correlation coefficient between inflation and money supply growth for this sample?

| Country | A | B | C | D | E | F | G |
|---|---|---|---|---|---|---|---|
| Average inflation | 9 | 7 | 8 | 11 | 12 | 16 | 4 |
| Average money growth | 11 | 6 | 8 | 14 | 15 | 25 | 5 |

## 3.3 Rank correlation

### 3.3.1 Introduction

The correlation coefficient as defined above can be used in circumstances where both variables take numeric values (**cardinal data**) as in our example, the two variables being profit and sales.

The idea of rank correlation may be applied where no numerical measure exists, although items may be ordered or ranked in some way (**ordinal data**). For example, if we can get people to select the best or most favoured item from a list along with the worst/least favoured we may be able to determine the consensus view as regards the rankings.

### 3.3.2 Calculating the rank correlation

Rank correlation can be calculated using the formula

$$r = 1 - \frac{6\Sigma d^2}{n(n^2 - 1)}$$

where

d = Difference between the rankings.
n = Number of rankings.

This formula may be derived from the correlation coefficient formula above (see appendix).

## Example

Eight companies are ranked by two different analysts in order of growth prospects next year as follows.

| A | B | C | D | E | F | G | H |
|---|---|---|---|---|---|---|---|
| 1 | 4 | 5 | 2 | 8 | 3 | 7 | 6 |
| 2 | 4 | 6 | 1 | 7 | 5 | 8 | 3 |

Determine the correlation between the two rankings.

## Solution

| Company | Analyst 1 | Analyst 2 | d | $d_2$ |
|---------|-----------|-----------|-----|-----|
| A | 1 | 2 | −1 | 1 |
| B | 4 | 4 | 0 | 0 |
| C | 5 | 6 | −1 | 1 |
| D | 2 | 1 | 1 | 1 |
| E | 8 | 7 | 1 | 1 |
| F | 3 | 5 | −2 | 4 |
| G | 7 | 8 | −1 | 1 |
| H | 6 | 3 | 3 | 9 |
| | | | | $\overline{\underline{18}}$ |

$$r = 1 - \frac{6\Sigma d^2}{n(n^2 - 1)}$$

$$= 1 - \frac{6 \times 18}{8(8^2 - 1)}$$

$$= 1 - \frac{108}{8 \times 63}$$

$$= 1 - \frac{108}{504}$$

$$= 1 - 0.214 = 0.786$$

This indicates a reasonably strong correlation between the two rankings.

Since the rank correlation formula is derived from the correlation coefficient, the values it may take and the meaning of those values are identical.

## 3.3.3 Application to cardinal data

Rank correlation would not normally be applied to situations where we already have numerical data as some of the information contained in those cardinal data would be lost if the data were ranked to use the above relationship. The following example illustrates how it may be applied to cardinal data, although as we have just said, this would be unusual.

Where one or both of the variables are judgemental rather than numerical, however, then the rank correlation is the only measure that can actually be calculated and will require the ranking of both sets of data.

## Example

Calculate the rank correlation for our sales/profit example above.

## Solution

| x (Sales) | y (Profit) | Sales Ranking | Profit Ranking | d | $d_2$ |
|---|---|---|---|---|---|
| 1,000 | 160 | 12 | 12 | 0 | 0 |
| 1,300 | 215 | 10 | 9 | 1 | 1 |
| 1,700 | 270 | 5.5 | 5 | 0.5 | 0.25 |
| 2,000 | 350 | 2 | 2 | 0 | 0 |
| 2,100 | 370 | 1 | 1 | 0 | 0 |
| 1,800 | 315 | 4 | 4 | 0 | 0 |
| 1,900 | 340 | 3 | 3 | 0 | 0 |
| 1,600 | 255 | 7 | 7 | 0 | 0 |
| 1,500 | 260 | 8 | 6 | 2 | 4 |
| 1,400 | 220 | 9 | 8 | 1 | 1 |
| 1,200 | 200 | 11 | 10 | 1 | 1 |
| 1,700 | 170 | 5.5 | 11 | −5.5 | 30.25 |
| | | | | | 37.50 |

$$r = 1 - \frac{6\Sigma d^2}{n(n^2 - 1)}$$

$$= 1 - \frac{6 \times 37.5}{12(12^2 - 1)}$$

$$= 1 - \frac{225}{12 \times 143}$$

$$= 1 - \frac{225}{1,716}$$

$$= 1 - 0.131 = 0.869$$

which, as we can see, is a different figure from the correlation coefficient establish above.

## Exercise 5

Two fund managers assess the research material provided by seven brokers as follo (marks out of 100).

| Brokers | I | II | III | IV | V | VI | VII |
|---|---|---|---|---|---|---|---|
| Manager A | 65 | 69 | 40 | 35 | 87 | 80 | 60 |
| Manager B | 68 | 52 | 53 | 40 | 62 | 65 | 69 |

What is the rank correlation between these two assessments?

## Exercise 6

Two groups of credit analysts recently completed eight training courses and were asked to assess the quality of each. The marks awarded by the two groups to each course was as follows.

| Course: | 1 | 2 | 3 | 4 | 5 | 6 | 7 | 8 |
|---------|----|----|----|----|----|----|----|----|
| Group A | 80 | 87 | 49 | 50 | 92 | 68 | 51 | 81 |
| Group B | 62 | 30 | 58 | 59 | 49 | 80 | 63 | 64 |

Calculate the rank correlation coefficient between the two assessments.

# 4 SIGNIFICANCE TESTING OF REGRESSION RESULTS

## 4.1 Introduction

Having established regression coefficients, the correlation coefficient and the equation of the regression line that we wish to use for projections, we will need to consider whether our results can be relied upon – i.e. are the coefficients statistically significant?

This will involve the use of hypothesis testing and, possibly, the student t-distribution, although note that since we are testing the coefficients measuring variations about a line, our degrees of freedom will be $n - 2$.

## Example

We are given the following relationship regarding consumption in the economy arising as a result of a regression analysis exercise undertaken on a sample of 32 (standard errors in parentheses).

$$C = £5,000 + 0.78Y \quad r = 0.87$$

$$(£450) \ (0.04) \ (0.23)$$

Determine whether, at the 5% significance level

- The a coefficient is not less than £6,500.

- The b coefficient is not less than 0.84.

- The positive correlation coefficient is statistically significant.

## Solution - a coefficient

**Null hypothesis**

$H_0$: $a \geq £6,500$

**Alternative hypothesis**

$H_1$: $a < £6,500$ $\quad \Rightarrow$ *a One-Tailed Test*

### Significance or error level

Significance level = 5%

### Critical values

With a sample size of 32 we have 30 degrees of freedom, i.e. $v = 30$, giving $t_{0.050}$ 1.697.

### Sample t value

$$t = \frac{\bar{x} - \mu}{SE} = \frac{5,000 - 6,500}{450} = 3.333$$

### Conclusion

The sample t-statistic exceeds the critical value, therefore we must reject the n hypothesis and conclude that the base level of consumption is below £6,500.

## Solution - b coefficient

### Null hypothesis

$H_0$: $b \geq 0.84$

### Alternative hypothesis

$H_1$: $b < 0.84 \Rightarrow$ *a One-Tailed Test*

### Significance or error level

Significance Level = 5%

### Critical values

With a sample size of 32 we have 30 degrees of freedom, i.e. $v = 30$, giving $t_{0.050}$ 1.697.

### Sample t value

$$t = \frac{\bar{x} - \mu}{SE} = \frac{0.78 - 0.84}{0.04} = 1.500$$

### Conclusion

The sample t-statistic is less than the critical value, therefore we must accept the hypothesis that the true marginal propensity to consume is not less than 0.84.

## Solution - correlation coefficient

To test whether any of the statistics are statistically significant we must compare them zero.

### Null hypothesis

$H_0$: $r = 0$ i.e. that it is not statistically significant.

**Alternative hypothesis**

$H_1$:  $r \neq 0$    $\Rightarrow$ *a Two-Tailed Test*

**Significance or error level**

Significance level  =  5%

**Critical values**

With a sample size of 32 we have 30 degrees of freedom, i.e. $\nu = 30$, giving $t_{0.050} = 2.042$.

**Sample t value**

$$t = \frac{\bar{x} - \mu}{SE} = \frac{0.87 - 0.00}{0.23} = 3.78$$

**Conclusion**

The sample t-statistic exceeds the critical value, therefore we must reject the null hypothesis and conclude that there is a significant positive correlation.

## 4.2 Standard errors

The one remaining question is how do we determine standard errors for correlation and regression coefficients. The formulae here are perhaps the most obscure, however they are

### 4.2.1 Correlation coefficient

$$SE = \frac{\sqrt{1 - r^2}}{\sqrt{n - 2}}$$

### 4.2.2 Regression b coefficient

$$SE = \sqrt{\frac{1 - r^2}{n - 2}} \times \frac{b}{r}$$

### 4.2.3 Regression y values for given x values

$$SE = \sqrt{\frac{1 - r^2}{n(n - 2)}} \times \sqrt{n\sum y^2 - \left(\sum y\right)^2} \times \sqrt{\frac{1}{n} + \frac{n(x - \bar{x})^2}{n\sum x^2 - \left(\sum x\right)^2}}$$

## 4.2.4 Illustrations of use

### Testing the significance of correlation

### Example

In our regression and correlation example earlier in the session, we calculated th correlation coefficient to be 0.86224 based on a sample size of 12. Let us now determin whether this positive correlation is significant by testing it against a null hypothesis tha there is zero or negative correlation, i.e. that r = 0, at the 10%, 5% and 2.5% levels.

### Solution

**Null hypothesis**

$$H_0: \ r \leq 0$$

**Alternative hypothesis**

$$H_1: \ r > 0 \Rightarrow a \ One\text{-}Tailed \ Test$$

**Significance or error level**

Significance level = 10%, 5%, 2.5%

**Critical values**

With a sample size of 12 we have 10 degrees of freedom, i.e. $v = 10$, giving

$$t_{0.100} = 1.372$$

$$t_{0.050} = 1.812$$

$$t_{0.025} = 2.228$$

**Sample t value**

$$SE = \sqrt{\frac{1-r^2}{n-2}} = \sqrt{\frac{1-0.86224^2}{10}} = 0.160169$$

Hence:

$$t = \frac{\bar{x} - \mu}{SE} = \frac{0.862240}{0.160169} = 5.3833$$

**Conclusion**

| Significance Level | Critical Value | | Sample Z Value | Conclusion re Null Hypothesis |
|---|---|---|---|---|
| 10% | 1.372 | < | 5.3833 | Reject |
| 5% | 1.812 | < | 5.3833 | Reject |
| 2.5% | 2.228 | < | 5.3833 | Reject |

The sample evidence indicates that the correlation coefficient is significantly different from zero at all levels, we can therefore conclude that this correlation is significant and the variables are positively correlated.

## Significance of b coefficient

### Example

In our regression example above, we calculated the b coefficient to be 0.18320 based on a sample size of 12. Let us now determine whether this coefficient, i.e. this slope, is significantly less than 0.3 by testing it against this as a null hypothesis, i.e. that b = 0.3, at the 10%, 5% and 2.5% levels.

### Solution

**Null hypothesis**

$$H_0: \ b \geq 0.3$$

**Alternative hypothesis**

$$H_1: \ b < 0.3 \quad \Rightarrow a \ One\text{-}Tailed \ Test$$

**Significance or error level**

Significance Level = 10%, 5%, 2.5%

**Critical values**

With a sample size of 12 we have 10 degrees of freedom, i.e. $v = 10$, giving

$$t_{0.100} = 1.372$$

$$t_{0.050} = 1.812$$

$$t_{0.025} = 2.228$$

**Sample t value**

$$SE = \sqrt{\frac{1-r^2}{n-2}} \times \frac{b}{r}$$

$$= \sqrt{\frac{1-0.86224^2}{10}} \times \frac{b}{r} = 0.160169 \times \frac{0.18320}{0.86224} = 0.034031$$

Hence

$$t = \frac{\bar{x} - \mu}{SE} = \frac{0.18320 - 0.30000}{0.034031} = 3.432$$

### Conclusion

| Significance Level | Critical Value | | Sample Z Value | Conclusion re Null Hypothesis |
|---|---|---|---|---|
| 10% | 1.372 | < | 3.432 | Reject |
| 5% | 1.812 | < | 3.432 | Reject |
| 2.5% | 2.228 | < | 3.432 | Reject |

The sample evidence indicates that the b coefficient *is* significantly different from 0.3 a
any levels.

## Confidence intervals for y values

## Example

What is the 95% confidence interval for values of y when x is 2,300?

## Solution

**Point estimate of value**

Profit = −32.70 + 0. 18320 × 2,300 = 388.66

**Confidence intervals**

With 10 degrees of freedom in a two-tailed test, the t-statistic is 2.228. Now

$$SE = \sqrt{\frac{1-r^2}{n(n-2)}} \times \sqrt{n\Sigma y^2 - (\Sigma y)^2} \times \sqrt{\frac{1}{n} + \frac{n(x-\bar{x})^2}{n\Sigma x^2 - (\Sigma x)^2}}$$

$$= 0.0462369 \times \sqrt{12 \times 868,875 - (3,125)^2} \times \sqrt{\frac{1}{12} + \frac{12(2,300-1,600)^2}{12 \times 31,940,000 - (19,200)^2}}$$

$$= 0.0462369 \times \sqrt{660,875} \times \sqrt{\frac{1}{12} + \frac{12(2,300-1,600)^2}{14,640,000}}$$

$$= 0.0462369 \times 812.942 \times 0.6964$$

$$= 37.5879 \times 0.6964 = 26.1762$$

Hence the 95% confidence interval spans the range

$$\mu = \bar{x} \pm t \times SE$$

$$= 388.66 \pm 2.228 \times 26.1762$$

i.e.

$$330.34 \le \mu \le 446.98$$

# 5 SUMMARY

## 5.1 Purpose

- Regression = Determine the relationship between variables
- Correlation = Determine the strength of that relationship

## 5.2 Linear regression coefficients a and b

### 5.2.1 Simultaneous equation approach

Solve simultaneously for a and b by either

$$\Sigma y = na + b\Sigma x$$

$$\Sigma xy = a\Sigma x + b\Sigma x^2$$

### 5.2.2 Formulae approach

Alternatively apply the formulae

$$b = \frac{n\Sigma xy - \Sigma x \Sigma y}{n\Sigma x^2 - (\Sigma x)^2}$$

and

$$a = \overline{y} - b\overline{x}$$

## 5.3 Multiple regression coefficients

Can only practically be calculated by the simultaneous equation approach where, for two input variables $x_1$, and $x_2$, we have

$$\Sigma y = na + b_1\Sigma x_1 + b_2\Sigma x_2$$

$$\Sigma x_1 y = a\Sigma x_1 + b_1\Sigma x_1^2 + b_2\Sigma x_1 x_2 = a\Sigma x_1 + b_1\Sigma x_1 x_1 + b_2\Sigma x_1 x_2$$

$$\Sigma x_2 y = a\Sigma x_2 + b_1\Sigma x_1 x_2 + b_2\Sigma x_2^2 = a\Sigma x_2 + b_1\Sigma x_2 x_1 + b_2\Sigma x_2 x_2$$

## 5.4 Correlation coefficient and coefficient of determination

Correlation Coefficient (r) given by

$$r = \frac{n\Sigma xy - \Sigma x \Sigma y}{\sqrt{[n\Sigma x^2 - (\Sigma x)^2][n\Sigma y^2 - (\Sigma y)^2]}}$$

Coefficient of determination = $r^2$

## 5.5 Rank correlation coefficient

Rank correlation coefficient determined by

$$r = 1 - \frac{6\Sigma d^2}{n(n^2 - 1)}$$

# 6 SOLUTIONS TO EXERCISES

1.

| Country | x | $x_2$ | y | xy |
|---|---|---|---|---|
| Australia | 8.7 | 75.69 | 2.4 | 20.88 |
| Belgium | 7.0 | 49.00 | 1.6 | 11.20 |
| Canada | 7.1 | 50.41 | 1.3 | 9.23 |
| France | 5.7 | 32.49 | 0.8 | 4.56 |
| Germany | 8.1 | 65.61 | −0.2 | −1.62 |
| Holland | 6.3 | 39.69 | 0.9 | 5.67 |
| Italy | 5.4 | 29.16 | 0.8 | 4.32 |
| Japan | −0.3 | 0.09 | 0.9 | −0.27 |
| | 48.0 | 342.14 | 8.5 | 53.97 |

**Simultaneous equations approach**

The first normal equation gives:

$\Sigma y = na + b\Sigma x$

$8.5 = 8a + 48b$

or

$8a = 8.5 - 48b$

$a = 1.0625 - 6b$

The second normal equation gives:

$\Sigma xy = a\Sigma x + b\Sigma x^2$

$53.97 = 48a + 342.14b$

or

$48a = 53.97 - 342.14b$

$a = 1.124375 - 7.1279116667b$

Solving simultaneously gives:

$1.0625 - 6b = 1.124375 - 7.1279116667b$

$1.127916667b = 0.061875$

$b = 0.05486$

Substituting this into the first normal equation gives:

$a = 1.0625 - 6 \times 0.05486 = 0.7333$

**Formulae approach**

$$b = \frac{n\sum xy - \sum x \sum y}{n\sum x^2 - (\sum x)^2}$$

$$= \frac{8 \times 53.97 - 48 \times 8.5}{8 \times 342.14 - (48)^2}$$

$$= \frac{23.76}{433.12} = 0.05486$$

$$a = \bar{y} - b\bar{x}$$

$$= \frac{8.5}{8} - 0.05486 \times \frac{48}{8}$$

$$= 1.0625 - 0.3292 = 0.7333$$

**Regression line**

$$y = 0.7333 + 0.05486\,M$$

2.

| $x$ | $x_2$ | $y$ | $xy$ |
|---|---|---|---|
| 1 | 1 | −16 | −16 |
| 2 | 4 | −22 | −44 |
| 3 | 9 | 10 | 30 |
| 4 | 16 | 15 | 60 |
| 5 | 25 | 6 | 30 |
| 6 | 36 | 5 | 30 |
| 7 | 49 | 6 | 42 |
| 8 | 64 | −8 | −64 |
| 36 | 204 | −4 | 68 |

**Simultaneous equations approach**

The first normal equation gives:

$\sum y = na + b\sum x$

$-4 = 8a + 36b$

or

$8a = -4 - 36b$

$a = -0.5 - 4.5b$

The second normal equation gives:

$\sum xy = a\sum x + b\sum x^2$

$68 = 36a + 204b$

or

$36a = 68 - 204b$

$a = 1.8888889 - 5.6666667b$

Solving simultaneously gives:

$-0.5 - 4.5b = 1.8888889 - 5.6666667b$

$1.1666667b = 2.3888889$

$b = 2.04762$

Substituting this into the first normal equation gives:

$a = -0.5 - 4.5 \times 2.04762 = -9.7143$

**Formulae approach**

$$b = \frac{n\Sigma xy - \Sigma x \Sigma y}{n\Sigma x^2 - (\Sigma x)^2}$$

$$= \frac{8 \times 86 - 36 \times (-4)}{8 \times 204 - (36)^2}$$

$$= \frac{688}{336} = 2.0476$$

$$a = \bar{y} - b\bar{x}$$

$$= \frac{-4}{8} - 2.0476 \times \frac{36}{8}$$

$$= -0.5 - 9.2143 = -9.7143$$

**Regression line**

$g = -9.7143 + 2.0476\,T$

3.

| $x$ | $x_2$ | $y$ | $xy$ | $y_2$ |
|------|--------|------|--------|--------|
| 8.0 | 64.00 | 7.2 | 57.60 | 51.84 |
| 8.4 | 70.56 | 8.5 | 71.40 | 72.25 |
| 7.5 | 56.25 | 7.3 | 54.75 | 53.29 |
| 7.8 | 60.84 | 7.9 | 61.62 | 62.41 |
| 8.7 | 75.69 | 7.5 | 65.25 | 56.25 |
| 40.4 | 327.34 | 38.4 | 310.62 | 296.04 |

$$r = \frac{n\Sigma xy - \Sigma x \Sigma y}{\sqrt{[n\Sigma x^2 - (\Sigma x)^2][n\Sigma y^2 - (\Sigma y)^2]}}$$

$$= \frac{5 \times 310.62 - 40.4 \times 38.4}{\sqrt{\left[5 \times 327.34 - (40.4)^2\right]\left[5 \times 296.04 - (38.4)^2\right]}}$$

$$= \frac{1.74}{\sqrt{[4.54][5.64]}}$$

$$= \frac{1.74}{5.0602} = 0.34386$$

4.

| $x$ | $x^2$ | $y$ | $xy$ | $y^2$ |
|-----|-------|-----|------|-------|
| 9 | 81 | 11 | 99 | 121 |
| 7 | 49 | 6 | 42 | 36 |
| 8 | 64 | 8 | 64 | 64 |
| 11 | 121 | 14 | 154 | 196 |
| 12 | 144 | 15 | 180 | 225 |
| 16 | 256 | 25 | 400 | 625 |
| 4 | 16 | 5 | 20 | 25 |
| 67 | 731 | 84 | 959 | 1,292 |

$$\mathbf{r} = \frac{n\sum xy - \sum x \sum y}{\sqrt{\left[n\sum x^2 - \left(\sum x\right)\right]\left[n\sum y^2 - \left(\sum y\right)^2\right]}}$$

$$= \frac{7 \times 959 - 67 \times 84}{\sqrt{\left[7 \times 731 - (67)^2\right]\left[7 \times 1,292 - (84)^2\right]}}$$

$$= \frac{1,085}{\sqrt{[628][1,988]}}$$

$$= \frac{1,085}{1,117.347} = 0.971$$

5.

| Broker | A | B | d | $d^2$ |
|--------|---|---|---|-------|
| I | 4 | 2 | 2 | 4 |
| II | 3 | 6 | −3 | 9 |
| III | 6 | 5 | 1 | 1 |
| IV | 7 | 7 | 0 | 0 |
| V | 1 | 4 | −3 | 9 |
| VI | 2 | 3 | −1 | 1 |
| VII | 5 | 1 | 4 | 16 |
| | | | | 40 |

$$r = 1 - \frac{6\sum d^2}{n(n^2 - 1)}$$

$$= 1 - \frac{6 \times 40}{7(7^2 - 1)}$$

$$= 1 - \frac{240}{336}$$

$$= 1 - 0.7143 = 0.2857$$

6.

| Course | Group A | Group B | d | d² |
|--------|---------|---------|-----|-----|
| 1 | 4 | 4 | 0 | 0 |
| 2 | 2 | 8 | −6 | 36 |
| 3 | 8 | 6 | 2 | 4 |
| 4 | 7 | 5 | 2 | 4 |
| 5 | 1 | 7 | −6 | 36 |
| 6 | 5 | 1 | 4 | 16 |
| 7 | 6 | 3 | 3 | 9 |
| 8 | 3 | 2 | 1 | 1 |
| | | | | 106 |

$$r = 1 - \frac{6\sum d^2}{n(n^2 - 1)}$$

$$= 1 - \frac{6 \times 106}{8(8^2 - 1)}$$

$$= 1 - \frac{636}{504}$$

$$= 1 - 1.2619 = -0.2619$$

# APPENDIX 1 - DERIVATION OF REGRESSION AND CORRELATION COEFFICIENTS

## Linear regression coefficients

### Setting up the problem

The regression coefficients aim to minimise the sum of squared deviation between the observed values of y and those predicted by the regression line which we will denote here as $y_e = a + bx$. The notation we will use is as follows.

x, y are the observed values

n is the number of observations

$y_e$ is the predicted value of y from the regression line $y_e = a + bx$

Based on this, if d is the sum of squared deviation then we will have

$$d = \Sigma(y - y_e)^2$$
$$= \Sigma(y^2 - 2yy_e + y_e^2)$$
$$= \Sigma y^2 - 2\Sigma yy_e + \Sigma y_e^2$$

and substituting $y_e = a + bx$ gives

$$d = \Sigma y^2 - 2\Sigma y(a + bx) + \Sigma(a + bx)^2$$
$$= \Sigma y^2 - 2a\Sigma y - 2b\Sigma xy + \Sigma(a^2 + 2abx + b^2x^2)$$
$$= \Sigma y^2 - 2a\Sigma y - 2b\Sigma xy + na^2 + 2ab\Sigma x + b^2\Sigma x^2$$

### Solving for the intercept - a

Partially differentiating this equation with respect to a gives

$$\frac{\partial d}{\partial a} = 2\Sigma y + 2na + 2b\Sigma x$$

To minimise the difference, d, with respect to a we need

$$\frac{\partial d}{\partial a} = 0$$

hence

$$-2\Sigma y + 2na + 2b\Sigma x = 0$$

or

$$-\Sigma y + na + b\Sigma x = 0$$

giving

$$\Sigma y = na + b\Sigma x$$

## Solving for the slope - b

Partially differentiating this equation with respect to b gives

$$\frac{\partial d}{\partial b} = 2\Sigma xy + 2a\Sigma x + 2b\Sigma x^2$$

To minimise the difference, d, with respect to b we need

$$\frac{\partial d}{\partial b} = 0$$

hence

$$-\Sigma xy + a\Sigma x + b\Sigma x^2 = 0$$

or

$$\Sigma xy = a\Sigma x + b\Sigma x^2$$

# Regression coefficients

## Simultaneous equations

The regression coefficients must satisfy each of these equations (referred to as the 'normal equations' for least squares regression, minimising the difference with respect both a and b):

$$\Sigma y = na + b\Sigma x$$

$$\Sigma xy = a\Sigma x + b\Sigma x^2$$

which must, therefore, be solved simultaneously.

The advantage of this method is that it can be easily extended to cover multiple regression calculations which is much more difficult to deal with under the algebraic formulation method below.

## Algebraic formulation

Alternatively, these normal equations for linear regression may be algebraically rearranged as follows:

*First normal equation*

$$\Sigma y = na + b\Sigma x$$

or

$$na = \Sigma y - b\Sigma x$$

Now dividing both sides by n gives

$$a = \frac{\Sigma y}{n} - b\frac{\Sigma x}{n}$$

and

$$\bar{y} = \frac{\Sigma y}{n} \quad \text{and} \quad \bar{x} = \frac{\Sigma x}{n}$$

hence

$$a = \bar{y} - b\bar{x}$$

*Second normal equation*

$$\Sigma xy = a\Sigma x + b\Sigma x^2$$

or

$$-\Sigma xy + a\Sigma x + b\Sigma x^2 = 0$$

and substituting a from above (a = $\bar{y}$ – b$\bar{x}$) we get

$$-\Sigma xy + \Sigma x(\bar{y} - b\bar{x}) + b\Sigma x^2 = 0$$

giving

$$-\Sigma xy + \bar{y}\Sigma x - b\bar{x}\Sigma x + b\Sigma x^2 = 0$$

Rearranging this with all the terms containing b on the left gives

$$b\Sigma x^2 - b\bar{x}\Sigma x = \Sigma xy - \bar{y}\Sigma x$$

and multiplying both sides by n gives

$$bn\Sigma x^2 - bn\bar{x}\Sigma x = n\Sigma xy - n\bar{y}\Sigma x$$

Now

$$\bar{x} = \frac{\Sigma x}{n} \quad \text{and} \quad \bar{y} = \frac{\Sigma y}{n}$$

hence

$$n\bar{x} = \Sigma x \quad \text{and} \quad n\bar{y} = \Sigma y$$

Substituting these gives

$$bn\Sigma x^2 - b\Sigma x\Sigma x = n\Sigma xy - \Sigma x\Sigma y$$

therefore

$$b[n\Sigma x^2 - (\Sigma x)^2] = n\Sigma xy - \Sigma x\Sigma y$$

hence

$$b = \frac{n\Sigma xy - \Sigma x \Sigma y}{n\Sigma x^2 - (\Sigma x)^2}$$

*Conclusion*

Thus the regression coefficients can, therefore, be found using:

$$b = \frac{n\Sigma xy - \Sigma x \Sigma y}{n\Sigma x^2 - (\Sigma x)^2}$$

and

$$a = \bar{y} - b\bar{x}$$

This may appear to be more convenient for linear regression, but cannot be eas extended to multiple regression.

# Multiple regression coefficients – 2 input variables

## Setting up the problem

The regression coefficients aim to minimise the sum of squared deviation between observed values of y and those predicted by the regression space which, using our ear notation, we will denote here as $y_e = a + b_1 x_1 + b_2 x_2$

Based on this, if d is the sum of squared deviation then we will have

$$d \quad = \quad \Sigma(y - y_e)^2$$

$$= \quad \Sigma(y^2 - 2yy_e + y_e^2)$$

$$= \quad \Sigma y^2 - 2\Sigma yy_e + \Sigma y_e^2$$

and substituting $y_e = a + b_1 x_1 + b_2 x_2$, gives

$$d \quad = \quad \Sigma y^2 - 2\Sigma y(a + b_1 x_1 + b_2 x_2) + \Sigma(a + b_1 x_1 + b_2 x_2)^2$$

$$= \quad \Sigma y^2 - 2a\Sigma y - 2b_1 \Sigma x_1 y - 2b_2 \Sigma x_2 y$$
$$+ \Sigma(a^2 + b_1^2 x_1^2 + b_2^2 x_2^2 + 2ab_1 x_1 + 2ab_2 x_2 + 2b_1 b_2 x_1 x_2)$$

$$= \quad \Sigma y^2 - 2a\Sigma y - 2b_1 \Sigma x_1 y - 2b_2 \Sigma x_2 y$$
$$+ na^2 + b_1^2 \Sigma x_1^2 + b_2^2 \Sigma x_2^2 + 2ab_1 \Sigma x_1 + 2ab_2 \Sigma x_2 + 2b_1 b_2 \Sigma x_1 x_2$$

## Solving with respect to a

Partially differentiating this equation with respect to a gives

$$\frac{\partial d}{\partial a} = -2\Sigma y + 2na + 2b_1 \Sigma x_1 + 2b_2 \Sigma x_2$$

To minimise the difference, d, with respect to a we need

$$\frac{\partial d}{\partial a} = 0$$

hence

$$-2\Sigma y + 2na + 2b_1\Sigma x_1 + 2b_2\Sigma x_2 = 0$$

giving

$$\mathbf{\Sigma y = na + b_1\Sigma x_1 + b_2\Sigma x_2}$$

## Solving with respect to $b_1$

Partially differentiating this equation with respect to $b_1$ gives

$$\frac{\partial d}{\partial b} = -2\Sigma x_1 y + 2a\Sigma x_1 + 2b_1\Sigma x_1^2 + 2b_2\Sigma x_1 x_2$$

To minimise the difference, d, with respect to b we need

$$\frac{\partial d}{\partial b} = 0$$

hence

$$-2\Sigma x_1 y + 2a\Sigma x_1 + 2b_1\Sigma x_1^2 + 2b_2\Sigma x_1 x_2 = 0$$

or

$$\mathbf{\Sigma x_1 y = a\Sigma x_1 + b_1\Sigma x_1^2 + b_2\Sigma x_1 x_2}$$

## Solving with respect to $b_2$

Partially differentiating this equation with respect to $b_2$ gives

$$\frac{\partial d}{\partial b} = -2\Sigma x_2 y + 2a\Sigma x_2 + 2b_2\Sigma x_2^2 + 2b_1\Sigma x_1 x_2$$

To minimise the difference, d, with respect to b we need

$$\frac{\partial d}{\partial b} = 0$$

hence

$$-2\Sigma x_2 y + 2a\Sigma x_2 + 2b_2\Sigma x_2^2 + 2b_1\Sigma x_1 x_2 = 0$$

or

$$\mathbf{\Sigma x_2 y = a\Sigma x_2 + b_1\Sigma x_1 x_2 + b_2\Sigma x_2^2}$$

## Regression coefficients

As a result, the regression coefficients may be determined by simultaneously solving the normal equations:

$$\Sigma y = na + b_1\Sigma x_1 + b_2\Sigma x_2$$

$$\Sigma x_1 y = a\Sigma x_1 + b_1\Sigma x_1^2 + b_2\Sigma x_1 x_2 = a\Sigma x_1 + b_1\Sigma x_1 x_1 + b_2\Sigma x_1 x_2$$

$$\Sigma x_2 y = a\Sigma x_2 + b_1\Sigma x_1 x_2 + b_2\Sigma x_2^2 = a\Sigma x_2 + b_1\Sigma x_2 x_1 + b_2\Sigma x_2 x_2$$

# Multiple regression coefficients – general expression

## Setting up the problem

The regression coefficients aim to minimise the sum of squared deviation between the observed values of y and those predicted by the regression space which, using our earlier notation, we will denote here as $y_e = a + b_1 x_1 + b_2 x_2 + b_3 x_3 + \cdots + b_n x_n$

Based on this, if d is the sum of squared deviation then we will have

$$d = \Sigma(y - y_e)^2$$

$$= \Sigma(y^2 - 2yy_e + y_e^2)$$

$$= \Sigma y^2 - 2\Sigma yy_e + \Sigma y_e^2$$

Substituting $y_e = a + b_1 x_1 + b_2 x_2 + b_3 x_3 + \cdots + b_n x_n$ gives

$$d = \Sigma y^2 - 2\Sigma y(a + b_1 x_1 + b_2 x_2 + b_3 x_3 + \cdots + b_n x_n)$$
$$+ \Sigma(a + b_1 x_1 + b_2 x_2 + b_3 x_3 + \cdots + b_n x_n)^2$$

$$= \Sigma y^2 - 2a\Sigma y - 2b_1\Sigma x_1 y - 2b_2\Sigma x_2 y - 2b_3\Sigma x_3 y - \cdots - 2b_n\Sigma x_n y$$

$$+ \Sigma(a^2 + b_1^2 x_1^2 + b_2^2 x_2^2 + \cdots + b_n^2 x_n^2$$

$$+ 2ab_1 x_1 + 2ab_2 x_2 + \cdots + 2ab_n x_n$$

$$+ 2b_1 b_2 x_1 x_2 + 2b_1 b_3 x_1 x_3 + \cdots + 2b_1 b_n x_1 x_n$$

$$+ 2b_2 b_3 x_2 x_3 + 2b_2 b_4 x_2 x_4 + \cdots + 2b_2 b_n x_2 x_n + \cdots + 2b_{n-1} b_n x_{n-1} x_n)$$

$$= \Sigma y^2 - 2a\Sigma y - 2b_1\Sigma x_1 y - 2b_2\Sigma x_2 y - 2b_3\Sigma x_3 y - \cdots - 2b_n\Sigma x_n y$$
$$+ na^2 + b_1^2\Sigma x_1^2 + b_2^2\Sigma x_2^2 + \cdots + b_n^2\Sigma x_n^2$$

$$+ 2ab_1\Sigma x_1 + 2ab_2\Sigma x_2 + \cdots + 2ab_n\Sigma x_n$$

$$+ 2b_1 b_2\Sigma x_1 x_2 + 2b_1 b_3\Sigma x_1 x_3 + \cdots + 2b_1 b_n\Sigma x_1 x_n$$

$$+ 2b_2 b_3\Sigma x_2 x_3 + 2b_2 b_4\Sigma x_2 x_4 + \cdots + 2b_2 b_n\Sigma x_2 x_n + \cdots + 2b_{n-1} b_n\Sigma x_{n-1} x_n$$

## Solving with respect to a

Partially differentiating this equation with respect to a gives

$$\frac{\partial d}{\partial a} = 2\Sigma y + 2na + 2b_1\Sigma x_1 + 2b_2\Sigma x_2 + 2b_3\Sigma x_3 + \ldots + 2b_n\Sigma x_n$$

To minimise the difference, d, with respect to a we need

$$\frac{\partial d}{\partial a} = 0$$

hence

$$-2\Sigma y + 2na + 2b_1\Sigma x_1 + 2b_2\Sigma x_2 + 2b_3\Sigma x_3 + \cdots + 2b_n\Sigma x_n = 0$$

giving

$$\mathbf{\Sigma y = na + b_1\Sigma x_1 + b_2\Sigma x_2 + b_3\Sigma x_3 + \cdots + b_n\Sigma x_n}$$

## Solving with respect to $b_k$

Partially differentiating this equation with respect to $b_k$ for each value of k from 1 to n, gives

$$\frac{\partial d}{\partial b} = 2\Sigma x_k y + 2a\Sigma x_k + 2b_1\Sigma x_k x_1 + 2b_2\Sigma x_k x_2 + \ldots + 2b_k\Sigma x_k x_k + \ldots + 2b_n\Sigma x_k x_n$$

To minimise the difference, d, with respect to b we need

$$\frac{\partial d}{\partial b} = 0$$

hence

$$-2\Sigma x_k y + 2a\Sigma x_k + 2b_1\Sigma x_k x_1 + 2b_2\Sigma x_k x_2 + 2b_3\Sigma x_k x_3 + \cdots + 2b_n\Sigma x_k x_n = 0$$

or

$$\mathbf{\Sigma x_k y = a\Sigma x_k + b_1\Sigma x_k x_1 + b_2\Sigma x_k x_2 + b_3\Sigma x_k x_3 + \cdots + b_n\Sigma x_k x_n}$$

## Regression coefficients

The regression coefficients may be determined by simultaneously solving the normal equations:

$$\Sigma y \quad = na + b_1\Sigma x_1 + b_2\Sigma x_2 + b_3\Sigma x_3 + \cdots + b_n\Sigma x_n$$

$$\Sigma x_1 y \quad = a\Sigma x_1 + b_1\Sigma x_1 x_1 + b_2\Sigma x_1 x_2 + b_3\Sigma x_1 x_3 + \cdots + b_n\Sigma x_1 x_n$$

$$\Sigma x_2 y \quad = a\Sigma x_2 + b_1\Sigma x_2 x_1 + b_2\Sigma x_2 x_2 + b_3\Sigma x_2 x_3 + \cdots + b_n\Sigma x_2 x_n$$

$$\Sigma x_3 y \quad = a\Sigma x_3 + b_1\Sigma x_3 x_1 + b_2\Sigma x_3 x_2 + b_3\Sigma x_3 x_3 + \cdots + b_n\Sigma x_3 x_n$$

$$\vdots \qquad\qquad \vdots \qquad\quad \vdots \qquad\quad \vdots$$

$$\Sigma x_n y \quad = a\Sigma x_n + b_1\Sigma x_n x_1 + b_2\Sigma x_n x_2 + b_3\Sigma x_n x_3 + \cdots + b_n\Sigma x_n x_n$$

## Correlation coefficient and coefficient of determination

### Definitions

### Coefficient of determination - $r^2$

The coefficient of determination shows what proportion of the total variation in the value of y can be explained by its association with x as established with the regression line. The total variation is defined here as $\Sigma(y - \bar{y})^2$ i.e. the sum of squared deviation. We could therefore write this as

$$r^2 = \frac{\text{Explained variation of } y}{\text{Total variation of } y} = \frac{\Sigma(y_e - \bar{y})^2}{\Sigma(y - \bar{y})^2}$$

### Correlation coefficient - r

The correlation coefficient is simply the square root of the coefficient of determination (or the coefficient of determination is the square of the correlation coefficient). Both measures have their uses as do variances and standard deviations which are equally related.

### Derivation of the correlation coefficient

We can derive the correlation coefficient formula from the above definitions. Our starting point is

$$r^2 = \frac{\text{Explained variation of } y}{\text{Total variation of } y} = \frac{\Sigma(y_e - \bar{y})^2}{\Sigma(y - \bar{y})^2}$$

Now

$$y_e = a + bx$$

and

$$\bar{y} = a + b\bar{x}$$

Subtracting the second equation from the first we have

$$y_e - \bar{y} = b(x - \bar{x})$$

and substituting this in the starting equation gives

$$r^2 = \frac{\Sigma[b(x - \bar{x})]^2}{\Sigma(y - \bar{y})^2}$$

$$= \frac{b^2\Sigma(x - \bar{x})^2}{\Sigma(y - \bar{y})^2}$$

$$= \frac{b^2 \Sigma(x^2 - 2x\bar{x} + \bar{x}^2)}{\Sigma(y^2 - 2y\bar{y} + \bar{y}^2)}$$

$$= \frac{b^2(\Sigma x^2 - 2\bar{x}\Sigma x + n\bar{x}^2)}{\Sigma y^2 - 2\bar{y}\Sigma y + n\bar{y}^2}$$

and multiplying top and bottom of this equation by n gives

$$= \frac{b^2(n\Sigma x^2 - 2n\bar{x}\Sigma x + n^2\bar{x}^2)}{n\Sigma y^2 - 2n\bar{y}\Sigma y + n^2\bar{y}^2}$$

Now

$$n\bar{x} = \Sigma x \quad \text{and} \quad n\bar{y} = \Sigma y$$

and substituting these gives

$$r^2 = \frac{b^2[n\Sigma x^2 - 2\Sigma x\Sigma x + (\Sigma x)^2]}{n\Sigma y^2 - 2\Sigma y\Sigma y + (\Sigma y)^2}$$

$$= \frac{b^2[n\Sigma x^2 - 2(\Sigma x)^2 + (\Sigma x)^2]}{n\Sigma y^2 - 2(\Sigma y)^2 + (\Sigma y)^2}$$

$$= \frac{b^2[n\Sigma x^2 - (\Sigma x)^2]}{n\Sigma y^2 - (\Sigma y)^2}$$

Now we established above that

$$b = \frac{n\Sigma xy - \Sigma x\Sigma y}{n\Sigma x^2 - (\Sigma x)^2}$$

and substituting this gives

$$r^2 = \frac{[n\Sigma xy - \Sigma x\Sigma y]^2}{[n\Sigma x^2 - (\Sigma x)^2]^2} \times \frac{[n\Sigma x^2 - (\Sigma x)^2]}{n\Sigma y^2 - (\Sigma y)^2}$$

and after cancelling the top of the second part of this equation with one power of the bottom of the first we have

$$r^2 = \frac{[n\Sigma xy - \Sigma x\Sigma y]^2}{[n\Sigma x^2 - (\Sigma x)^2]} \times \frac{1}{n\Sigma y^2 - (\Sigma y)^2}$$

or

$$r^2 = \frac{[n\Sigma xy - \Sigma x\Sigma y]^2}{[n\Sigma x^2 - (\Sigma x)^2][n\Sigma y^2 - (\Sigma y)^2]}$$

If we now simply take the square root we have the equation of correlation coefficient, i.e.

$$r = \frac{n\Sigma xy - \Sigma x\Sigma y}{\sqrt{[n\Sigma x^2 - (\Sigma x)^2][n\Sigma y^2 - (\Sigma y)^2]}}$$

## Rank correlation

If we rank data in order (both x and y) we will assign values between 1 and n where n the number of values. Given this

$$\Sigma x = \Sigma y = \frac{n(n+1)}{2}$$

and

$$\Sigma x^2 = \Sigma y^2 = \frac{n(n+1)(2n+1)}{6}$$

Also

$$\Sigma d = \Sigma(x - y)$$

hence

$$\Sigma d^2 = \Sigma(x - y)^2$$
$$= \Sigma x^2 - 2\Sigma xy + \Sigma y^2$$
$$= 2\Sigma x^2 - 2\Sigma xy \quad (\text{since } \Sigma x = \Sigma y)$$

and therefore

$$\Sigma xy = \Sigma x^2 - \frac{\Sigma d^2}{2}$$

$$= \frac{n(n+1)(2n+1)}{6} - \frac{\Sigma d^2}{2}$$

Hence substituting these in the above correlation coefficient gives

$$r = \frac{n\Sigma xy - \Sigma x\Sigma y}{\sqrt{[n\Sigma x^2 - (\Sigma x)^2][n\Sigma y^2 - (\Sigma y)^2]}}$$

$$r = \frac{n\Sigma xy - \Sigma x\Sigma y}{[n\Sigma x^2 - (\Sigma x)^2]}$$

$$= \frac{\dfrac{n^2(n+1)(2n+1)}{6} - \dfrac{n\sum d^2}{2} - \dfrac{n^2(n+1)^2}{2^2}}{\dfrac{n^2(n+1)(2n+1)}{6} - \dfrac{n^2(n+1)^2}{2^2}}$$

$$= 1 - \dfrac{\dfrac{n\sum d^2}{2}}{\dfrac{n^2(n+1)(2n+1)}{6} - \dfrac{n^2(n+1)^2}{2^2}}$$

Multiplying the top and bottom lines of the fraction by 12 gives

$$r = 1 - \dfrac{6n\sum d^2}{2n^2(n+1)(2n+1) - 3n^2(n+1)^2}$$

$$= 1 - \dfrac{6n\sum d^2}{2n^2(2n^2 + 3n + 1) - 3n^2(n^2 + 2n + 1)}$$

$$= 1 - \dfrac{6n\sum d^2}{4n^4 + 6n^3 + 2n^2 - 3n^4 - 6n^3 - 3n^2}$$

$$= 1 - \dfrac{6n\sum d^2}{n^4 - n^2}$$

$$= 1 - \dfrac{6\sum d^2}{n^3 - n}$$

giving

$$r = 1 - \dfrac{6\sum d^2}{n(n^2 - 1)}$$

# APPENDIX 2 - CALCULATION OF STANDARD ERRORS

## General

### Introduction

The normal formula for the standard error based on data from a sample is

$$SE = \frac{s}{\sqrt{n}}$$

where

$$s = \sqrt{\frac{\Sigma f(x-\bar{x})^2}{n-1}}$$

i.e. where the sample standard deviation has been calculated by dividing by the degree of freedom. Putting these two equations together gives

$$SE = \sqrt{\frac{\Sigma f(x-\bar{x})^2}{n(n-1)}}$$

If, however, we had not adjusted our calculation of the standard deviation, and calculate the sample standard deviation as we would for the population, i.e.

$$s = \sqrt{\frac{\Sigma f(x-\bar{x})^2}{n}}$$

then we could correct for this in the standard error calculation by dividing by the degre of freedom, i.e.

$$SE = \frac{s}{\sqrt{n-1}} = \frac{\text{Unexplained variability about expected value}}{\sqrt{\text{Degrees of freedom}}}$$

since when we put these two equations together, we once again get the equation not above, i.e.

$$SE = \sqrt{\frac{\Sigma f(x-\bar{x})^2}{n(n-1)}}$$

## Relevance

The relevance of this is that when we calculate regression and correlation coefficients do not distinguish between whether we are dealing with the full population or simp sample, hence if we are dealing with a sample (almost certainly the case) we will need to account for the degrees of freedom in the calculation of the standard error.  We should therefore calculate the standard error as

$$SE = \frac{\text{Unexplained variability about expected value}}{\sqrt{\text{Degrees of freedom}}}$$

## The correlation coefficient

The correlation coefficient, r, is a relative measure of the goodness of fit, with $r^2$ giving the proportion of the y values observed that can be explained by the regression line and the value of x.  Hence for this coefficient

- Unexplained variability about expected value $= \sqrt{1-r^2}$
- Degrees of freedom $= n - 2$

Hence

$$SE = \frac{\sqrt{1-r^2}}{\sqrt{n-2}} = \sqrt{\frac{1-r^2}{n-2}}$$

## The b coefficient

The standard error for the relative measure r was

$$SE = \sqrt{\frac{1-r^2}{n-2}}$$

The b coefficient is an absolute value measure and we therefore need to scale this measure for the values involved, giving

$$SE = \sqrt{\frac{1-r^2}{n-2}} \times \frac{b}{r} \quad \text{or} \quad \sqrt{\frac{1-r^2}{n-2}} \times \sqrt{\frac{n\Sigma y^2 - (\Sigma y)^2}{n\Sigma x^2 - (\Sigma x)^2}}$$

## Y values for given values of x (and a coefficient)

The original relative measure firstly needs to be scaled for absolute value of the average variability in the value of y around the regression line, giving

$$SE = \sqrt{\frac{1-r^2}{n-2}} \times \sqrt{\Sigma y^2 - \frac{(\Sigma y)^2}{n}}$$

$$= \sqrt{\frac{1-r^2}{n-2}} \times \sqrt{\frac{n\Sigma y^2 - (\Sigma y)^2}{n}}$$

$$= \sqrt{\frac{1-r^2}{n-2}} \times \sqrt{n\Sigma y^2 - (\Sigma y)^2} \times \sqrt{\frac{1}{n}}$$

$$= \sqrt{\frac{1-r^2}{n(n-2)}} \times \sqrt{n\Sigma y^2 - (\Sigma y)^2}$$

To then cater for the greater inherent uncertainty as we move further away from the observed range of values of x, or the mean of those values of x, we then make an adjustment to the last term to expand the SE the further away we go, giving

$$SE = \sqrt{\frac{1-r^2}{n(n-2)}} \times \sqrt{n\Sigma y^2 - (\Sigma y)^2} \times \sqrt{\frac{1}{n} + \frac{n(x-\bar{x})^2}{n\Sigma x^2 - (\Sigma x)^2}}$$

# 10 Time series analysis

## Contents

# 1 INTRODUCTION

## 1.1 The components of a time series

A time series is a relationship where the value of a variable is in some way dependent upon time. Examples of such series would include population expansion, global warming effects, economic output, etc.

Since the measured variable is dependent upon time we may wish to graph the relationship, plotting time along the horizontal axis and the value of the dependent variable on the vertical axis. Although such graphs often appear to demonstrate considerable random movement, there is frequently some underlying pattern that can be determined.

The pattern of observed values against time is considered to be a function of four factors, specifically

- Trend – T.
- Cyclical variations – C.
- Seasonal variations – S.
- Random variations - R.

### 1.1.1 Trend

The trend is the underlying general long-term movement in the value of the observed variable over time. In the graph below we have illustrated this as a linear growing trend. The trend could be growing, stable or falling, and the form of the change could be linear, exponential or polynomial. These represent the most likely trends but are by no means an exhaustive list.

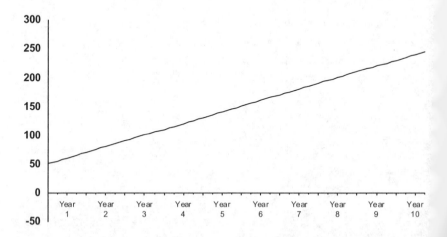

Before the trend of a particular time series can be determined it is generally necessary to standardise its measurement. For example, if the time series was measuring the sales generated per month it may be necessary to revise the monthly data to take account of the differing number of business days in a month. Indeed, it may be more appropriate to take the measurement of sales per day for that month.

Even when the original data are in annual form, they may still require some standardisation before a meaningful analysis can be carried out. In the context of long-term trend measurement, changes in the population size often need to be adjusted for by dividing the originally measured values by the population size to state the series in a per capita form. Frequently comparison of trends on a per capita basis is far more meaningful than a corresponding analysis of unadjusted figures.

Establishing the trend is the first element of time series analysis and may be achieved by either

- Linear regression analysis; or
- Moving averages.

Both of these methods are discussed below.

## 1.1.2 Cyclical variations

Cyclical variations represent long-term regular fluctuations which take several years to complete. Many types of cyclical variation have been suggested in an economic and business context although their justification, explanation and measurement has proved difficult.

The main problem in trying to measure cyclical variations is in obtaining sufficient information from which conclusions can be drawn. If we are to remove the effects of any chance factors from our readings we need to have observed and accurately measured several cycles. When a cycle itself spans several years this poses an immense practical difficulty.

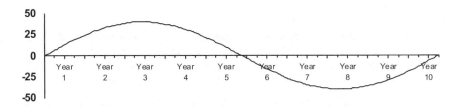

Examples of proposed economic/business cycles include

- *Kondratieff cycles* - an economic cycle of 40-60 years duration.
- *Kuznets cycles* - a 8-10 year business/building economic cycle.

As we noted above, with such long time scales involved the determination and measurement of such cycles poses many great problems, if indeed they exist at all.

### 1.1.3 Seasonal variations

Seasonal variations represent regular repeating short-term fluctuations which complete a full cycle within a given period, regularly one year. Examples of such cycles would include temperature variations across a year, toy store sales across a year showing a regular peak at Christmas, general business reporting cycles culminating in the annual report and accounts, etc.

The effect of seasonal variations may appear as follows.

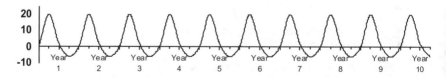

Due to the frequency of their occurrence compared to cyclical variations, the determination and measurement of seasonal fluctuations proves to be much more practical.

### 1.1.4 Random variations

Random fluctuations occur as a result of unpredictable factors such as floods, strikes, elections, etc. The effect of random fluctuations in isolation may appear as follows.

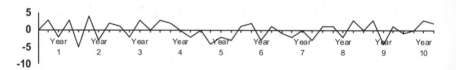

The general view in time series analysis is that the trend, cyclical variations, and seasonal fluctuations can be viewed as resulting from systematic influences, the effects of which can be measured. Random fluctuations, on the other hand, are considered to be so erratic that it would be fruitless to attempt to model them.

Since the random element is totally unpredictable and may be either positive or negative, we make the assumption throughout that its long-term average is zero and hence if sufficient measurements can be taken and averaged, the effect of random fluctuations will be cancelled.

### 1.1.5 Actual result

The actual observed measurements therefore represent some combination of these four factors which may be illustrated in the graph below.

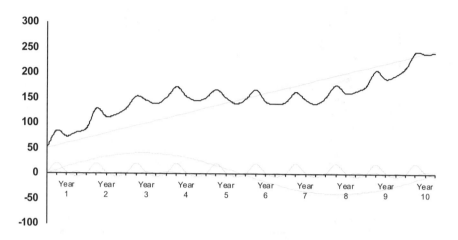

## 1.2 Time series models

### 1.2.1 Introduction

The method of measuring and combining these factors (the appropriate time series model) is dependent upon if and how the factors are related. The two alternatives we may wish to use are

- The additive model.
- The multiplicative model.

### 1.2.2 The additive model

In the additive model the factors are measured in the same units (e.g. £) and simply added to explain the actually observed value, i.e.

$$A = T + C + S + R$$

For many models, there will be insufficient data to correctly identify the cyclical factors for reasons we noted above and therefore the model will be reduced to

$$A = T + S + R$$

The additive model will be most appropriate where the value of the seasonal (or cyclical, if determined) variations are the same regardless of the value of the underlying trend. This could be graphically illustrated as follows.

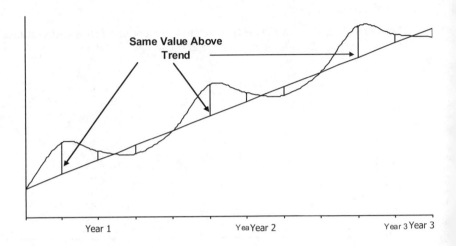

### 1.2.3 The multiplicative model

The multiplicative model is considered to be more appropriate where the variation about the trend are in *proportion* to the value of the underlying trend itself. This i probably a more appropriate assumption in most circumstances.

The multiplicative model is

$$A = T \times C \times S \times R$$

where A and T are measured in units (e.g. £) and S, C and R are proportions c percentages demonstrating how far these factors have caused the actual value to mov from that trend. Note, in this model R is assumed to have an average value of 1, c 100%.

Once more the time scales involved and probable lack of data will mean that the cyclic elements cannot be identified and the model reduces to

$$A = T \times S \times R$$

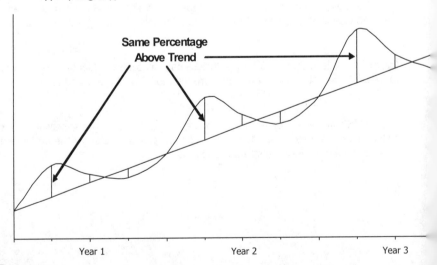

# 2 APPROACH TO TIME SERIES ANALYSIS

## 2.1 Introduction

The problem that we are faced with is that we are presented with the actual data and we are trying to decompose the actual observed variations into the above four factors. Clearly, the selection of the right model (additive or multiplicative) will be essential if we are to get a correct analysis.

Initially below we will only consider relatively short-term timescales making the determination of cyclical fluctuations impractical for reasons noted above. Having dealt with short-term fluctuations we will then go on to consider how we may be able to determine these cyclical fluctuations.

The basic approach that we adopt is as follows.

■    *Determine the trend:* determine the long-term general movement using either

  –    Linear regression; or
  –    Moving averages.

■    *Determine the seasonal plus random variations:* determine the scale of the seasonal and random variations combined by measuring how far the actual observations differ from the underlying trend line.

■    *Isolate the seasonal variations:* by averaging the seasonal and random variations measured above for each season, we should cancel out the effects of the random element leaving us with a measure for just the seasonal fluctuations.

■    *Isolate the random variations:* the random variations then represent any residual difference.

It is worth trying to appreciate this idea up front as it is all too easy to get bogged down in the calculations later on and lose track of the overview.

It should be noted that throughout this session we will be using linear trends for clarity. As we noted above trends may take many different forms (e.g. exponential growth) in which case these ideas would need some modification such as measuring the logarithmic value of the dependent variable rather than the absolute value.

## 2.2 Trend

### 2.2.1 Introduction

The trend is often the most important element in the time series. It is the first factor that we must identify in order to isolate all the other factors.

The first thing to do will be to try to determine the general shape of the trend by constructing a graph of the data. This graph should help us identify

■    Whether a trend exists.
■    The direction of the trend (up or down).
■    Whether the trend is linear or exponential.

Having determined the general form of the trend we must then quantify it using either

- Linear regression; or
- Moving averages.

We will illustrate the ideas involved by considering the following example throughout the remainder of this session.

## Example

The following data have been obtained regarding the quarterly sales achieved by a company. Determine how these figures appear to be fluctuating with time and project the quarterly sales for the next two years.

| Quarter | Year 1 £'000 | Year 2 £'000 | Year 3 £'000 | Year 4 £'000 | Year . £'00( |
|---------|--------------|--------------|--------------|--------------|--------------|
| 1 | 97 | 101 | 102 | 109 | 114 |
| 2 | 70 | 74 | 79 | 83 | 88 |
| 3 | 41 | 44 | 47 | 48 | 50 |
| 4 | 58 | 63 | 66 | 68 | 74 |

## 2.2.2 Linear regression

Linear regression gives us the mathematical equation of a straight line which best fits ∶ number of observed values. If we are to utilise linear regression in a time serie∶ problem we must plot the variable as the *y* value, with the *x* value representing time.

If the relationship we ascertain from our graph turns out to be non-linear we will need t∘ rescale the axes in order to produce a linear relationship which can then be used. Thi∶ rescaling has already been discussed in our session on regression analysis.

Applying our linear regression ideas to the above data we get the following.

| x (Time) | $x^2$ | y £'000 | xy |
|---|---|---|---|
| 1 | 1 | 97 | 97 |
| 2 | 4 | 70 | 140 |
| 3 | 9 | 41 | 123 |
| 4 | 16 | 58 | 232 |
| 5 | 25 | 101 | 505 |
| 6 | 36 | 74 | 444 |
| 7 | 49 | 44 | 308 |
| 8 | 64 | 63 | 504 |
| 9 | 81 | 102 | 918 |
| 10 | 100 | 79 | 790 |
| 11 | 121 | 47 | 517 |
| 12 | 144 | 66 | 792 |
| 13 | 169 | 109 | 1,417 |
| 14 | 196 | 83 | 1,162 |
| 15 | 225 | 48 | 720 |
| 16 | 256 | 68 | 1,088 |
| 17 | 289 | 114 | 1,938 |
| 18 | 324 | 88 | 1,584 |
| 19 | 361 | 50 | 950 |
| 20 | 400 | 74 | 1,480 |
| 210 | 2,870 | 1,476 | 15,709 |

Hence

$$b = \frac{n\sum xy - \sum x \sum y}{n\sum x^2 - (\sum x)^2}$$

$$= \frac{20 \times 15,709 - 210 \times 1,476}{20 \times 2,870 - (210)^2}$$

$$= \frac{4,220}{13,300} = 0.31729$$

$$a = \bar{y} - b\bar{x}$$

$$= \frac{1,476}{20} - 0.31729 \times \frac{210}{20}$$

$$= 73.80 - 3.33158$$

$$= 70.468$$

Giving the equation of the relationship as

$$y = 70.468 + 0.31729x$$

i.e.

Sales $= 70.468 + 0.31729 \times$ Time

where time is measured in quarters from the beginning of Year 1.

## 2.2.3 Moving averages

The calculation of a moving average represents an alternative means for determining the trend. The approach is to calculate the average observed value across a period that represents the full seasonal cycle so that the average will eliminate the effects of the seasonal and random fluctuations leaving just the underlying trend.

If, for example, we were given the following daily sales figure for our above company over a two-week period and we believed there was a weekly cycle to the level of sales, then we would ascertain the following moving average figures.

| Week | Qtr | Value (A) £ | M. Av. (T) £ |
|------|-----|-------------|--------------|
| 1 | Monday | 975 | |
| | Tuesday | 900 | |
| | Wednesday | 885 | 936 |
| | Thursday | 910 | 938 |
| | Friday | 1010 | 939 |
| 2 | Monday | 985 | 940 |
| | Tuesday | 905 | 942 |
| | Wednesday | 890 | 945 |
| | Thursday | 920 | |
| | Friday | 1025 | |

The moving average figure represents the average for the five days centred on that point, i.e. the first figure of 936 against the Wednesday of Week 1 is the average of the Monday to Friday figures of Week 1. The figure of 938 next to Thursday of Week 1 is the average of the Tuesday Week 1 figure to Monday Week 2 figure. As a result, each moving average figure is the average of all the sales in five working days (one weekly cycle) and therefore eliminates the ups and downs on any particular days.

Since there are an odd number of days in each week in the above example, we can plot the moving average against the central one, i.e. it represents that day, the two days before that day and the two days after that day. If, on the other hand, there were an even number of measurements taken across one cycle (e.g. a six day week) then we could not assign the moving average to any one particular day, it would need to lie between the third and fourth items in the cycle. If we just wish to identify the trend itself this is of no consequence. However, if we wish to use the trend to extrapolate forward, then we need to put a value against each day (or each measurement) rather than between days (or measurements).

The general example we are working on throughout this session illustrates this feature which will help emphasise the problem and show the solution.

In this example, we first calculate the total of each four quarters' sales, noting the midway between the second and third quarters in each sequence. We can now see the general trend, but since no figure is allocated to any quarter, how can we predict particular future quarter's value?

Our next step is to add together the value of consecutive pairs of four-quarter totals produce one total, which now represents eight quarters. This eight-quarter total need to be placed between the two four-quarter totals and as such will now appear to be in relation to one of the original quarters.

We can now calculate the moving average by dividing this figure by eight as follows.

| Year | Qtr | Value (A) £'000 | 4 Qtr £'000 | 8 Qtr £'000 | M. Av. (T) £'000 |
|------|-----|-----|-----|-----|-----|
| 1 | Q1 | 97 | | | |
| | Q2 | 70 | | | |
| | | | 266 | | |
| | Q3 | 41 | | 536 | 67.000 |
| | | | 270 | | |
| | Q4 | 58 | | 544 | 68.000 |
| | | | 274 | | |
| 2 | Q1 | 101 | | 551 | 68.875 |
| | | | 277 | | |
| | Q2 | 74 | | 559 | 69.875 |
| | | | 282 | | |
| | Q3 | 44 | | 565 | 70.625 |
| | | | 283 | | |
| | Q4 | 63 | | 571 | 71.375 |
| | | | 288 | | |
| 3 | Q1 | 102 | | 579 | 72.375 |
| | | | 291 | | |
| | Q2 | 79 | | 585 | 73.125 |
| | | | 294 | | |
| | Q3 | 47 | | 595 | 74.375 |
| | | | 301 | | |
| | Q4 | 66 | | 606 | 75.750 |
| | | | 305 | | |
| 4 | Q1 | 109 | | 611 | 76.375 |
| | | | 306 | | |
| | Q2 | 83 | | 614 | 76.750 |
| | | | 308 | | |
| | Q3 | 48 | | 621 | 77.625 |
| | | | 313 | | |
| | Q4 | 68 | | 631 | 78.875 |
| | | | 318 | | |
| 5 | Q1 | 114 | | 638 | 79.750 |
| | | | 320 | | |
| | Q2 | 88 | | 646 | 80.750 |
| | | | 326 | | |
| | Q3 | 50 | | | |
| | Q4 | 74 | | | |

You will have noticed above that the effect of undertaking this moving average calculation is that we lose data at the beginning and the end of the observed series since we do not have earlier or later quarters' measurements on which to continue our moving average calculation. We need to be aware of this factor when using the moving average trend information to project forward as we illustrate below.

## Exercise 1a

Car sales by quarter have been as follows over the last five years.

| Qtr | Year 1 '000 | Year 2 '000 | Year 3 '000 | Year 4 '000 | Year 5 '000 |
|-----|-----|-----|-----|-----|-----|
| Q1 | 70 | 74 | 76 | 66 | 84 |
| Q2 | 71 | 77 | 92 | 89 | 100 |
| Q3 | 144 | 153 | 130 | 122 | 147 |
| Q4 | 98 | 102 | 94 | 82 | 93 |

Ascertain the moving average trend assuming a linear relationship.

## 2.3 Seasonal variation

### 2.3.1 Introduction

Having identified the trend using either linear regression or moving averages we need to go on to identify the seasonal variations.

As we noted above, the basic approach is to calculate the scale of the difference between the actually observed values and the trend for each period. This difference represents the summation of the effects of the seasonal and random variations. If we then average these variations by season we should be able to eliminate the effect of the random variations leaving us with just the seasonal factors.

Although this is a general outline of the approach, the exact maths involved will depend on whether we are using the additive or the multiplicative model.

### 2.3.2 Additive model

Using the additive model

$$A = T + S + R$$

gives

$$A - T = S + R$$

That is, the sum of the seasonal and random fluctuations can be ascertained by subtracting the trend values from the actually observed values.

It is irrelevant which method has been used to calculate the trend (linear regression o moving averages) although clearly with the moving averages method some tren measurements are missing at the start and end of the period.

We should always remember that in the additive model all the factors take on the same units, in this case £.

### 2.3.3 Multiplicative model

Using the multiplicative model

$$A = T \times S \times R$$

gives

$$\frac{A}{T} = S \times R$$

That is, the product of the seasonal and random variations can be determined dividing the actually observed values by the trend value.

Once again it is irrelevant which method has been used in determining the tren although some figures will be missing at the start and end if the moving averag method has been used.

We should also remember that in the multiplicative model S and R will be proportiona or percentage measures and A and T are absolute value measures.

## 2.3.4 Seasonal and random variations

Applying these ideas to our initial example, using the moving average trend figures (although the approach would be identical for the linear regression trend figures), we can calculate our seasonal and random variations under either model as follows.

| Year | Qtr | Value (A) | 4 Qtr | 8 Qtr | M. Av. (T) | Seasonal & Random Variation Add | Seasonal & Random Variation Mult. |
|------|-----|-----------|-------|-------|------------|------|------|
| | | £'000 | £'000 | £'000 | £'000 | £'000 | % |
| 1 | Q1 | 97 | | | | | |
| | Q2 | 70 | | | | | |
| | | | 266 | | | | |
| | Q3 | 41 | | 536 | 67.000 | (26.000) | 61.194 |
| | | | 270 | | | | |
| | Q4 | 58 | | 544 | 68.000 | (10.000) | 85.294 |
| | | | 274 | | | | |
| 2 | Q1 | 101 | | 551 | 68.875 | 32.125 | 146.642 |
| | | | 277 | | | | |
| | Q2 | 74 | | 559 | 69.875 | 4.125 | 105.903 |
| | | | 282 | | | | |
| | Q3 | 44 | | 565 | 70.625 | (26.625) | 62.301 |
| | | | 283 | | | | |
| | Q4 | 63 | | 571 | 71.375 | (8.375) | 88.266 |
| | | | 288 | | | | |
| 3 | Q1 | 102 | | 579 | 72.375 | 29.625 | 140.933 |
| | | | 291 | | | | |
| | Q2 | 79 | | 585 | 73.125 | 5.875 | 108.034 |
| | | | 294 | | | | |
| | Q3 | 47 | | 595 | 74.375 | (27.375) | 63.193 |
| | | | 301 | | | | |
| | Q4 | 66 | | 606 | 75.750 | (9.750) | 87.129 |
| | | | 305 | | | | |
| 4 | Q1 | 109 | | 611 | 76.375 | 32.625 | 142.717 |
| | | | 306 | | | | |
| | Q2 | 83 | | 614 | 76.750 | 6.250 | 108.143 |
| | | | 308 | | | | |
| | Q3 | 48 | | 621 | 77.625 | (29.625) | 61.836 |
| | | | 313 | | | | |
| | Q4 | 68 | | 631 | 78.875 | (10.875) | 86.212 |
| | | | 318 | | | | |
| 5 | Q1 | 114 | | 638 | 79.750 | 34.250 | 142.947 |
| | | | 320 | | | | |
| | Q2 | 88 | | 646 | 80.750 | 7.250 | 108.978 |
| | | | 326 | | | | |
| | Q3 | 50 | | | | | |
| | Q4 | 74 | | | | | |

## Exercise 1b

Continuing on from Exercise 1a, determine the combined seasonal and random variations using each of the additive approach and multiplicative approach.

## 2.3.5 Isolating the seasonal variation

### Introduction

We must now isolate just the seasonal fluctuations by averaging the above seasonal and random fluctuations for each quarter to cancel the effect of the random element.

### Additive model

Undertaking this on our additive model figures gives the following.

Note the average figures are calculated as the sum divided by four, since even though there are five years there are only four moving average measures for each quarter.

That arises as a consequence of the moving average calculation and would not be the case if we had used a linear regression trend.

| Year | Q1 £'000 | Q2 £'000 | Q3 £'000 | Q4 £'000 |
|---|---|---|---|---|
| 1 | – | – | (26.000) | (10.000) |
| 2 | 32.125 | 4.125 | (26.625) | (8.375) |
| 3 | 29.625 | 5.875 | (27.375) | (9.750) |
| 4 | 32.625 | 6.250 | (29.625) | (10.875) |
| 5 | 34.250 | 7.250 | – | – |
| Sum | 128.625 | 23.500 | (109.625) | (39.000) |
| Average | 32.156 | 5.875 | (27.406) | (9.750) |

Having now calculated the average variation in each season and eliminated the effect of random factors, we should be in a position to move on through our analysis, however, another problem has arisen.

Since these figures are supposed to represent *average* variations around the long-term trend we would expect them to net out to zero. If we add up all of these average values, however, we will find that they do not come to zero, rather their total is +0.875, slightly *above* what we would expect. We therefore need to make a minor adjustment to these average figures in order to arrive at our seasonal variation which we do by *deducting* 0.219 (0.875 ÷ 4) from each of these quarterly averages giving

| Year | Q1 £'000 | Q2 £'000 | Q3 £'000 | Q4 £'000 | Net £'000 |
|---|---|---|---|---|---|
| 1 | – | – | (26.000) | (10.000) | |
| 2 | 32.125 | 4.125 | (26.625) | (8.375) | |
| 3 | 29.625 | 5.875 | (27.375) | (9.750) | |
| 4 | 32.625 | 6.250 | (29.625) | (10.875) | |
| 5 | 34.250 | 7.250 | – | – | |
| Sum | 128.625 | 23.500 | (109.625) | (39.000) | |
| Average | 32.156 | 5.875 | (27.406) | (9.750) | 0.875 |
| Correction | (0.219) | (0.219) | (0.219) | (0.219) | |
| Seasonal | 31.938 | 5.656 | (27.625) | (9.969) | |

Subject to some very minor roundings in our calculations, these figures now net out to zero across one full year and hence represent our best estimate of seasonal variations.

## Multiplicative model

Applying exactly the same idea of averaging the observed quarterly variations across each year in the multiplicative model we get the following.

| Year | Q1 % | Q2 % | Q3 % | Q4 % | Net % |
|------|------|------|------|------|-------|
| 1 | – | – | 61.194 | 85.294 | |
| 2 | 146.642 | 105.903 | 62.301 | 88.266 | |
| 3 | 140.933 | 108.034 | 63.193 | 87.129 | |
| 4 | 142.717 | 108.143 | 61.836 | 86.212 | |
| 5 | 142.947 | 108.978 | – | – | |
| Sum | 573.239 | 431.059 | 248.524 | 346.901 | |
| Average | 143.310 | 107.765 | 62.131 | 86.725 | 399.931 |
| Correction | 0.017 | 0.017 | 0.017 | 0.017 | |
| Seasonal | 143.327% | 107.782% | 62.148% | 86.743% | |

*Note*: This time we would expect the sum of the four quarters' averages to add to 400% (4 × 100%). In this case the average of the four quarters is slightly *below* that amount (399.931) and hence we need to *add* a small correction to each quarter, being 0.017 = [(400.000 – 399.931) ÷ 4].

Once again, we have now isolated the effect of the seasonal fluctuation alone.

## Exercise 1c

Continuing Exercise 1b, isolate the seasonal variations using both the additive and multiplicative models.

## 2.4 Random variations

### 2.4.1 Introduction

Having now isolated the seasonal variations we are in a position to measure the experienced random fluctuations, although you will recall that we will never try to predict these.

### 2.4.2 Additive model

Using the additive model

$$A = T + S + R$$

gives

$$A - T - S = R$$

but since we have calculated S + R (= A – T) as the effects of our seasonal and random variations in one of the columns above, we simply need to deduct the determined seasonal variations, S, from these figures, effectively using

$$R = (S + R) - S \qquad (R = (A - T) - S)$$

### 2.4.3 Multiplicative model

Using the multiplicative model

$$A = T \times S \times R$$

gives

$$\frac{A}{T \times S} = R$$

but since we have calculated S × R (= A/T) as the effects of our seasonal and random variations in one of the columns above, we simply need to divide these figures by S to determine the random variation experienced, effectively using

$$R = (S \times R) \div S \qquad \left( R = \frac{A}{T} \div S = \frac{A}{T \times S} \right)$$

### 2.4.4 Application

Applying these ideas extends our tabular calculation, giving

| Year | Qtr | Value (A) | 4 Qtr | 8 Qtr | M. Av. (T) | Seasonal & Random Variation | | Average Seasonal Variation (S) | | Random Variation (R) | |
|---|---|---|---|---|---|---|---|---|---|---|---|
| | | | | | | Add | Mult. | Add | Mult. | Add | Mult. |
| | | £'000 | £'000 | £'000 | £'000 | £'000 | % | £'000 | % | £'000 | % |
| 1 | Q1 | 97 | | | | | | | | | |
| | Q2 | 70 | | | | | | | | | |
| | Q3 | 41 | 266 | 536 | 67.000 | (26.000) | 61.194 | (27.625) | 62.148 | 1.625 | 98.465 |
| | Q4 | 58 | 270 | 544 | 68.000 | (10.000) | 85.294 | (9.969) | 86.743 | (0.031) | 98.330 |
| 2 | Q1 | 101 | 274 | 551 | 68.875 | 32.125 | 146.642 | 31.938 | 143.327 | 0.187 | 102.313 |
| | Q2 | 74 | 277 | 559 | 69.875 | 4.125 | 105.903 | 5.656 | 107.782 | (1.531) | 98.257 |
| | Q3 | 44 | 282 | 565 | 70.625 | (26.625) | 62.301 | (27.625) | 62.148 | 1.000 | 100.246 |
| | Q4 | 63 | 283 | 571 | 71.375 | (8.375) | 88.266 | (9.969) | 86.743 | 1.594 | 101.756 |
| 3 | Q1 | 102 | 288 | 579 | 72.375 | 29.625 | 140.933 | 31.938 | 143.327 | (2.313) | 98.325 |
| | Q2 | 79 | 291 | 585 | 73.125 | 5.875 | 108.034 | 5.656 | 107.782 | 0.219 | 100.234 |
| | Q3 | 47 | 294 | 595 | 74.375 | (27.375) | 63.193 | (27.625) | 62.148 | 0.250 | 101.683 |
| | Q4 | 66 | 301 | 606 | 75.750 | (9.750) | 87.129 | (9.969) | 86.743 | 0.219 | 100.441 |
| 4 | Q1 | 109 | 305 | 611 | 76.375 | 32.625 | 142.717 | 31.938 | 143.327 | 0.687 | 99.57 |
| | Q2 | 83 | 306 | 614 | 76.750 | 6.250 | 108.143 | 5.656 | 107.782 | 0.594 | 100.33 |
| | Q3 | 48 | 308 | 621 | 77.625 | (29.625) | 61.836 | (27.625) | 62.148 | (2.000) | 99.49 |
| | Q4 | 68 | 313 | 631 | 78.875 | (10.875) | 86.212 | (9.969) | 86.743 | (0.906) | 99.38 |
| 5 | Q1 | 114 | 318 | 638 | 79.750 | 34.250 | 142.947 | 31.938 | 143.327 | 2.312 | 99.73 |
| | Q2 | 88 | 320 | 646 | 80.750 | 7.250 | 108.978 | 5.656 | 107.782 | 1.594 | 101.11 |
| | Q3 | 50 | 326 | | | | | | | | |
| | Q4 | 74 | | | | | | | | | |

## Exercise 1d

Following on from Exercise 1c, determine the random variations observed in each quarter.

# 2.5 Cyclical variations

The calculation of cyclical fluctuations follows a very similar fashion to that of the calculation of seasonal variations, though clearly over a much longer timescale.

The approach is firstly to take annual measures throughout each cycle and thus eliminate the effect of the seasonal fluctuations within each year. If we then calculate the difference between these actually observed values and the calculated trend figures for each year, this must represent the cyclical and random variations.

If we do this over a number of cycles and then average these readings for the corresponding parts of those cycles, we will eliminate the effects of any random variations. What we will then be left with will be just the cyclical fluctuations that we are trying to identify.

# 2.6 Projections

## 2.6.1 Introduction

In order to undertake projections we now need to extrapolate forward our trend, seasonal and random fluctuations.

## 2.6.2 Projecting the trend

The method for projecting the trend differs slightly depending on whether we have used the linear regression or the moving average method of calculation.

### Linear regression

If we have used linear regression analysis in order to establish the underlying trend, then we have established an equation into which we can feed a time value in order to read out the appropriate trend value.

In our example above the relationship we established was

Sales = $70.468 + 0.31729 \times$ Time

where Time = Number of quarters measuring from the start of year 1 (e.g. Year 6 Quarter 1 is Quarter 21).

Hence we can predict the trend figures for each quarter of Years 6 and 7 as

| Qtr | 21 | 22 | 23 | 24 | 25 | 26 | 27 | 28 |
|------|-------|-------|-------|-------|-------|-------|-------|-------|
| | £'000 | £'000 | £'000 | £'000 | £'000 | £'000 | £'000 | £'000 |
| Sales | 77.131 | 77.448 | 77.766 | 78.083 | 78.400 | 78.718 | 79.035 | 79.352 |

## Moving average method

If we have used the moving average method in order to determine the underlying trend, then to predict forward we need to determine an average growth rate across the measured period and apply this moving forward.

*Linear growth*

If there appears to have been linear growth then the relationship we need to use is

$$\text{Growth per period} = \frac{\text{Latest Moving Average Value} - \text{Earliest Moving Average Value}}{\text{Number of Values} - 1}$$

*Note*: The number of values − 1 gives the number of periods' growth, e.g. two consecutive periods' measurements will give one period's growth. Here growth is in value terms (i.e. here £'000)

## Example

$$\text{Growth per period} = \frac{80.750 - 67.000}{161} = 0.91667, \text{ i.e. £916.67 per period.}$$

*Compound/exponential growth*

If, on the other hand, growth appears to be exponential then the relationship we should use to calculate this compound growth is

$$(1 + \text{Growth per period}) = \sqrt[n-1]{\frac{\text{Latest Moving Average Value}}{\text{Earliest Moving Average Value}}}$$

*Note*: n − 1 gives the number of periods' growth once again, and the Growth per period is in proportionate or percentage terms.

## Example

$$(1 + \text{Growth per period}) = \sqrt[16-1]{\frac{80.750}{67.000}} = 1.0125221$$

corresponding to growth of 0.0125221 or 1.25221% per quarter.

## 2.6.3 Projecting the seasonal variations

The seasonal fluctuations used are the average seasonal fluctuations we calculate earlier, i.e. those that eradicated the effects of the random variations. These are added/applied to the trend figures to give us our best estimates of what the actual figures will be for those relevant quarters.

## 2.6.4 Projecting the random variations

Since the random fluctuations are defined as being unpredictable it would be more appropriate for us to ignore them in our calculations and concentrate upon the trend and seasonal factors only.

### 2.6.5 Additive prediction

## Linear growth

Applying a linear growth trend as established from the above data gives the following trend information.

| Year | Qtr | T £'000 | S £'000 | A = T + S £'000 |
|------|-----|---------|---------|-----------------|
| 6 | Q1 | 83.500 | 31.938 | 115.438 |
|   | Q2 | 84.417 | 5.656 | 90.073 |
|   | Q3 | 85.333 | (27.625) | 57.708 |
|   | Q4 | 86.250 | (9.969) | 76.281 |
| 7 | Q1 | 87.167 | 31.938 | 119.105 |
|   | Q2 | 88.083 | 5.656 | 93.739 |
|   | Q3 | 89.000 | (27.625) | 61.375 |
|   | Q4 | 89.917 | (9.969) | 79.948 |

*Note:* Year 6 Quarter 1's trend figure is based on the Year 5 Quarter 2's trend figure (the last trend figure that we have above) plus three quarters' growth, i.e.

$$80.750 + (0.917 \times 3) = 83.500$$

Each subsequent quarter's trend is simply determined by adding the average growth rate to the preceding quarter's figures.

## Compound growth

Applying a compound growth trend as established from the above data gives the following trend information.

| Year | Qtr | T £'000 | S £'000 | A = T + S £'000 |
|------|-----|---------|---------|-----------------|
| 6 | Q1 | 83.822 | 31.938 | 115.760 |
|   | Q2 | 84.871 | 5.656 | 90.527 |
|   | Q3 | 85.934 | (27.625) | 58.309 |
|   | Q4 | 87.010 | (9.969) | 77.041 |
| 7 | Q1 | 88.100 | 31.938 | 120.038 |
|   | Q2 | 89.203 | 5.656 | 94.859 |
|   | Q3 | 90.320 | (27.625) | 62.695 |
|   | Q4 | 91.451 | (9.969) | 81.482 |

*Note:* Year 6 Quarter 1's trend figure is based on the Year 5 Quarter 2's trend figure (the last trend figure that we have above) applying three quarters' growth, i.e.

$$80.750 \times 1.0125221^3 = 83.822$$

Each subsequent quarters' trend is simply determined by multiplying the preceding quarter's figure by (1 + Growth per period).

### 2.6.6 Multiplicative prediction

The *trend* figures in the multiplicative model are established in exactly the same way as for the additive model, the trend figures representing values (here £) in both cases. As you can see, they are exactly the same figures for both linear growth and compound growth.

We must remember in this model that the seasonal fluctuations represent *proportional* or *percentage* changes from those trend figures and hence to establish the actual figures we anticipate we must *multiply* the trend figures by the seasonal fluctuations.

### Linear growth

| Year | Qtr | T £'000 | S % | A = T × S £'000 |
|------|-----|---------|------|-----------------|
| 6 | Q1 | 83.500 | 143.327 | 119.678 |
|   | Q2 | 84.417 | 107.782 | 90.986 |
|   | Q3 | 85.333 | 62.148 | 53.033 |
|   | Q4 | 86.250 | 86.743 | 74.816 |
| 7 | Q1 | 87.167 | 143.327 | 124.934 |
|   | Q2 | 88.083 | 107.782 | 94.938 |
|   | Q3 | 89.000 | 62.148 | 55.312 |
|   | Q4 | 89.917 | 86.743 | 77.998 |

### Compound growth

| Year | Qtr | T £'000 | S % | A = T × S £'000 |
|------|-----|---------|------|-----------------|
| 6 | Q1 | 83.822 | 143.327 | 120.140 |
|   | Q2 | 84.871 | 107.782 | 91.476 |
|   | Q3 | 85.934 | 62.148 | 53.406 |
|   | Q4 | 87.010 | 86.743 | 75.475 |
| 7 | Q1 | 88.100 | 143.327 | 126.271 |
|   | Q2 | 89.203 | 107.782 | 96.145 |
|   | Q3 | 90.320 | 62.148 | 56.132 |
|   | Q4 | 91.451 | 86.743 | 79.327 |

### Exercise 1e

Continuing Exercise 1d, predict quarterly sales for the next two years assuming a linear trend.

## 2.7 Limitations of time series analysis

Time series analysis is, as we have seen, an averaging process and the limitations of time series come directly from this, i.e

- Time series analysis assumes that random and seasonal factors will cancel over complete seasonal cycles. While this assumption may be OK for small variations in the long run, it is less valid for larger variations (remember that arithmetic means are heavily distorted by extreme items) or shorter periods where this cancellation is unlikely to occur
- End values in the moving averages are 'lost' as a result of the averaging process
- Time series results cannot be statistically evaluated in the same way as linear regression.

# 3 SUMMARY

## 3.1 Time series assumption

The pattern of observed values against time is considered to be a function of four factors, specifically

- Trend – T.
- Cyclical variations – C.
- Seasonal variations – S.
- Random variations - R.

## 3.2 Models

### 3.2.1 Additive

$$A = T + C + S + R$$

### 3.2.2 Multiplicative

$$A = T \times C \times S \times R$$

## 3.3 Determine trend

Determine the trend through either

- Moving averages
- Regression analysis

## 3.4 Determine seasonal variations

Determine seasonal variations by averaging each season to eliminate random effects, adjusting as necessary such that the net seasonal variation is

- Additive Model: net = 0, ie nothing added or subtracted overall
- Multiplicative model: net = 1, ie nothing scaled up or down overall

## 3.5 Forecast

Forecast by extrapolating trend and adjusting for seasonal element.

# 4 SOLUTIONS TO EXERCISES

### 1. Additive and multiplicative model

| Year | Qtr | Value '000 | 4 Qtr '000 | 8 Qtr '000 | Moving Average '000 | Seasonal + Random Additive '000 | Multipl % | Av. Seasonal Var. Additive '000 | Multipl % | Random Additive '000 | Multipl % |
|---|---|---|---|---|---|---|---|---|---|---|---|
| 1 | Q1 | 70 | | | | | | | | | |
| | Q2 | 71 | | | | | | | | | |
| | Q3 | 144 | 383 | 770 | 96.250 | 47.750 | 149.610 | 39.805 | 140.792 | 7.945 | 106.264 |
| | Q4 | 98 | 387 | 780 | 97.500 | 0.500 | 100.513 | −4.789 | 94.872 | 5.289 | 105.945 |
| 2 | Q1 | 74 | 393 | 795 | 99.375 | −25.375 | 74.465 | −24.789 | 74.712 | −0.586 | 99.669 |
| | Q2 | 77 | 402 | 808 | 101.000 | −24.000 | 76.238 | −10.227 | 89.623 | −13.773 | 85.064 |
| | Q3 | 153 | 406 | 814 | 101.750 | 51.250 | 150.369 | 39.805 | 140.792 | 11.445 | 106.802 |
| | Q4 | 102 | 408 | 831 | 103.875 | −1.875 | 98.195 | −4.789 | 94.872 | 2.914 | 103.502 |
| 3 | Q1 | 76 | 423 | 823 | 102.875 | −26.875 | 73.876 | −24.789 | 74.712 | −2.086 | 98.881 |
| | Q2 | 92 | 400 | 792 | 99.000 | −7.000 | 92.929 | −10.227 | 89.623 | 3.227 | 103.689 |
| | Q3 | 130 | 392 | 774 | 96.750 | 33.250 | 134.367 | 39.805 | 140.792 | −6.555 | 95.437 |
| | Q4 | 94 | 382 | 761 | 95.125 | −1.125 | 98.817 | −4.789 | 94.872 | 3.664 | 104.158 |
| 4 | Q1 | 66 | 379 | 750 | 93.750 | −27.750 | 70.400 | −24.789 | 74.712 | −2.961 | 94.228 |
| | Q2 | 89 | 371 | 730 | 91.250 | −2.250 | 97.534 | −10.227 | 89.623 | 7.977 | 108.827 |
| | Q3 | 122 | 359 | 736 | 92.000 | 30.000 | 132.609 | 39.805 | 140.792 | −9.805 | 94.188 |
| | Q4 | 82 | 377 | 765 | 95.625 | −13.625 | 85.752 | −4.789 | 94.872 | −8.836 | 90.386 |
| 5 | Q1 | 84 | 388 | 801 | 100.125 | −16.125 | 83.895 | −24.789 | 74.712 | 8.664 | 112.291 |
| | Q2 | 100 | 413 | 837 | 104.625 | −4.625 | 95.579 | −10.227 | 89.623 | 5.602 | 106.646 |
| | Q3 | 147 | 424 | | | | | | | | |
| | Q4 | 93 | | | | | | | | | |

Average trend growth rate: $g = \dfrac{\text{Highest} - \text{Lowest}}{n-1} = \dfrac{104.625 - 96.250}{16-1} = 0.5583$ per qtr

### Additive seasonal variations

| Year | Q1 '000 | Q2 '000 | Q3 '000 | Q4 '000 | |
|---|---|---|---|---|---|
| 1 | | | 47.750 | 0.500 | |
| 2 | −25.375 | −24.000 | 51.250 | −1.875 | |
| 3 | −26.875 | −7.000 | 33.250 | −1.125 | |
| 4 | −27.750 | −2.250 | 30.000 | −13.625 | |
| 5 | −16.125 | −4.625 | | | |
| Sum | −96.125 | −37.875 | 162.250 | −16.125 | |
| | | | | | |
| Average | −24.031 | −9.469 | 40.563 | −4.031 | 3.031 |
| Correction | −0.758 | −0.758 | −0.758 | −0.758 | |
| Av. Seasonal | −24.789 | −10.227 | 39.805 | −4.789 | 0.000 |

## Multiplicative seasonal variations

| Year | Q1 | Q2 | Q3 | Q4 | |
|------|------|------|------|------|------|
| | % | % | % | % | |
| 1 | | | 149.610 | 100.513 | |
| 2 | 74.465 | 76.238 | 150.369 | 98.195 | |
| 3 | 73.876 | 92.929 | 134.367 | 98.817 | |
| 4 | 70.400 | 97.534 | 132.609 | 85.752 | |
| 5 | 83.895 | 95.579 | _____ | _____ | |
| Sum | 302.637 | 362.281 | 566.955 | 383.277 | |
| | | | | | |
| Average | 75.659 | 90.570 | 141.739 | 95.819 | 403.787 |
| Correction | −0.947 | −0.947 | −0.947 | −0.947 | ↵ |
| Av. Seasonal | 74.712 | 89.623 | 140.792 | 94.872 | 400.000 |

## Additive prediction

| | | Trend | Seasonal | Predicted |
|------|------|--------|----------|-----------|
| | | '000 | '000 | '000 |
| 6 | Q1 | 106.300 | −24.789 | 81.511 |
| | Q2 | 106.858 | −10.227 | 96.632 |
| | Q3 | 107.417 | 39.805 | 147.221 |
| | Q4 | 107.975 | −4.789 | 103.186 |
| 7 | Q1 | 108.533 | −24.789 | 83.744 |
| | Q2 | 109.092 | −10.227 | 98.865 |
| | Q3 | 109.650 | 39.805 | 149.455 |
| | Q4 | 110.208 | −4.789 | 105.419 |

## Multiplicative prediction

| | | Trend | Seasonal | Predicted |
|------|------|--------|----------|-----------|
| | | '000 | % | '000 |
| 6 | Q1 | 106.300 | 74.712 | 79.419 |
| | Q2 | 106.858 | 89.623 | 95.770 |
| | Q3 | 107.417 | 140.792 | 151.234 |
| | Q4 | 107.975 | 94.872 | 102.438 |
| 7 | Q1 | 108.533 | 74.712 | 81.088 |
| | Q2 | 109.092 | 89.623 | 97.772 |
| | Q3 | 109.650 | 140.792 | 154.378 |
| | Q4 | 110.208 | 94.872 | 104.557 |

Where the Year 6 Quarter 1 trend figure is based on the Year 5 Quarter 2 trend above plus three quarters growth, and each subsequent quarters' trend is one quarter's growth larger still.

### Additive Model

| Year | Qtr | Value | 4 Qtr | 8 Qtr | Moving Average | Seasonal + Random | Average Seasonal Variation | Random |
|------|-----|-------|-------|-------|----------------|-------------------|---------------------------|--------|
| | | £m | £m | £m | £m | £m | £m | £m |
| 1 | Q1 | 120 | | | | | | |
| | Q2 | 131 | | | | | | |
| | Q3 | 139 | 548 | 1,118 | 139.750 | −0.750 | 1.354 | −2.104 |
| | Q4 | 158 | 570 | 1,161 | 145.125 | 12.875 | 18.354 | −5.479 |
| 2 | Q1 | 142 | 591 | 1,206 | 150.750 | −8.750 | −14.396 | 5.646 |
| | Q2 | 152 | 615 | 1,254 | 156.750 | −4.750 | −5.313 | 0.563 |
| | Q3 | 163 | 639 | 1,285 | 160.625 | 2.375 | 1.354 | 1.021 |
| | Q4 | 182 | 646 | 1,305 | 163.125 | 18.875 | 18.354 | 0.521 |
| 3 | Q1 | 149 | 659 | 1,329 | 166.125 | −17.125 | −14.396 | −2.729 |
| | Q2 | 165 | 670 | 1,354 | 169.250 | −4.250 | −5.313 | 1.063 |
| | Q3 | 174 | 684 | 1,375 | 171.875 | 2.125 | 1.354 | 0.771 |
| | Q4 | 196 | 691 | 1,384 | 173.000 | 23.000 | 18.354 | 4.646 |
| 4 | Q1 | 156 | 693 | 1,389 | 173.625 | −17.625 | −14.396 | −3.229 |
| | Q2 | 167 | 696 | 1,394 | 174.250 | −7.250 | −5.313 | −1.938 |
| | Q3 | 177 | 698 | | | | | |
| | Q4 | 198 | | | | | | |

$$\text{Average trend growth rate: } g = \frac{\text{Highest} - \text{Lowest}}{n-1} = \frac{174.250 - 139.750}{12-1}$$

$$= \text{£3.136 per qtr}$$

### Additive seasonal variations

| Year | Q1 | Q2 | Q3 | Q4 | |
|------|-----|-----|-----|-----|---|
| | £m | £m | £m | £m | |
| 1 | | | −0.750 | 12.875 | |
| 2 | −8.750 | −4.750 | 2.375 | 18.875 | |
| 3 | −17.125 | −4.250 | 2.125 | 23.000 | |
| 4 | −17.625 | −7.250 | | | |
| Sum | −43.500 | −16.250 | 3.750 | 54.750 | |
| | | | | | |
| Average | −14.500 | −5.417 | 1.250 | 18.250 | −0.417 |
| Correction | 0.104 | 0.104 | 0.104 | 0.104 | |
| Av Seasonal | −14.396 | −5.313 | 1.354 | 18.354 | 0.000 |

**Additive prediction**

|   |     | Trend | Seasonal | Predicted |
|---|-----|-------|----------|-----------|
|   |     | £m | £m | £m |
| 5 | Q1 | 183.659 | −14.396 | 169.263 |
|   | Q2 | 186.795 | −5.313 | 181.483 |
|   | Q3 | 189.932 | 1.354 | 191.286 |
|   | Q4 | 193.068 | 18.354 | 211.422 |
| 6 | Q1 | 196.205 | −14.396 | 181.809 |
|   | Q2 | 199.341 | −5.313 | 194.028 |
|   | Q3 | 202.477 | 1.354 | 203.831 |
|   | Q4 | 205.614 | 18.354 | 223.968 |

Where the Year 5 Quarter 1 trend figure is based on the Year 4 Quarter 2 trend above plus three quarters growth, and each subsequent quarters' trend is one quarter's growth larger still.

# INDEX